Dojo Knights

Dojo Knights

-A Randori From Munich to Moscow-

Christo Murphy

YOUCAXTON
PUBLICATIONS

Dojo Knights is dedicated to the affectionate memory of

Tony MacConnell

who did so much for British Judo

Contents

Dojo Knights

Foreword

I LAY NAKED and peacefully drunk, on the ancient stones of a Catalan pavement. I was smoking a fine cigar. Peter Donnelly danced his midnight waltz with a Spanish waiter; a small man with no option but to comply, his feet flapping helplessly six inches above the tiled floor of Bar Loco. Royston Muller was holding important discussions with a wall, or perhaps the cat that looked down upon him with sleepy disinterest. I lazily wished that either I could retrieve my shorts, draped over a nearby lamppost, or that I was more substantially endowed.

I was seventy-one years old and thought it time that I should write our story...

⌐

Dojo Knights is a meander through the judo scene of the nineteen sixties and seventies. It follows the lives of two working-class judoka, Danny Murphy, a minor player and Peter Donnelly who progresses to become British champion, an elite fighter on the world and Olympic stage. This book is not a factual history but most of what I have written is true, especially any judo events referenced. I have tried to capture the *Zeitgeist,* the 'ghost' or spirit of the age. I have deliberately allowed the book to flow laterally in many places attempting to give the reader a feel for the times. I have 'peeped in,' as it were, into the lives of judo players, some important and some not. I apologise if you don't like these sideways forays.

I have tried to make this book enjoyable to non-judoka, but I am assuming that most who read it will have some familiarity with the sport, hence I have not gone into any lengthy explanations regarding techniques or terminology. The book ends, an appendix if you like, with brief biographies of the 'Dojo Knights.' These have all been provided by the players themselves. I cannot help but note that so many lads from rough backgrounds used judo as an escape from tedium, and as an escape route to a better life.

There is very little that is unsavoury in these pages – one or two swear-words where to leave them out would be silly. There are some scenes which are sexual in nature, but nothing coarse nor explicit. The book simply reflects the lives of those whose story it tells.

I have tried to ensure that real events are not distorted. If a judo contest took place then I have done my best to report it accurately. My metaphor when writing this account was to imagine an archipelago of islands as the 'judo facts.' For the water between them I make no such truth claims – some of it happened and some did not. But I have tried to recreate the spirit of the times which, in truth, was damn good!

To conclude, this is my homage to judo and the 'hard knocks' who practice and compete. It is a unique sport in that it marries hard fighting with a gentle philosophy. I believe it gives more than it takes back – chief amongst such gifts are lifelong friendships forged in the fire of martial combat.

Christo Murphy 2021

...And From David Starbrook MBE; 9th Dan

I'd like to thank Christo for writing DOJO KNIGHTS in the first place. It has been a privilege to have been asked to be a part of the factual and fictional stories, (even the fiction is pretty much how things were back in the day!)

Many memories have been evoked for me from reading the book and I would like to pay homage to all those that we have lost along the way, including my great friend Keith Remfry and mentors such as T.P. Leggett, Alan Petherbridge, Dr Kingsbury, Phyllis Elliot and of course Tony Mac. I should also like to give a shout out to all those that have formed part of my coaching team including the Great Britain coach Ray Ross.

Taking up the sport so late any friendships made were developed in training with partners such as Angelo, Brian, Bobby Sullivan and later on Peter Donnelly; also those lesser-known club players from the Renshuden including Ray Neenan, Joe Dougherty and Derek Ryman the oldest known blue belt to ever don a kit.

For those reading DOJO KNIGHTS enjoy and hold tight because you're in for a bumpy ride!

Good luck!

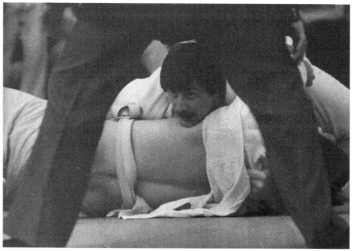

Peter Donnelly – Moscow, 1980

Chapter One
The Grand Joust Mockba - 1980

THE EMPEROR NAPOLEON entered Moscow to find the city empty and on fire. I find it amusing to note that the French, in their revolution of 1789, hated the aristocracy so much that in the terror which followed, they lopped off every noble head that they could find. Fourteen years after severing *'la tete'* of King Louis XVI they changed their minds and the people of *'Liberte, Egalite, Fraternite'* placed the dead King's crown firmly on the braincase of a Corsican, proclaiming Napoleon Buonaparte, Emperor. (Also interesting is the fact that the guillotine used in thousands of head disconnections was the promotion of a doctor, a kind man, who wanted to find a humane way of killing people quickly and without too much pain).

Napoleon was unhappy with the Russians: they had left little of value in the city, and of course, what army does not like to loot? It is a well-accepted part of the fun of war. The retreating citizens had also taken all the grub with them and so the invading French had nothing to eat. This was hardly playing fair. Russian food is certainly not *haute cuisine*. In fact, I believe it to be overall, tasteless muck. No, such food is an acquired taste which funnily enough is disliked the world over – even in Russia. But an army must eat, and the Russians had left not a crumb. What to do? Napoleon sat on his beautiful war-horse and patted him tenderly on the neck. The French Emperor loved Marengo and as far as we know the Irish horse loved the 'Little General' in return. They looked around Red Square, deserted except for a few of Napoleon's staff - Princes, and Dukes dressed in madly elaborate uniforms with preposterous, tall hats; they were in poor humour as they had missed lunch. Horse and rider looked upwards at

1

the mad beauty which is St Basil's Cathedral. The Emperor spoke to his horse. '*Cette cathedrale est stupide! C'est comme des oignons peints. Nous avons des meilleures cathedrals a Paris!*'

He gently spurred his horse forward. 'Stuff this for a game of soldiers Marengo. There's nothing to eat and the weather's turning decidedly nippy. Better get back to France or we're in deep shit! The retreat to France is well documented and is the subject of a great symphony by Tchaikovsky – the 1812.

⌐

Peter Donnelly, Arthur Mapp and John Holliday, British judo champions all, stood in Red Square their heads tilted far back, looking up at the unique beauty which is St Basil's Cathedral Moscow.

'What do you think Arthur?'

'Impressive enough – a bit mad though, like a load of painted onions.'

Without fuss or fanfare, the British judo team had arrived in Moscow and were quartered in the Olympic village a short distance from the centre of the famed city. The departure from London had been low key. There had been a pleasant enough hotel send off to toast them and wish them success, but no formal reception. Officially, the team was to compete under the banner of the International Olympic Committee, a compromise as the British Government wished to support the American led boycott. They had therefore not attended the Games opening ceremony and had travelled directly to the Olympic village, an austere set of structures, angular, brutal and unadorned concrete. The Soviets liked this sort of image, they regarded it as a symbol of the strength of their state – down to earth, not frivolous but undaunted and solid. The Russians had at this time a national inspirational figure Olga Levantova, who had received the highest honour, an award for her services to the USSR. She was a 'Hero of the Soviet Union, First Class,' richly deserved as she had born sixteen healthy children who would no doubt grow up to make Mother Russia proud. There were awards in different categories: for the woman who had dug most coal or smelted a thousand tons of iron, that sort of thing. She was pictured in the local newspapers kissing the Soviet President, Leonid Brezhnev, an ugly brute if ever there was one but I have no sympathy for the man. She also won a car, a Moskvitch. To give such a vehicle as a prize was cruel; a sadistic trick which well demonstrated the psychopathology of the Russian state.

⌒

A mere week earlier Peter Donnelly, the team captain, had wondered if they would make the Olympics at all. He cast his mind back to the day he had received a letter urging him to boycott the games and encourage his team-mates to do likewise:

The breakfast table at Crystal Palace was full of lean and hungry men – particularly hungry! Tony MacConnell and David Starbrook were hard taskmasters. Their mission objective was to deliver eight men in the best physical condition possible to contest the judo events at the Moscow Olympic games of 1980. These two, each a colossus of British judo, would not fail in their joint task. A Japanese sword master will take an ingot of raw iron and furnace heat it until it rages incandescent white. A mighty hammer will forge and fold, heat and flatten again and again until the sword has an unimaginable, laminated strength. Then, and only then will it be honed to perfection. These eight had endured the unendurable and became harder in the process. The British judo team had lived and trained together at Crystal Palace for almost a year. It was late June and the honing was almost complete.

Peter, still young at twenty-eight but a seasoned veteran, sat at the pine refectory table and stared unenthusiastically at the segment of melon and slice of wholemeal toast that was to be his breakfast. He and the team had already endured the tense agony of the morning weigh-in. But for a week now there had been no drama. Each day, after toileting and the daily run, his weight had been eighty-six point nine kilogrammes – a weight that suited him and more importantly, 'Mac' perfectly. Tony MacConnell had made it very clear that he expected each team member to meet his exact weight specification and if they did not, they would simply be 'off the team.' No one doubted him;

no-one would test his resolve. Peter's morning had gone according to schedule and he had enjoyed the compulsory pre-breakfast run, the early summer weather being sunny and warm.

He ate the melon and toast and sat quietly pondering events to come. He sipped a glass of squeezed orange juice. He noticed with mild interest that the team were sitting in weight order; John Holliday, Ray Neenan, and Chris Bowles at the far end with himself, Mark Chittenden and Paul Radburn in the middle spaces, and Arthur Mapp at the end. Neil Adams walked towards them carrying a bundle of letters. He dropped a beige envelope in front of Peter, uttered the single word 'Post,' and then moved to his seat further along.

Peter looked at the envelope with some surprise at the neatly typed heading and address.

Peter Donnelly Esq; Captain of the British Olympic Judo Team, c/o National Sports and Recreation Centre, Crystal Palace, London.

This was odd; this was not a personal communication. He had no idea as to its contents, and curiosity roused, he wiped his toast knife on a napkin and opened the letter.

⤺

In December 1979, during the Cold War, the Soviet 40th Army invaded Afghanistan in order to prop up the communist government of the People's Democratic Party of Afghanistan. At the time, the United States had been making diplomatic headway in the Middle East at Moscow's expense, successfully influencing Egypt, Israel, Saudi Arabia, Pakistan, and others. The Soviet Union feared the loss of its communist proxy in Afghanistan. This invasion was, of course, condemned by western powers, in particular the United States and Great Britain.

⤺

In 1950 the brothers Ross and Norris set up 'The McWhirter Twins Corporation' to sell facts to newspapers. At that time, Sir Hugh Beaver, managing director of Guinness, had an argument with a friend about which was the fastest bird in Europe. There was no reference book with such information. Thus, was the start of The Guinness Book of Records which was developed by the McWhirter twins and funded by the Guinness company. The murder of brother Ross McWhirter by the provisional IRA in November 1975, (after he had offered a £50,000 reward for information leading to the conviction of Irish terrorists,) caused Norris great grief. He took on something of his brother's militancy and, just days after the murder, helped launch the National Association for Freedom. He used his wealth to support many libertarian causes and became increasingly anti-communist.

⌣

Peter Donnelly opened the expensive beige vellum envelope, and withdrew its contents, a sheet of twice folded heavyweight bond – this was no throw-a-way circular. He shoved away his breakfast plate and smoothed the paper flat on the pine table. He read:

Dear Peter,

We have not met so I hope you will excuse this informality of address. I am comfortable that you will understand that we have a connection, a familiarity as athletes although my zenith is twenty-five years passed.

Do we both not wish it were the case that politics never reared its ugly head in Olympic sport? Sadly, this is wishful thinking. The disgraceful way in which Adolph Hitler used the 1936 games in Berlin to show off his despicable Nazis, and the horrors of the terrorist attack in Munich only eight short years ago, show the impossible nature of this dream.

Once again, a despotic regime, and I mean the Soviet Union, has used force of arms to subdue a sovereign nation. The Russian Bear has marched into Afghanistan and placed its people in bondage to their vile communist ideology, and yet this same nation is to host the most prestigious sporting event the world ever sees in just a few short weeks. Attending it can only give support to the barbarous actions of the Soviets. Other countries have already decided not to go; the United States, Japan, Pakistan amongst others. Our own

Prime Minister, The Rt Hon Margaret Thatcher has urged the British Olympic committee to join these nations in showing disapproval and disavowal of the Soviet state. But we, unlike those under the yoke of communism, are a free people. It is right and proper in a democracy such as ours that the choice of participating or not in these Olympic games is left to the conscience of the individual athlete.

> Peter, with all my heart I wish it were otherwise, but as chairman of the National Association for Freedom I urge you to boycott the Moscow games and use your influence as team captain to encourage your friends and fellow judo players to do the same. It is the right and courageous thing to do.
> Yours sincerely,
> Norris McWhirter

Peter walked from the restaurant to the Crystal Palace dojo, lost in thought and confused by the letter. Of course, he knew about the stance President Jimmy Carter had taken, for the Moscow games to be boycotted. He also knew this was far from popular even in the United States and that it was not supported by the British Olympic committee. Margaret Thatcher was vociferous that this call be heeded, but could not get the agreement of her own government. Lost in thought he was startled when a strong hand rested upon his shoulder from behind.

Tony MacConnell had many fine qualities. He was large and powerful to be sure but by no means a giant. He stood just over six feet tall and weighed a commendable hundred kilos, heavier than in his recent fighting days, but there was something about him that exuded steadfastness; his physical strength was legendary - but that was not it. No, his craggy countenance and mop of careless blond hair radiated security. He was the man that could lift the heaviest burden from the soul of a depleted athlete and carry it on his unbending shoulders. He was the father figure that could tell world-class judo player, suffering after a defeat, 'Don't worry, everything's gonna be alright' and be believed. His northern tones comforted and eased. He was the oil that calmed troubled waters.

'Summat up Peter? You seem lost in thought, and you know it worries me when you start to think.' He looked round to see Mac.

'Oh, hello Tony. Sorry about the thinking – I won't do it again.' They both smiled. Peter removed the McWhirter letter from his blue Great Britain tracksuit and passed it to MacConnell. 'I got this today – have a squint.' They sat together on a nearby concrete bench in the sunshine of late June, Peter rested still and quiet while Mac read. He finished and passed the paper back. 'What do you think Tony?'

'I think it's your letter – nowt to do wi' me. You're the team captain - says so on the envelope! What do you intend to do?' The simple question clarified Peter's thoughts that had jumbled for the past half-hour.

'Nothing! He screwed up the paper and dropped it into a waste-bin as they walked to the dojo to begin morning training.

⌒

The first Moscow breakfast turned out to be a poor affair. It was served in a huge refectory in which athletes queued at a long bar. It reminded Peter of a motorway service café of the 1960s. He stood next to his room-mate Mark Chittenden the U95 kilo champion of Great Britain. Yesterday's flight and bus transfer to the Olympic village had been tedious. At Moscow's Sheremetyevo Airport passports and papers had been thoroughly checked and checked again. The terminal smelled of paint and was obviously new. The transfer to the shuttle bus which was to take the team to the village was organised by a large, angular Russian dressed in a black suit, black tie and white shirt. He wore heavy framed sun-glasses and a neat trilby hat. In the manner of a tour guide, he introduced himself using a microphone while standing at the front of the speeding bus, his back braced against the luggage rack.

'Pay attention! Pay attention! Hello Great Britain! My name is Vitaly Brezhnev. I am your guide and helper. Any problems you see me and I will fix them. Pay attention! Welcome to Mother Russia, 'The land of the tree's and the home of the slaves!' He looked up and waited for appreciative laughter at his pun, which did not arrive.

'Okay – I make joke. A big joke but you no laugh. Why not? You think I will have you shot? No problem, pay attention. We hardly shoot anyone in Russia since Stalin died!' He looked along the length of the coach at the tired and puzzled athletes. 'You still no laugh... My God you're a tough crowd. Yesterday I make all the Germans laugh. Mind you, they were East Germans and so they had to...'

Peter was surprised to see him supervising at breakfast. The team had arrived quite late the previous evening and had each been allocated a room in a very plain block of flats, his was on the fourth floor. The lift, though new, seemed antiquated and clanked and squealed as it hauled them upwards. At the required floor, he alighted with Mark leaving Chris Bowles and Ray Neenan to continue upwards. Mark opened the door to room 404, and he and Peter entered to find two single beds, one wardrobe, a small chest of drawers and one chair. The bare walls were painted off-white and there was no shade around the single light bulb that hung centrally.

'What do you think Peter?' Donnelly looked out of the window and could see the great city of Moscow in the distance. In the fading summer's light, his eyes were drawn to a tall building with a red star shining brightly. He recognised it as that depicted upon all the posters and advertisements for the Olympic games – The Moscow State University. 'What do you think?' persisted Mark. Peter swatted two or three mosquitoes resting on the glass.

'It's a little...' he paused, struggling to find the word. 'It's a little – sparse. And I think we might get bitten to death.' Both young men were too tired to consider eating that evening but were ready for breakfast when they awoke the next morning. The single beds were cramped and a little hard but, all-in-all, not too bad - both men had slept well. The bathroom was tiny but contained all that was necessary. And neither man had a weight problem, Tony MacConnell had seen to that; both athletes were ready for a substantial meal.

Peter surveyed the food on offer. He had developed a breakfast routine which kept him from feeling hungry and provided the nutrients and energy necessary for his morning training routine. Today was a rest day, nevertheless he would stick with two boiled eggs for protein, porridge and fruit for energy and tea. They were under orders not to drink un-boiled water; salad was forbidden and fruit had to be peeled to avoid the ever-present problem of stomach bugs.

There was an abundance of porridge and bread, both a dull grey colour – hardly appealing. The fruit offered consisted of apples, pears and oranges all dehydrated and unappetising. Someone spoke and Peter turned in response.

'Hello Peter. It's not so good eh?' It was Bertil Strom, a Swedish judoka he knew from previous competitions. 'We've been here for a few days getting used to things. The food is not exactly bad, but it's not good either. Poor quality – don't eat the steak otherwise you'll be chewing for a month.' The pleasantries of their conversation were interrupted by the guide from the previous evening, still dressed in black, complete with hat and sunglasses. The Swede smiled and shook his outstretched hand. 'Why if it isn't Karl Gustav Brezhnev – still looking for spies?'

'You Swedish are the big jokers. Looking for spies indeed. I am just a humble guide and interpreter. But you know this! And you know my name is Vitaly, but I understand your joke. The initials, K.G.B! It is very funny - you jokers! Without warning Bertil rapped him with his knuckles, striking a bulge under his left armpit. He was rewarded with a metallic thud.

'And what's that then Karl? Your wallet?' The Russian did not lose his composure nor affable good humour.

'You joker. Of course, it is my radio - but don't do that again in case it goes off! You betcha!' He seemed to find this genuinely funny and was smiling as he joined them at table keen to continue the conversation. 'But the food is good? The rooms are good?' He looked at Peter's identity pass. 'What do you think Peter?'

'Well, we've only just arrived, but everything seems very basic. There is plenty of food, if you like bread and potatoes - and last night our room was full of mosquitoes, was it not Mark?' The Russian seemed crestfallen.

'But this is so sad. This is the best food in Moscow provided especially for our guests. Most certainly it is! But pay attention to me. The shops are empty to supply the athletes. But you haven't tried the food at night. It is very good and there is a great deal of meat. Each person can have enough for one family.' Mark Chittenden decided to change the subject and rescue the Russian from his genuine distress and puzzlement.

'We've got the day off today. Where should we go? Anything good to see?' Vitaly visibly cheered.

'Where to go? Why, Moscow is a city of wonders – a city of one thousand years. Pay attention! There is so much to see. Red Square; The Kremlin; St Basil's Cathedral; GUMP department store; the metro system – every station is a palace. There is the biggest canon ever made and the biggest bell. There is so much.'

'Where is this bell? Hanging in a cathedral or church? When does it ring?' asked Peter. Vitaly shook his head.

'No, it is not in a cathedral – it's too big. It's near the Kremlin Palace, just inside the walls, and it doesn't ring. In fact, it's broken nearly in half - but it is very big, easily as big as a house.'

'But it doesn't work? How about the gun?' asked Mark.

'That doesn't work either. I don't think it ever has. But, pay attention, it is very big!' Peter chipped in brightly.

'So, you've got a big bell that doesn't clang and a big gun that doesn't bang?'

'You joker – you betcha! But the metro stations are like palaces. My father had something to do with their construction. Peter considered their afternoon mooching about an unfamiliar city.

'Is Moscow safe for tourists?'

'Safe? It's completely safe! At least it is now. Pay attention! We've thrown all the derelicts, vagrants, criminals and prostitutes into gaol for a few weeks to keep them off the streets. Stalin would have been proud! I hear that the girls kicked up one helluva fuss, you betcha. They expected to make a fortune...'

⌇

Alfred John Latham Tomkins was born in 1905 into a respectable middle-class family who lived in a large house in Reading. The entirety of the household consisted of his father Bertram, who did 'something in the city,' and his mother, who did not. There were two maids, two cats and two dogs. Whatever the employment of his father, it paid for 'little Alfie' to attend a private preparatory school and then a few years at Harrow before his education took him up the river Thames to while away time at Oxford. (It must be mentioned here that England being England and Oxford being Oxford, the river at this point in its roam is called the Isis.) To say 'while away' is not quite fair. Alfie was both intelligent and industrious, a sure recipe for success. He was also sportingly inclined and managed to find time to pick up a rowing blue. Alfie was an all-round good egg. He was a boy and then a young man of his time; by the luck of his age, he had missed the horrors of the First World War. His father expected him to trudge in his footsteps and do a well-paid 'something in the city.' But Alfie was unusual in that he liked making things, like bridges out of twigs and underground chambers in which to hide. Against his father's, not very ardent wishes he studied engineering at university and was fortunate to come under the wing of an eminent professor.

His interview for a place at Brasenose College to study engineering science was interesting. He sat nervously in front of the desk occupied by the eminent Professor Charles Frewen Jenkins who offered him an apple. 'I don't really like them myself but my wife fusses and she is a good soul. If you eat it when she quizzes me this evening I can reply with complete honesty 'My love, the apple was eaten.' Take it boy and do us both good! Alfie took the apple and held it, unsure as to when the eating process should begin. 'So, you want to be an engineer do you boy?'

'Yes Sir.' Alfie had his answers prepared but the Professor did not ask him his reasons.

'Can you speak any language except English?' This confused young Alfred who could only reply monosyllabically.

'No.'

'Oh, that is a pity, it really is. I speak eight languages – it's a sort of hobby of mine. Some people collect stamps or coins – I collect languages. Not as many of course!' This amused the professor and he laughed at his own wit. Alfie laughed as well and now more relaxed, he unconsciously bit into the apple. This further amused the eccentric don. 'That's the spirit boy. Eat up!' He looked at the papers before him. 'I'll tell you what, young Alfred. If you promise to learn a language, properly mind, I'll let you become an engineer. How does that sound?' Alfred was pleased but perplexed and had difficultly replying through a mouthful of apple pith.

'Yeff fleas,' he swallowed. 'That would be excellent. Thank you, Sir.' He further considered what to do as the professor seemed to have lost interest in the interviewing process and was reading a book written in Catalan. He sat still, dangling the apple core by its stalk. Professor Jenkins looked up from his tome.

'Yes? What do you want?' The professor now seemed irritated at Alfie's presence.

'Two things Sir. What shall I do with the apple core and what language shall I learn?'

'Bin. Russian. Goodbye.'

The professor was as good as his word, and Alfie as good as his. Three years later he graduated from Oxford University, with First Class honours in Engineering Science, and a fluent speaker of the Russian language.

〜

In October 1926, Alfie began working as a junior engineer for Metropolitan-Vickers Electrical Company. He was not too sure how he had got the job – his father knew somebody else's father, that sort of thing probably. But he liked the work and was good at it. He rose quickly in status and competency and in 1932, as a senior engineer he was invited into the office of the company's managing director and asked if he would like to be the project manager of an exciting development. 'Don't worry, your salary will be greatly enhanced in line with the considerable responsibilities that come with the position,' said Sir Hubert Vickers. 'This is the opportunity for you to stamp your mark on the world's stage, young fella. The perfect job for you. I see you speak fluent Russian?'

'Well, I might be a little rusty. But how does it matter? I don't see...'

'Oh dear! Didn't I mention? It's in Moscow man! What an adventure for an up-and-coming young blade. You'll lead our team of consulting engineers building the Moscow underground – Metro they call it, like in Paris. Perfect job. You'll come back with a cartload of money and a pretty Russian wench if I'm any judge. Slap my boots I'm damned if you won't! How about it, young Alfie?'

Alfie rose to the challenge. He and his team arrived in Moscow by plane which he found very exciting. The two-day flight, with only a half-dozen stops; Stockholm, Riga, Minsk and other, nameless aerodromes to refuel - seemed a miracle of the age. He met the great and the good of the Communist Party – but few engineers and none with the knowledge or experience to organise and expedite a project of such magnitude. His go-between, guide, translator – in truth Alfie was not sure of his formal role – was an affable black suited, white shirted, black hatted permanently smoking man of about forty who introduced himself as Alexei Brezhnev. 'You will have every co-operation. Nothing will be a problem – so when do we start? This evening or tomorrow morning, you betcha?' Alexei maintained a stern look and spoke in low dull tones.

'What!' groaned Alfie. 'No! No! No! We must make plans first. I have a team of architects, surveyors, mechanical engineers, electrical engineers, quantity surveyors, draughtsmen - it will be months before we are ready to begin. Men, machinery, materials - the logistics are complex. Everything has to be organised. Alexei, forgive me – it will be months.' Alexei became very pale.

'This cannot be. No, we must start tomorrow at the latest. Comrade Stalin is coming in to see our progress. There must be work! There must be action!' Alfie was surprised at this outburst, Alexei seemed close to genuine panic. He grabbed Alfie by the arm and marched him to the far end of the palatial room in which they were meeting. He talked in an urgent gabbling whisper. 'There must be something for him to see. Otherwise, I will be shot. He might have you shot as well but that is not so likely. But if there is no work happening, I'm dead and that's for sure. Comrade Stalin has promised the Russian people that they will have the best underground railway in the world in honour of the glorious revolution. Tomorrow is October 25th an important day. It must happen. Save my life my friend. What can we do?' Alfie grimaced.

'I suppose you could dig. Get a gang digging a hole. Say it will be the entrance to the first station.'

'There must be plans! He likes looking at paperwork...' Alfie thought for a few seconds and then answered.

'No problem – I'll knock something up overnight.

'Alfred, my friend. You have saved my life. I will be forever grateful - as will be my son Vitaly, long after I am dead. Digging – of course!' He thought for a moment. 'Where shall we dig?'

'Oh, anywhere you like really. It doesn't matter.'

The next morning Comrade Josef Stalin was well pleased at the sight of a thousand men and women furiously digging in a local park. He turned to Lavrentiy Beria, the murderous head of the dreaded secret police the NKVD as they drove slowly past in a bullet-proof limousine. 'Shall we shoot anyone today, Comrade?'

'It's up to you of course dear Comrade – but to be honest I'm not in the mood.'

'I might have you shot Comrade Beria.'

'Not if I have you shot first you won't Comrade General Secretary.'

Both men laughed but in each case with an underlying nervousness. (*Author's Note – Joseph Stalin was not shot. He died on 1st March 1953 of a cerebral haemorrhage. He was found unconscious on the floor of his country house three days earlier and moved to a couch where he stayed until his death. None of the members of his government wished to take charge of the situation in case he recovered and had them shot.*

Lavrentiy Beria, the head of Stalin's secret police, was shot - on 23rd December 1953. He was accused of 357 counts of rape and treason and executed on the orders of Nikita Khrushchev the new Soviet head of state. Between them, Stalin and Beria were responsible for the deaths of at least 20 million people – most of them Russian.)

⌒

Five years later, the massive project was completed to perfection. Each station a veritable palace dedicated to the glory of the workers of the Soviet Union and its paranoid, 'Dear Leader,' Comrade General Secretary Josef Stalin. It was he who had Alfie arrested for spying –

success was as dangerous as failure in Stalinist Russia. The arrest was carried out by none other than Alexei Brezhnev. Alfie was in bed with the beautiful young Russian countess, Anna Petrova, who seemingly came as a fixture with the magnificent apartment, also supplied by Alexei. It was three in the morning when a loud knocking awoke Alfie and he answered the door, puzzled to see his friend.

'Oh, hello Alexei – a bit early isn't it? What's up?' He was further surprised and alarmed to see a troop of six soldiers brandishing fearsome machine guns and Alexei waving a pistol.

'By order of the Supreme Soviet you, imperialist lackey and revisionist pig, are under arrest for crimes against the state.' Alfie was clubbed to the ground by the butt of Alexei's gun where he lay, confused and hurt. Alexei shouted into the bedroom. 'Thank you and good-night Comrade.' Anna Petrova did not reply but turned over and went back to sleep as her lover, the unfortunate Alfred, was hauled out and bundled into an awaiting car.

They sat together in the backseat of the spacious sedan as it rumbled through the deserted streets of the Moscow night. 'Sorry about that old chum,' said Alexei, 'but listen to me carefully and do exactly as I say or that mad bastard Beria will have us both shot. Don't speak just listen. This is the last time we will have any privacy. Once we get out of the car every word spoken will be heard. Don't worry about the driver, he's deaf. There are microphones everywhere and lip-readers with binoculars. You have been arrested for spying. It doesn't matter that you are innocent – as far as we are concerned you are guilty. We are going to the Lubyanka, the Headquarters of the secret police – I am a Colonel, you know that don't you? You will be interrogated, mostly by me. I apologise in advance that I will have to beat you up a little – not too much, just keeping up appearances so to speak. Protest your innocence for a day or two but then give in and agree that you are a spy. There will then be a trial and you will be found guilty and sentenced to life imprisonment. After a week or so, I will come in the middle of the night, have you put in a truck and taken to a field outside Moscow. There you will kneel and I will shoot you in the back of the head. It will be a blank of course, but might still sting. You pitch forward and lie still. Do not move at all, not at all! About an hour later a car will arrive and your 'body' will be put in the back. You will be given transit papers, a new passport and put on a train for Germany. And that's it. A week or so later you will be home in your parent's house in Reading. Thank you for saving my life those few years ago – one good turn deserves another as you say. One last thing, you built a bloody fine Metro system Alfie – you should be proud.'

Alfie Tomkins missed the grand opening celebrations to mark his magnificent accomplishment. Anna Petrova, his former lover, sat next to his reserved but vacant seat, and watched the Bolshoi ballet perform Swan Lake under the spectacular octagonal roof of Komsomolskaya Metro station.

⌐

Forty-five years later Peter Donnelly, Mark Chittenden, Arthur Mapp and Chris Bowles gazed in admiration at the splendour of the same station. No-one could be immune to its spectacular beauty. Above their heads hung a huge chandelier of filigree metalwork gilded, according to the guidebook, with pure gold leaf. It was centrally attached to the vaulted ceiling which displayed the red star of Russia embedded in a shining aura of shimmering gold mosaic. They walked towards the platform along an avenue of marble arches each illuminated above by a lesser chandelier burning sixteen electric candle lights; blazing torchieres graced every pillar. Peter stopped to examine a mosaic scene worthy of a place in any museum. It showed a maiden standing on the piled banners and bodies of defeated Nazis, holding a hammer and sickle in one hand and a palm branch in the other. The symbolism was unmistakeable. The guide-book did not mention that this mosaic had been changed six times since the day Alfie Tomkins had commissioned it, each time removing political figures who had fallen out of favour with changing Soviet regimes – and adding new favourites.

'Let's go and see the big bell and gun.' Said Mark. The idea found favour and the quintet left the station and trooped into Red Square. Arthur commented upon the unique oriental architecture of St Basil's Cathedral and then partnered with John Holliday, contrived to get lost. They wandered off into the Moscow sunshine, the frame of the heavyweight briefly eclipsing that of the lightweight fighter. There was nothing comedic about the sixty-kilo weight difference between the men. Any person with eyes to look would see only two perfectly fettled combat athletes. The remaining *judoka*, now a trio, entered the imposing perimeter walls and found the Tsar Bell mounted near the mighty, foreboding walls of the Kremlin. This was now the official home of the Russian President but for over five-hundred years was the fortified palace of successive Tsars. It was indeed a big bell, as high as a house with a massive crack down one side large enough to accommodate a London bus. The guide book helpfully explained that this bell was the third in a series of failures, the previous two being flawed and had cracked during cooling. This, the last one, had almost worked. In 1737 Mikhail Motorin succeeded in casting the giant. He had added 525 kilogrammes of silver and 75 kilos of gold to the molten bronze. The resultant alloy did not crack and great celebrations were held to celebrate Mikhail's success. The bell wasn't finished – a great deal of ornamentation was to be added. Curlicues and relief portraits of the Tsar and Tsarina, angels, cherubs and every form of baroque paraphernalia were brazed onto the bell. Unfortunately, in all this creative turmoil, the workshop which housed it caught fire. This shouldn't have been a problem, but some well-meaning dope responsible for eighteenth century fire-fighting had hosepipes run from the nearby Moskva river, and doused the building, bell included, with copious amounts of ice-cold water. The resulting speedy cooling of the bronze caused it to crack – sod's law I suppose!

'Follow me!' ordered Peter Donnelly. The gun must be inside the museum.' Chris Bowles and Mark Chittenden dutifully followed - but not without question.

'Are you sure?'

'Pretty sure – this way.' They climbed a set of stone steps leading into the imposing fortress. Peter waved his Olympic competitors pass at the soldiers at the top - and saluted. The guards came to attention and the three athletes passed into the building without hindrance. The long corridor was devoid of pictures or statuary - surprising for a museum. Two more guards stood dutifully on either side of the distant double doors towards which they marched. 'Keep in step,' said Peter, 'the Russians like it.' It seemed to do the trick. Once more Olympic passes were waved and this time one soldier politely opened the door. They found themselves in a featureless corridor, empty but for two more guards standing at far-away black double doors.

'This is the first museum I've been in with no paintings.' Chris Bowles nodded in agreement to Mark's comment, 'and where are the other visitors?'

'It's fine,' said Peter beginning to enjoy himself. 'It's probably a quiet day.' This time the passes shown elicited a different response. Both guards blocked their way, machine guns menacingly pointing forwards. From behind, doors crashed open and six soldiers stamped down the corridor, guns raised. The squaddies spoke little, but the one word 'Up!' accompanied by the matching gestures of several gun barrels was sufficient communication. Three pairs of arms were immediately raised. There are an estimated 72 million AK-47 machine guns in the world and one of them prodded Peter Donnelly in the back. He fleetingly remembered the tale told by his old Sensei, Kevin Murphy, that the best defence against a knife was a machine gun and appreciated the irony of the position he was in; judo is generally ineffective against a Kalashnikov. They were roughly bundled down the corridor with much shouting and posturing. The judoka were separated and each shoved through a different heavy black door.

'Peter, Peter, Peter! You joker, it's good for you that I'm here, you betcha! Pay attention! Sit down and don't worry.' Vitaly Brezhnev sat behind a plain desk, the room being otherwise empty except for one other chair. Vitaly, complete with sun-glasses and black hat was smoking and seemingly relaxed with his feet up and his chair tilted back on two legs. 'Sit down. You make big joke yes? Mind you, if you had gone through the last door you would have been in the President's office and then we would have no choice but to shoot you. Lucky fellow! Not so lucky for the guards you tricked – tomorrow they'll be in Afghanistan fighting the Taliban. Such is life. How are you Peter? Tell your friend Vitaly everything, you joker.' Vitaly seemed to be in good humour but Peter Donnelly could not be sure, the sunglasses masking the Russians eyes.

'Hello 'Pay Attention' – somehow I'm not surprised to see you. We were just looking for the big gun; the biggest canon in the world. Isn't this the museum?' Vitaly roared with laughter and rocked forward. He slapped the desk in front of him and laughed even louder.

''Pay attention?' You call me that? I get it, you betcha! You make big joke. Of course! That will do. A simple mistake. Anyway, don't worry. We have orders not to shoot anyone during the Olympics - Uncle Lenny does not want any incidents. No, no – you and the boys are quite safe.'

'Uncle Lenny? Who's Uncle Lenny?'

'Brezhnev, President Brezhnev. We have the same name did you not notice Peter? We have the same name. Yes, he is my uncle, my great uncle but it does me no good. He does not like me so much.' Peter listened but with little interest. His concerns were elsewhere.

'What will happen to us? What are you going to do?' Vitaly Brezhnev put out his cigarette, stubbing it on the desk.

'Do with you? We're not going to do anything with you – providing you keep your mouths shut that is. Let me explain. If 'we' make a fuss it will show our security to be bad and that will mean the soldiers will never even make it to Afghanistan and I will spend the rest of my life freezing in Siberia – if I'm lucky. If 'you' make a fuss the same thing will happen. No, the best thing is that we throw you out of a side door and we forget all about today, you betcha. You are very lucky Peter that this did not happen at a different time.'

'What? If we'd gotten lost at a different time of day there would have been more trouble?' Peter was genuinely confused.

'No! If you had charged around the Kremlin years ago when Uncle Joe was in charge, everyone would have been shot – you betcha!'

'You had another uncle who was President?'

'Again no! Pay attention! No, of course not. 'Uncle Joe' – Josef Stalin. He was the nation's uncle – everyone loved him. Mind you, he did have a lot of people killed, so people had to love him if they wanted to stay alive – but things are much better now. We hardly shoot anyone and absolutely nobody during the Olympics.' The

Russian rose to his feet and put his arm around Peter's shoulders. 'Come on, time to get the others and throw you out. Have you ever been to Reading?' Peter was now calmer but still shaken and now confused by the question.

'Reading? Once or twice – it's a nice little town by the river. Why?'

'No reason. My father had a friend there. Papa dreamed of going, but they shot him before he had chance.'

'Shot him! My God!' Peter felt genuine alarm at this casual statement. 'I'm so sorry.'

'Oh, it's nothing, so long ago. He was denounced as an imperialist revisionist and disappeared. A pity, he was a nice man, but it was his own fault.'

'Why? Why was it his own fault?' Vitaly took off his sunglasses to reveal pale blue, sad and tired eyes. He looked at Peter without emotion.

'He was sleeping with a Russian countess and my mother found out. Mama was a good communist with high up connections in the secret police.'

'Good God! She had your father shot for adultery!'

'No, no you must not think that – she was a good woman. It was more that Papa was shagging an aristocrat. It offended her socialist principles.'

⌐

On the evening of July 30th 1980 Neil Adams and Ezio Gamba stood on their respective podium positions and watched the flags rise at the conclusion of their medal presentation ceremony. Neither heard the national anthem of their country played in the Lenin Palace of Sports and neither saw the Union flag of Great Britain raised nor the tricolour of Italy. Instead, the Olympic anthem rang out and two flags depicting the five Olympic rings hung in honour of the winners of the gold and silver medal. But the unthinkable had happened. Neil Adams, often regarded as the greatest player in the world, a hot favourite for the gold medal had lost. No-one in the British judo community expected this result. They had fought before and Adams had twice beaten his great Italian rival – but Gamba had won at their last encounter the previous December. Neil had raced through the four earlier rounds – no fight lasting longer than a minute and a half, each terminating in a full *ippon*. Gamba's performance had been good but not quite as impressive: Christian Dyot of France had taken him the distance with Gamba winning by decision. But in the final against Adams, he had a lucky break – or perhaps he had done his homework well?

Peter Donnelly had watched his friend, the talisman of the British judo team, unexpectedly lose. He was saddened. Neil was a once in a generation judoka, but anyone could be thrown – sometimes you won fights you should have lost and lost fights you should have won - a fundamental judo truth. His own event had finished two days earlier and finally he had achieved a level of calmness. He felt physically and emotionally drained but had had an epiphany, a life changing moment. In the repechage semi-final he had fought Detlef Ultsch, the current world champion, to a standstill. Time had been called and both men, exhausted, sat back on their haunches struggling for the energy to rise. Ultsch spoke to him, each word a gasping effort. 'Donnelly! Donnelly! Donnelly!' Nothing else was said but Peter recognised it for what it was – the salute of one great player to another. They adjusted their *judo-gi*, stood and awaited the referee's decision which went to Ultsch. Peter accepted the call completely. He knew it could have gone either way as did the German. He also knew it was the last decision he would ever face on a judo mat. His competitive days in his beloved sport were now irrevocably over.

That evening he lay in his room, grateful to be alone particularly from the heartfelt commiserations received from his team mates. His chest was tight and he felt strange, oddly detached from everything around him. He was cocooned, as if he was seeing the world clearly but insulated from it by a thick pane of plate glass. He did not feel upset or disappointed by his performance, but try as he might he could not but continually review his fights:

The Cuban was the unknown quantity. The draw for the U86 kilogramme category had been posted first thing in the morning and Peter, in company with the other competitors gathered around the events board. There were two pools, both even regarding the quality of competitors. Fleetingly he wished he was in the alternative half where the two favourites were undoubtedly the Swiss, Rothlisburger and the Soviet Yatskevitch. Peter knew he had the beating of Jurg Rothlisburger; Yatskevitch was tough and had won the recent European championships in Vienna where Peter had picked up the bronze but... He forced his mind away from such daydreams to concentrate on the job in hand. Who was Isaac Azcuy? He was not on the international circuit – the Cubans did not travel much. He was probably good. Cuba was building a reputation for excellence in a variety of sports including judo. If he could defeat Ascuy it would be either him or Detlef Ultsch in the final – of this Peter Donnelly felt sure.

If Peter had a defensive weakness it was to attacks made with right-handed *ippon seoi-nage*, He'd lost to this throw in the Polish Open. Gary Haroise had turned him with the same technique in the final of the Dutch, fortunately without scoring – but it had given him a fright. Subsequently he had trained and trained to develop a strong right-legged defence. He had put in the hours; he should be alright.

The contest against Azcuy was going well. Little had happened and Peter felt strong and comfortable. He had put in one big *uki-goshi* attack which the Cuban blocked easily enough with both players falling to the floor. Azcuy had the dominant position but chose not to transition into ne-*waza* – something which Peter mentally recorded. The referee restarted the contest and there was a brief but intense period of grip fighting. Azcuy cross gripped to the left and then threw in a big *ippon-seoi*. Peter was ready and braced hard with his right leg simultaneously dropping his weight backwards. Azcuy collapsed his left leg and rolled Peter 'off the other side' scoring an unexpected *ippon*. Peter felt calm but cold. He understood the loss meant his chance of a gold medal was gone - but he seemed detached. He saw the bout awarded to Azcuy as if he was watching through the eyes of another. His world seemed unreal. He won his other repechage fights with ease – until the decision loss against Ultsch...

His carousel of thoughts was mercifully interrupted by a knock, at the door. The unmistakeable head of Duncan Goodhew came into sight; the famous bald head that had been on every television screen a week earlier when he won his 100-metre breaststroke gold medal.

'Hello Peter. How's tricks?' Donnelly levered himself up onto his elbows but stayed on his bed.

'Not so bad Duncan. Come in. Take a seat. How about yourself?' Duncan Goodhew sat at the end of the single bed.

'Pretty good, all in all. I'm glad that the interviews have stopped. It was great to begin with but it became too much. Now I walk past the reporters and most don't even say hello. Such is life! But it all seems unreal. To be honest Peter I feel flat – as if there should be something more. Very strange, very odd.' He squirmed a little on the bed and changed the focus of the conversation. 'And you? Any plans? Going for the top spot next time?' Peter paused and then gave his reply clearly and without emotion.

'No... I'm done. I've climbed the judo ladder and stood near the top. The scrap with Ultsch was my last fight.' Duncan Goodhew, Olympic champion recognised the finality of a fellow athlete's words.

'Well, what's next then?'

'I don't know for sure. One thing is certain though, judo has given me a different view of myself. I've fought a hundred international events in a dozen or more countries. I'm one of the best players in the world – not bad for a scrawny council estate kid with a weak chest. I've climbed the hill and like the view, so whatever I do I won't be going back to being a tool-maker in a car factory.'

'Sounds like a plan Peter. Good luck!'

'Nothing to do with luck Duncan - we both know that. You got your gold medal through hard work and I'll hammer out my future in the same way.' The great swimmer leaned on the bed and held out his hand which Peter grasped firmly. The tightness in the *judoka's* chest vanished and he breathed easily. He looked out of the window and saw the star that topped Moscow State University twinkling redly in the fading evening light.

He felt that the city was his friend.

⌣

Chapter Two
A Young Esquire

THE VICTORY HALL was one of a thousand similar built to commemorate the triumph of the massed armies of the British Empire in defeating those of Kaiser Bill 1918, thus concluding the Great War. In fairness the French and American forces helped a bit as well, albeit in the case of the Americans, they arrived three years late and the French were at times a little half-hearted. To be even more precise, it turned out that the great victory of 1918 was in fact merely half-time as the whole shooting match started up again in 1939.

But at least we had the Victory Hall in which to play, and play we did. Every Tuesday and Friday night it became the dojo of the Budokan Judo Club. Half-way through a junior training session my brother, *Sensei* Kevin took me aside and asked, 'Who's the cheeky little sod?'

'Which cheeky little sod? They're all cheeky little sods.' In truth I was still a kid myself, but at twelve years old big enough to arrive early with Kevin and put out the mats – forty ex-army flock mattresses held in place by a wooden frame and covered with sailcloth. The mats were stored under the four-foot stage and it was my job to get them out – a task not made easier by Kevin insisting that this was to be done from the squatting position.

'Makes your thighs strong,' he said. 'It's one of the reasons the Japs are so good at judo. They sit on the floor and eat at low tables – they're forever getting up and down. They've got muscles like rocks have the Japs. Kenshiro Abbe would tense his thighs in the squat position and get young Dan grades to hit them with broom handles. I tell you now Danny, I've seen this happen with my own eyes and more than once the staves snapped across his legs. As I say – muscles like rocks. Now you get under that stage and throw out those mats!' I must have been stupid, but there again Kevin did have the knack of saying the most ridiculous of things and making you believe them. I suppose sports psychologists would say that he instilled self-belief. (I say he could get you to believe the proverbial ox-droppings – like the time he said I could beat Parisi as he was vulnerable to a left-handed *uchi-mata*. In the event, when I did fight Angelo, I could not have thrown him with a left-handed JCB.) Anyway, I digress.

'Get under that stage,' ordered Kevin, 'in a squat mind - the kids will be here soon.'

I saw him arrive, the slim torso of a lad dressed in jeans, tee-shirt and black school shoes. To begin with that was all I saw from my position as his head and shoulders were above the level of the stage door's opening. I heard him speak to Kevin in the otherwise empty hall.

'Is this where they do the judo mister?'

'It is where *we* do judo son. And don't call me mister – call me *Sensei*.'

'*Sensei*? What's a *Sensei*?'

'I'm the *Sensei* - the instructor, the person in charge of the club.'

'Can you break a brick with your bare hands?'

'No son, I'm not stupid. If I wanted to break a brick, I'd use a hammer, or maybe your head. Sod off we're busy.'

'Can I do judo *Sensei*?' The boy was comfortably persistent.

'No, I've told you bugger off. We're busy – anyway it's not free you have to pay. Have you got sixpence?'

'No, but I've got fourpence.'

'Oh, bloody hell. I'll find you a kit - get under the stage and get the mats out. Danny! I've found you a helper.'

The young boy of maybe ten years old jumped through the stage storage doors and immediately grabbed a mattress. In the dim light I could see he had straight black hair, even features and a lop-sided tooth. 'Hiya,' he said. Who are you?'

'I'm Danny, and *Sensei* is my big brother so watch yourself.' This attempted threat was ignored.

'Do you do judo – are you any good?' He took a mat from me and hurled it through the trap door. I noticed he had big hands and that he handled the mattresses with little effort - as easily as me and it was obvious that I was a few years older.

'I'm okay. I'm a junior blue belt which is quite good.'

'I want to be a black-belt. Will that take long?'

'Depends on all sorts of things. Anyway, you can't be a black belt until you're sixteen.'

'Well, I'm ten so I'll be a black belt in six years then. Oh – forgot. My name's Peter Donnelly.'

⌒

'The kid who helped you with the mats is a good lad. Do you know anything about him?' asked Kevin. The class had paired off and all were practising *o-goshi* which was the first throw Kevin taught. Other throws came along of course but without fail *o-goshi* was practised every night. ('Judo is like an Oak tree,' said Kevin. 'Every branch is a throw, and the smaller branches are the variations – but *o-goshi* is the trunk.)'

'His name is Peter Donnelly, that's all I know. Oh yes, he says he will be a black-belt by the time he's sixteen.'

'He will be – no doubt about it.'

'What do you mean, *Sensei*? This is the first time he's been on the mat. He probably won't stick at it – his sort never does.'

'What do you mean, 'his sort?''

'You know, gobby little brats.'

'Well Danny, that's fine coming from you! I tell you now he's the best kid I've seen on the mat – yourself included and you're pretty good.' I was annoyed at his statement.

'How can you tell? He's only been on the mat for five minutes?'

'You're right. He has - but I haven't! He's got judo born into him – it's coming out of his ears. He's smart and a quick learner.' I was even more childishly annoyed.

'What about me! I'm clever, I've passed all my exams and won a scholarship – one of only ten in Birmingham!'

'You're university smart. He's judo smart. Go and help those two over there with their body positioning and get them to bend their legs and keep their backs straight.'

⌒

Big brothers can be very blunt and quite crushing, particularly so in Kevin's case who was twenty years older than me. My late birth was the result of my father returning from the Second World War, my mother wrongly assuming she was beyond childbearing age and Roman Catholicism – a religion with quaint views on contraception.

Kevin had first encountered martial arts while serving in the Royal Navy. Unarmed combat was taught to all troops, but Kevin took to jiu-jitsu like the proverbial duck to water. He was conscripted in 1944 as a callow youth, Irish born but from the slums of Birmingham and soon found himself on board His Majesty's Ship, Indefatigable – 'The Indyfat.'

'I suppose every person had a different war...' Kevin held court in our parents' house in Alum Rock. After training on Friday, the routine was always the same – fish and chips from 'Stevie Pops' chippy, and then back to the house where mom always left piles of bread and butter. She was usually in bed by the time we arrived. The 'we' varied over the years but was normally Kevin, me, Tony Underwood, Dave Law, and Peter Donnelly. Peter was a few years younger than the rest of us but was always under our feet. In the end we gave up trying to get rid of him and as we grew older smuggled him into pubs and clubs as the easier option. Kevin swallowed a mouthful of chips and carried on speaking.

'My war was pretty good all in all – quite exciting. You feel bloody safe on a big aircraft carrier protected by a hundred anti-aircraft guns, heavy machine guns, rockets, torpedoes and fifty planes - Sea-fires, Avengers and Fireflies. We were sent to the far-east to join the Pacific Fleet in preparation for the invasion of Japan. Thank God the war came to an end before that happened. We were attacked by about ten Japanese bombers in January, but our Sea-fires saw them off. I think we shot them all down. But the scariest time, and I thought my number was up, was when we suffered a Divine Wind attack – a *Kami-kaze*. How it got through our defences God knows! We threw everything at it - Oerlikons, Bofors, cannons, heavy machine guns, rockets, the lot! But somehow it got through and hit just at the base of the control tower. The old Indyfat was heavily armoured and little damage was done – mind you the bomb it was carrying didn't go off or the story could have had a different ending. I was crewing an Oerlikon, a bit of a light-weight gun but with a good rate of fire. As I say every gun the ship could bear was banging away – you never heard such a racket. When it was all over, I thought I'd wet myself – my trousers were soaking – but it turned out just to be sweat.'

'How do you know *Sensei*?' interrupted Donnelly through a mouthful of chips.'

'Because I tasted it, young Peter! How do you think?' Everyone laughed. The conversation quickly returned to judo. 'Now you might find it strange to know that we had a few Japanese on board, as we were at war with Japan. But these were interpreters I think second generation lads from Hawaii, anyway they spoke English with an American accent. One of them – we called him 'Tojo' which looking back on it was in bad taste as that was the name of the Prime Minister of Japan, gave us jiu-jitsu lessons. We had all had unarmed combat training but what Tojo showed us was something else, a completely higher level of skills. We had made a little dojo in the corner of one of the aircraft hangars. It was noisy, stank of grease and aviation fuel, was hotter than an oven but it did the job. There was no *tatami* of course but we found padded engine covers which we put under canvas sheets. It was a bit lumpy but gave some protection from the floor, which remember was one-inch steel plate.'

'Now you guys, let's get one thing straight,' said Tojo. 'I'm in charge and you're not. What you call me off the mat is up to you – I really don't care a flying fish. On the mat you call me 'Sempai'. If you stick to martial arts long enough, you will come across another word – 'Sensei', which you will never call me as I am not worthy of that honour. Guys, do you understand me?'

'Yes,' we mumbled.

'Jesus H. Christ! That was a waste of breath. Yes *Sempai*! Shout it out for Christ sake!'

'Yes *Sempai*!'

'Lesson number one. Defence against a knife attack. What is the best defence? Anyone?'

'Twenty foot of fresh air and a machine gun?'

'What's your name son? Groucho Marx?' *Sempai* Tojo adopted a pained, long suffering expression.

'Murphy *Sempai*!'

'Murphy. I am forty-two years old and am missing my mother, wife and children. They are locked up in a camp in Hawaii because some mad baskets from the old country, a country I've never even seen, decided to bomb the American fleet. Your answer, although technically correct, annoys me. So, if you don't mind, pick up that bayonet over there and attack me. You will note that I do not have a machine gun. If you kill me don't worry. The other guys here will swear it was my own fault and the navy police will only be pleased that you've killed another dirty Jap.'

'Well lads, I realised that I'd gotten myself into a tight spot though opening my big mouth – a lesson to be learned young Donnelly.'

'What did you do?'

'Nothing I could do – I picked up the bayonet and attacked him. I supposed the outcome could have been worse though. He turned into my thrust, locked the wrist and knife with both hands and then turned out. I thought my wrist would break but I managed to release the pressure by rolling forwards. He flew into an arm-lock - I was still holding the knife. Now, both my wrist and elbow were locked and causing great pain. He took the bayonet from my hand and gently put the point up my nose.

'Listen up,' said Tojo, 'one of two things can happen...'

'Sorry *Sempai*! Sorry!'

'No Murphy, that's not it. You can either sing 'Mary had a little lamb' a song which I have always liked or...I'll accidentally break your arm.'

'What did you do?' Peter sat wide-eyed at *Sensei* Kevin's feet.

'What do you think? The sing-song wasn't so bad really, young Peter, the rest of the lads joined in. That was it – I was hooked! Jiu-jitsu, judo whatever, I could not get enough and still can't. Tojo was my first instructor and to me he was '*Sensei*.' If he wasn't worth the title, then Lord knows who is.'

⌇

Training at the Budokan carried on, the weeks, months and years methodically clicked on as if an eccentric metronome ticked off Tuesday and Friday evenings. Boys and girls grew up; new players joined and many left, judo not for them. Those that stayed improved and Peter never missed a session. Even when laid low with a cough or chest infection, of which he had more than his fair share, he always turned up, invariably early to help with the mats.

'Not going on the mat tonight young Peter?' Kevin ruffled his hair as he sat mat-side whilst the rest of the club were getting changed.

'I don't think so *Sensei*. I've got a terrible cough and can hardly breathe.'

Now this perfectly reasonable statement was the wrong thing to say to Kevin. His list of good attributes did not include any form of medical training. He did have a variety of cures and remedies, which would not have been out of place at the time of the Black Death. He also had the unshakeable, but misplaced, conviction that he knew what he was doing. In the nineteen-fifties and sixties judo still had a hint of eastern mystery about it and many of the early *Sensei*s dabbled in oriental healing, massage, bone manipulation, that sort of thing. In some respects, they acquired mystical status – most of them were benign cranks. Kevin had without doubt incredible knowledge of judo, which was more or less where his compass ended. But that did not stop him from being regarded as some sort of wise man to the judo community – a position which he did nothing to discourage. For example, Tony Underwood who then had a fine head of hair was plagued with dandruff. Kevin had a cure. 'Try paraffin – it works a treat. Guaranteed to cure dandruff. Wash your hair and rub paraffin into your scalp. The dandruff will be gone in no time.'

We did not see Tony out and about for a while and when we did, he smelled and continued to smell of paraffin oil. He was also wearing a cotton sun hat - strange for February.

'What did you rub on your head Tony?' asked Kevin puzzled.

'Esso Blue. Dad keeps a gallon in the shed for his green-house heater.'

'You daft so-and-so, Tony. I meant liquid paraffin - not paraffin oil!'

'I didn't know there were two types of paraffin.'

'Well, there are. Liquid paraffin is good for the skin and paraffin oil is for burning in lamps and oil heaters.' After a while Tony did get sympathy of a sort.

'Did it hurt Tony?' I asked. I had gotten used to his aroma which reminded me of a hardware shop.

'It slowly began to sting and then got worse – as if my head was on fire. I put my it under the cold tap in the kitchen but too late; the damage was done. It killed all the skin on the top of my scalp.'

'Is that why you're wearing the sun hat?'

'No – it's because the dead skin is worse than the dandruff. I've got so much now it's like a snowstorm. I'm wearing the hat to keep it in.'

⌐∽

But we had complete trust in him, *Sensei* Kevin's word was law. When he suggested to the young Peter that a massage would help his congested chest this was not questioned. 'I've got some homemade liniment which is perfect for the job. It will ease your chest in no time. Get your shirt off Peter and lie at the edge of the mat.'

'What is it *Sensei*?' Asked Peter as Kevin massaged the creamy lotion into his back and chest.

'It's basically horse liniment but I've added some other stuff to beef it up a bit. Trust me it will open your lungs up in no time.'

'Horse liniment *Sensei*!' said Peter in some alarm.

'Yes, but don't concern yourself lad. Horses and people are much the same - and there's a bit of wintergreen oil and turpentine as well. You'll soon be back on the mat.'

This was important to Peter who was now twelve and due to enter his first major competition, the under sixteen event at the Amateur Judo Association of Great Britain's national championships. For the past year or so, he had trained at both the junior and senior sessions at the Budokan and we had both added an extra Thursday night's practice at the Morris Commercial Judo Club. Kevin's first day prediction that he would be extraordinarily talented had proved to be correct. He had started to win local junior events with predictable ease, but the AJA nationals only had two age groups – under sixteen and seniors. He was completely committed to his training and we had our own additional regime - a thousand Saturday *uchi-komi*. We were now close friends. and he at almost thirteen and me a gawky two years older were well matched for size.

Kevin rolled Peter over and began once more to massage and pummel his back using much of his home-made potion. The dojo began to fill with the not unpleasant vaguely medicinal smell of horse embrocation and wintergreen. Peter began to cough violently.

'See what did I tell you.' Said *Sensei* Kevin. 'The muck on your chest is loosening and you'll soon be breathing fine. How're you feeling?'

'Much better *Sensei* – I think I'll put my kit on.'

'Well just do some *uchis* to loosen up and maybe a bit of light randori with Danny. Throw for throw! Nothing else! I'm sick of telling you two to save the *shiai* for competition.' Peter and I moved to the edge of the tatami, bowed and took a grip both adopting a left-handed posture at the insistence of *Sensei* Kevin. ('Most people fight right-handed. So, if you fight left there is a slight advantage. You get more practice defending against right-handed attacks than they do defending left. Not much of an advantage but worth having.')

'How's your chest Pete? Are you OK?'

'Well, we all know *Sensei* Kev is a bit off his head with his Japanese mumbo-jumbo and everything. But I tell you Danny I can breathe better than I've been able to do for weeks. My back and chest feel lovely and warm. A real nice glow – like being under a heat lamp. What shall we start with?'

'Blocks of twenty *o-goshi* each and change throw after one hundred?'

There is something very satisfying about *uchi-komi* practice; the repetitive action can become absorbing. Muscle memory takes over and the mind is free to wander or wonder – or do nothing but relax. Except of course landing on a hard mat every twentieth movement tends to jar you back to reality. Kevin's voice boomed out across the mat. 'Danny, there is no point in practicing a mistake. Your *uchi-komi* practice builds up the muscles you use in the throw. Bend your bloody knees! You couldn't lift a car if the jack was already straight could you? And you make sure your *tsukuri* is right in practice so that it's a habit in competition. What's your right arm doing?'

'Pulling *Sensei*.'

'Well, it shouldn't be; it should be pulling *and* lifting. Point your right elbow and lift. Get him on his toes.'

'And what are you doing Donnelly?'

'Everything perfectly *Sensei*.' Came the reply.

'Cheeky sod!' But *Sensei* Kevin smiled contentedly and drifted away to annoy someone else. We worked hard and after a hundred each I called the change to *taio-toshi*. Peter began to look at me in a peculiar manner and started to squirm and continually pull at the crotch of his *judo-gi*.

'What's up Pete?'

'Bollocks.'

'Bollocks yourself you little ...'

'No, no. My bollocks are on fire. Bloody hell!'

Peter ran off the mat, realised that he had not bowed, stepped back on and bowed off – and ran screaming for the toilet.

'What's up with him,' asked *Sensei* Kevin.

'He says his bollocks are on fire.'

'That'll be the wintergreen I suppose,' said Kevin his voice without concern. 'It must have mixed with sweat and dripped down onto his private parts. I better go and check on him.' Practice had ground to a halt with forty young men and women looking at the only toilet come changing room, listening to the moaning that came from within. After five minutes or so Kevin came out wearing a lop-sided grin. He addressed the class. 'He'll be fine but don't go in – he's sitting with his wedding tackle in the sink filled with cold water.' He spoke to me in a quieter tone. 'Mind you, unless it's temporary swelling brought on by the wintergreen, the ladies are in for a shock.'

⌒

It was four o'clock on a cold November morning and forty or so judoka, friends, family, supporters and associated hangers-on, waited in the cold autumn air - sunrise still a few hours distant. Things were different in the mid-sixties. Few people had cars and motorway travel was non-existent, except for the M1 which went only part way to London. The AJA championships were at the De Montfort Hall, Leicester. The only practical way to such events was by coach. One had been ordered, paid for but was late. The group was mainly assembled under the awning of the Grand Cinema, which provided some shelter from the fine rain now falling, and gave soft yellow illumination from the foyer lights.

A few adults nervously smoked; many did in those days as the health risks were largely unknown. But not the fighters – banned from this activity by *Sensei*. 'You can't fight with your lungs full of soot – no arguments. If I catch you smoking or if you smell of smoke, then you're out of the team!'

'But Mom and Dad smoke. That's not fair *Sensei* my clothes always smell of cigarettes.' Kevin, who never admitted being wrong about anything simply said, 'Peter, I don't care – don't smoke and don't come to judo smelling of smoke. Figure it out.'

In the end there were no dramas: the coach arrived ten minutes late but still in time to get to Leicester for the eight o'clock weigh-in. Peter sat on the back-bench seat of the coach with other young teenagers and I sat with Kevin and discussed the day's prospects. I was just sixteen, a senior brown belt, and more than held my own against the club's Dan grades and most of those who visited. 'How do you think I'll get on Kev?'

'Hard to say Danny. You're good on the mat and stand a fair chance in the Kyu grade events. There are not many brown belts better than you. But in truth this growth spurt you've had has done you no favours. How tall are you now? How heavy?'

'Almost six foot and seventy-three kilos.'

'To be honest, you need to put on ten kilos of muscle. No problem - you will when you get older with training and the right diet; but tall and skinny ain't the best shape for a judo player. You put a lot of people over with the left *taio-toshi* and the *uchi-mata* so that's good. But your defence is weak against short powerful players. You could do well – depends on who you fight.'

'Well, I won't be fighting Tony Underwood. Thank God he's got his Dan grade!'

'Yes, he is a bit special – a couple of years older than you which counts at your age.' I had met Tony a year or so earlier and he made an impression:

⌒

It seems to be a natural thing amongst judo players that when you get to that level of ability when you are winning more than losing you look around for someone new to fight. Peter Donnelly and I had both taken to training an extra evening at the Morris Commercial JC. The club was building a reputation as a place to go for a 'hard knock' and there were few harder knocks than the club's instructor, Bob Trevis. One Thursday night unknown face entered the dojo, bowed and was granted permission to step onto the mat. He was sandy haired with a wispy moustache and very heavily muscled across his back but lean elsewhere. 'Who's that,' asked Peter as we practiced together.

'I don't know, but he's only a brown belt same as me. He shouldn't be much trouble.'

The training session progressed as they always did; Bob coaching a new technique or variations; *uchi-komi*; *nage-komi*; *ne-waza* etc. with the last half-hour called as a free mat, which inevitably meant fighting. The newcomer came over to me.

'Do you fancy a pull?' He spoke the judoka's universal challenge to fight.

'OK.' I attempted to appear off-hand, perhaps even bored.

We took hold, both with a double lapel grip and prepared to do battle. While I was still preparing, I found myself flat on my back with no real idea as to what had happened. I was shocked. I had obviously been thrown but how and with what was a mystery. Perhaps I had tripped or momentarily blacked out? I got up and with more caution again took hold, locked my elbows and adopted a low *jigotai* defensive posture. After a minute it happened again but at least this time more slowly. I was being thrown with a left-handed hip technique. His *kuzushi* was so powerful that I was drawn onto tiptoes and his hips so low that his buttocks were below my knees. For the first time I fully understood why Jigaro Kano named 'Judo'- the Gentle Way. (In later years the great international player, Roy Inman who fought Tony twice in event finals referred to him as a 'floater', a player who would adopt the lightest of touches until he attacked and then explode into the throw.) By the end of the session, he had thrown me seven times with the same technique.

'I'm Tony Underwood', he said, as he shook my hand and left the mat.

⌐

The coach made its bumpy way to Leicester, there was no motorway route and the suspension of the coach and the surface of the road left much to be desired. Dawn was beginning to break. Some tried in vain to sleep but Kevin and I continued analysing the prospects for the day ahead. 'What about Peter, how do you think he'll do?' Kevin replied.

'He's in the same boat as you in a way. He's a great little player – we all know that, but he's not yet thirteen. He'll be fighting guys a year or two older, and at his age that counts. There's a lad from Northampton who I've seen on the circuit and he's good, older and heavier. He's won a lot of events; Peter will have his work cut out.'

Peter Myles Donnelly, the subject of our conversation, was not thinking about judo at all. He sat in the corner of the back seat of the coach next to a very pretty girl of his own age. They were both grateful for the dimmed lights. She was ridiculously pretty with perfect skin, blue eyes and ash blonde hair. Her teeth were even and Colgate white. I turned around to see that Peter had his hand, shall we say, on her knee and his tongue down her throat. I was annoyed, in truth I should better say, I was jealous. I was a lusty lad who, in those Rolling Stone words, was getting 'no satisfaction.' Donnelly seemed to be getting plenty, which was unfair. I had no luck with girls whatsoever and he seemed to be getting my share. I don't know why this was. I was tall, athletic, good looking in a certain light and passably hygienic. There were plenty of young ladies in the judo scene at that time. I remember in particular two buxom farm-girls, let's call them Rose and Heather for the sake of discretion. I was interested in either of these two lovelies but this was not reciprocated.

Tony Underwood did well in that department. Rose and Heather were both enamoured with him and he seemingly did not disappoint. I first noticed that something was going on when he volunteered to give both a lift home in his Triumph Vitesse. This was a sporty little number, a two-seater sports car really with a useless rear courtesy seat. One of the luckless girls had to cram in the back. At first this caused no fuss – the girls were young and bendy. After a while though, they would bicker, not unreasonably, as to whom should sit in the front. Tony also began arriving at training sessions wearing a shirt and tie. This continued for several months and each Friday night Tony would dutifully give the girls a lift home. The huffing and puffing regarding the occupancy of the front seat became worse, culminating in sulks and one full blown argument with Heather storming off into the Warwickshire night screaming abuse. The girls were not seen again – and Tony stopped wearing a tie.

It took me forty years to find out what had occurred:

Seemingly both Heather and Rose were willing to accept Tony's sexual ardour. However, the occupant of the front seat was the first to be satisfied and before round two could commence there was a lengthy wait. To add further insult the supporting event was invariably a less passionate affair, his urgency, shall we say, being softer. This caused no problem to begin with as the car had a radio and they listened to pop music for a half hour. The trouble arose when Tony began to favour one over the other regarding seating arrangements.

'And what was the tie all about?' I asked him.

'Oh, Heather liked to hold it while we were, well you know...' I did know. Perhaps it gave her a better grip on the proceedings.

The coach journey to De Montfort hall continued. First light became dawn and then full daylight. I turned round to see that Peter had finished his adolescent shenanigans and was now fast asleep, his head nestled in the pretty girl's lap. I wanted to punch him in the face.

⌒

Peter was failing at school and it was not clear to me why. My sixth form studies were going well, and I offered to help him with his maths – a particular struggle. He accepted this and his mom and dad were grateful so for a while we would sit in their kitchen and go through his homework. It was obvious to me that he was very bright but also deficient in the basics, the rules of number and the like, primary school stuff really. And then he started to cough...

Peter was diagnosed with COPD which plagued his early life. These letters stand for 'chronic obstructive pulmonary disease.' This sounds so much better than 'bad chest' but in truth means much the same - both terms being equally imprecise. They form a well-known medical deceit 'the fallacy of nomination' which means by giving something a fancy name it sounds as if the medics have a better handle on things. (I remember going to the doctors many years ago with a very unpleasant itchy bum. I explained my symptoms in embarrassing detail at the end of which the learned doctor said, 'Well boy, it seems you have 'anus pruritis.' I understand Latin and could not resist saying to the old quack, 'I came with an itchy arse and you have just told me I've got an itchy arse in Latin. Are you going to tell me how to cure it in Latin too?' He threw me out and said, 'Don't be cheeky.'

Peter's mother fussed benevolently and provided cake. Sister Lynne had her entrances and exits. The gummy dog, McGregor was interested for a while but then chewed at an old slipper. Mr Donnelly did as fathers did in those day and kept out of the way of things he deemed not of his concern. (I must waste a sentence in favour of Mrs Donnelly's cake. It was excellent, light, moist with the slightest tendency to crumble. I believe women baked better in those days and I think I know why. Mothers who guided their families through the war years and rationed sugar, used less of it. Cake had flavour rather than gooey sweetness.) As I tutored him it became obvious that the young Peter Donnelly had no learning difficulties whatsoever. What he did have was gaping holes in his basic education caused by school non-attendance which in turn was caused by both his illness and its treatment. As they say, success breeds success and just as importantly failure breeds failure. The more he fell behind, the less he was inclined to catch up.

⌒

The City of Birmingham, the hot house of the industrial revolution, the 'city of one thousand trades,' was grounded in old ideas of philanthropy and civic responsibility. This was still alive in the 1950s but sadly in decline, soon to be a history book memory. The city parks, open spaces in which the city's workers could play and relax, were beautifully maintained. The great employers of the city, Cadbury's, Dunlop, Lucas 'The Austin' and others provided social clubs and sports and recreation grounds. Free concerts were held weekly at the Town Hall where one could listen to the world-renowned City of Birmingham Symphony Orchestra. The free to enter Art Gallery displayed great masterpieces including a magnificent collection of Pre-Raphaelite art. The clock-tower bell at Birmingham University is called 'Big Joe' in honour of the visionary Joseph Chamberlain who founded this prestigious centre for learning. Brummies proudly slaked their thirst with 'Corporation Pop' the purest, sweetest of waters gushing from every lowly tap but originating in the Elan Valley of Wales. The hospitals were amongst the best in the world but were of their time. The care of the young was ever present in the minds and deeds of the city elders.

So, Peter Donnelly received sunray treatment for his bad chest. Two or three times a week he was taken out of school and dragged unwillingly to the Children's Hospital. There he was stripped naked, equipped with opaque goggles and stood reluctantly under heavy ultra-violet lamps referred to then as 'black light.' There was an idea prevalent at the time that sunlight was good – I mean medically good. It does have one confirmed use – it is a reasonable preventative of rickets – a bone-bending leg disease brought on through the lack of the sunlight produced vitamin D. This was common in the early part of the twentieth century amongst city children deprived of sunshine due to indoor living and smoke-filled air. Many was the child who clanked to school in surgical boots and metal callipers fixed at the knee. A Danish physician invented the 'Finsen' lamp, named after him. This blasted out a goodly wattage of UV and is effective in killing bacteria – but not those inside the lungs which to me seems self-apparent. But it was a treatment of its time and the doctors obviously thought it worth a bash. Of course, we know now that sunray treatment has no curative effect on lung disease and is a bit harmful – high doses of UV being a cause of skin cancer.

With one thing and another Peter's school attendance was less than fifty per cent hence, at the appropriate age, he sat and duly failed his 'Eleven Plus' examination. Most children in Great Britain took this test from nineteen forty-four onwards - but few knew what it was. To begin with it was not a true intelligence test; it was more a measure of what had been learned at primary school. It was designed to sort out what type of secondary education most fitted the child's abilities – in practice either academic Grammar or practical Secondary. It was about eighty-five per cent accurate which is either very good or very bad depending on your point of view. There really was a big problem though. Secondary schools were very badly resourced for decades and did not, by and large, provide the quality of education which children deserved.

Peter meandered through five years of inadequate secondary schooling and waved it good-bye clutching a solitary Certificate of Secondary Education in Art.

⌒

It was seven-thirty when the coach turned into the car park of De Montfort Hall. The colonnaded façade was not quite what I had expected. Rather than mediaeval it gave the impression of a Grecian storage facility or Palladian picture house. Nevertheless, my stomach churned, and I realised the day was to begin. I was nervous. I turned around to look at him, expecting that by now he would be fully awake. He was not but had shifted his position so that he was now resting his head in the lap of another pretty girl who caressed him tenderly. I wished him ill and woke him up with my foot.

'Oi! Donnelly, we're here!'

Peter Donnelly and Colin Draycott – British Champions (AJA), 1964

Chapter Three
A Joust at De Montfort Hall

THERE IS SOMETHING magnificent about a judo championship. It is wonderful in a chaotic, noisy, excitable way – and then there is the smell. In the 'old days' a competition had a unique aroma; a combination of sweat, liniments, curative ointments, and above all, the mustiness of judo kits. At that time, many were bought from J. Milom Ltd, Manchester. The Milom *judo-gi* was made of unbleached hessian, and like Levi jeans, had to be purchased one size too large as they shrank. These judo suits also needed a good bath, with a cupful of bleach added to render them white instead of their normal colour of washed out urinary yellow. Eventually, after about a year of wearing and washing, they settled down to being soft, comfortable and white. At a competition you would see suits worn ranging from brand-new, and thus stained as mentioned, with the musty smell of old horse-manure, to older kits, gleaming white and hygienic. Suit control was very lax, and it was rare to see anyone disciplined for an ill-fitting or grubby suit. Washing and drying was by no means easy back then. Not every house had a washing machine, and tumble driers were unheard of. Quite commonly a player turned up to fight with a suit still wet from the last club practice, stored in the meanwhile rolled up in the duffel bag – also supplied by Milom's. The stink was disgusting.

The chaos of a competition was helped by the high numbers in each event category, inadequate mat areas (except at national venues like Crystal Palace), poor quality or non-existent loudspeaker systems, hopeless weigh-in procedures and a general lack of professionalism regarding event management. But we didn't care much and for the most part went along for the ride. You would arrive at a venue, find somewhere to sit with your mates, weigh-in (which took forever) and then hang about, often for hours, waiting for something to happen. British Judo Time was invariably at least two hours later than any other time zone. The De Montfort Hall championship was about normal. The players and supporters from the Budokan and the Morris JC found seats together, the two clubs had developed a very friendly relationship. I was sitting with Bob Trevis, Kevin was nearby, and Peter was getting changed as the under sixteen events were the first to run. A strange commotion was taking place around one of the mat areas. A young man of about twenty, medium built with brown hair and an innocent face was behaving oddly. He wore jeans and a tee-shirt and had a good physique. He walked around the mat with his arms spread out as if in triumph and shouted various admonishments at the crowd.

'Stand for the King! The King is here! Rise peasants – stand for your king!' I had never seen anything like it and was confused.

'What's going on Bob? Who's that?' The shenanigans below us continued with people in the crowd shouting back.

'Sod off Muller, you mad basket.'

'Pack it in Roy. Come and take a seat.' Royston Muller was immune to such pleadings.

'Stand, I say for I am Le Roi – The King! The Muller of mullahs! The Tsunami on the tatami! The Master on the mat!'

'Who is it Bob.' I repeated and he replied.

'It's that mad sod from Great Barr. His name is Roy Muller – they call him the Mad Muller,'

'Is he a bit cracked? He certainly seems it.'

'No, he's just a big wind-up merchant, that's what he is. I think he just does this sort of thing to give him an edge when he fights.'

'Well, I've not seen him before – is he any good?'

'He's mainly a BJA lad, He trains at Great Barr and Solihull with Hudspith, Cannaby and that mob. I've asked him to come down to the Morris. As for how good he is – he's very good. He fought Gerry White in the final of the BJA Midland Area, (White was the reserve for the Tokyo Olympics) and Gerry only just got the decision. If you ever fight him watch his *ashi-waza*. I've never seen anyone as good with foot sweeps.' It was the first time I had seen the Mad Muller and his exhibitionist behaviour made a lasting impression.

⤶

As mentioned, a lot of people entered judo competitions in the sixties and seventies. A category might have eighty or more competitors. The weigh-in and what might loosely be called 'competition control' was the conventional mess. One lad, Martin Piovesana, a good player, turned up with the tips of three fingers bandaged but still seeping blood. He worked as a steel press operator and had neatly sliced the tops off these digits the week before. This was a regular occurrence in industrial Birmingham and men with maimed hands were commonplace. He was spotted.

'You can't fight mate, sorry' said one official.

'Why not?' Asked Martin.

'Your hands are a mess. You won't be able to grip – it's not safe...' Martin was having none of it.

'That's up to me innit? If I can't grip it's my own fault. Where does it say in the rules that I can't fight with a bad hand?' He had a point. The rules were quite hopeless and covered no such eventuality. The disagreement halted the already slow weigh-in. Opinion amongst the players were divided. 'Let him fight!' asserted one faction. 'I don't want his blood on my suit' countered the other. In the end the Chairman of the association, Harry Ewen, said that he could not fight; there was a vague rule which prohibited unsafe play and said Harry 'fighting with half a hand is definitely unsafe lad. Don't be so bloody stupid!'

Peter's event, the under sixteen open, conveniently had sixty-two entrants and was split into two halves. These large numbers meant that competitions were often run on a straight knockout basis.

'That's good Peter. The kid who is likely to be your main opposition is on the second sheet. If you meet at all it will be in the final.' Kevin spoke enthusiastically but Peter was unimpressed.

'I wish he was on my side of the draw – then I could beat him sooner. Anyway, where is he?' Kevin pointed out a round faced lad with blond hair standing with a gaggle of other teenagers from Northampton.

'He's the big lad wearing a brown belt.' Kevin indicated the group larking about, laughing pushing and shoving in the manner of youngsters nervously excited.

'He doesn't look much to me *Sensei*. He's fat – he must train on chips and pies!'

'He's a good lad Donnelly. Underneath the flab there is a lot of muscle and he moves well. He won the Northwest's a few months back. He must be twenty kilos heavier than you which is a lot of weight to move and a lot of power in attack. Watch him fight – he's got a powerful *harai-goshi*. His balance is all over the place mind but it's still a powerful attack.'

Now, of course such a weight mismatch would not be allowed in a junior event. The sport has moved on and is properly organised into categories which are designed to look after the health and safety of the players. It was not always thus.

⌒

Peter's first fight was against a taller lad of similar weight to himself and lasted about one second – maybe two.

Every player is taught a full range of techniques. No throw is better than any other; the range is there to suit the player and the specific circumstances of the fight. Kevin taught all the throws in the *go-kyu* but there is no doubt that he favoured hip techniques. He was not a great fan of sacrifice throws. 'Too much to go wrong Danny. It's your opponent's job to get you onto your back. Don't help him! The simpler the throw the better as far as I'm concerned! Concentrate upon doing the basics well! There is no such thing as a bad throw – just a throw done badly!' *Sensei* Kevin Murphy is now long gone, but I can hear his admonishments and words of judo wisdom clearly. At training he would ask, 'What are the two most important things in judo?' He expected the reply to be shouted out.

'*Tsukuri and kuzushi* – body positioning and breaking of the opponents balance.'

'Why is Peter Donnelly's *o-goshi* so good?'

'Because he's an overgrown lump with hands like hams and feet like paving slabs, *Sensei*.' One of the young Dan grades gave this helpful answer.

'Exactly! He has got great *kuzushi and tsukuri*. He lifts his opponents forward onto their toes; he turns in and his feet are planted between their feet in a perfect 'V' shape; he then rotates and tries to look up his own back. Kenshiro Abbe called this '*kyu-shin-do*' and then he dumps them gently down in front of him.'

His first win, in no more than two seconds was with a foot-sweep, *de-ashi-barai*.

'Great throw' I said as Peter left the mat, 'but I thought you would have warmed up your *o-goshi*.'

'Kev said to save it for best. I won't use it at all before the final - unless I have to.'

⌒

The De Montfort Hall was an international venue used for all sorts of events, and hence had a loudspeaker system that worked. This was not often the case with many competitions taking place in school halls, hotels, clubs and so forth. The more usual notification system was a harassed organiser shouting perhaps aided by a megaphone. The final was announced over the Tannoy. The junior events had proceeded swiftly.

'Peter Donnelly, Budokan – Red! John Holmes, Northampton – White. Mat two!'

The competition had progressed as predicted with Peter and the Northampton lad in the final. I had taken an interest in Holmes' progress and watched his fights while Kevin kept an eye on Peter. Holmes did indeed move well. His favourite attack was a right-sided *harai-goshi* which he delivered with a lot of power. But his balance was not so good and his *kuzushi* sometimes very weak. His right-hand position tended to 'chicken wing' and he lost a lot of momentum. On the other hand, he must have weighed eighty kilos and had won his six fights so far with three *harai-goshis* and three hold-downs.

'Good luck Peter.' I muttered.

'Don't need luck Danny. We put in three nights a week on the mat and do our 'Saturday Thousand' *uchi-komis*. I work harder than he does and deserve to win – I will win.'

'How do you know you work harder?' In reply he slapped his hard-muscled stomach and laughed. 'He's scared of me anyway...' Kevin joined us:

'*Koshi-garuma!* Roll him, Peter. He's too heavy for you to lift.'

'I can beat him *Sensei*.

'I know you can Peter. *Koshi-garuma!* Now be told Peter I don't want you doing yourself an injury. Be told!'

After two and a half minutes of hard judo, Donnelly turned in for his favourite left-handed *o-goshi*. Holmes blocked the attack, but Peter dug in again and crashed his luckless opponent to the mat. Many of the crowd rose to stand, applauding and shouting their appreciation of this near perfect throw from the much lighter, younger player. Peter bowed with difficulty and left the mat with his right hand shoved into the trousers of his *gi*.

'*Sensei* – I've hurt myself down below.' Kevin removed Peter's jacket and laid him down; he began prodding and examining his lower abdomen. At a certain spot Peter squealed. 'What is it *Sensei*? What's up?'

'You're a stupid sod Peter, that's what's up. You've won a gong and bust a gut - ruptured yourself in the process. It's hospital for you young Donnelly.'

'What now?'

'Of course not. You'll have to put up with it until we get back to Brum. I'm not missing the rest of the day chasing round after you. You did it - you put up with it; your mom can take you tomorrow. Idiot! Roll your socks into a ball and press them into the spot that hurts – and keep them there!'

'But I won *Sensei*.'

'Yes! And you could have won with *koshi-garuma* and saved us all a lot of fuss.

⤶

(Author's Note: Peter Donnelly, multiple British Champion, Olympian, European medallist, with a laundry list of international and national wins has many fine qualities. He has never, however been very good at 'being told.' If you are ever lucky enough to be invited to his rather beautiful home in a discreet part of leafy Devon, you will see that he only has two trophies on display; a small silver cup from the event above and his competitors medal from the 1980 Moscow Olympics.)

Judo is an individualistic sport and by its very nature attracts more than its fair share of odd-balls and cranks. Missing from the pages of judo history are the ranks of players who, in other sports, would be remembered with distinction. They say that 'history is written by the winners.' This has the ring of truth about it, but it is also written about the winners. Judo has legions of players that simply 'went their own way' and hence their skills, wins and exploits are forgotten or not afforded the merit due. Some of their names litter this account.

Tony Underwood is one such crank. He was entered in the Dan grade open and though young was developing a deserved reputation. He had recently won the BJA prestigious Goldberg-Vass competition. Of course, he had a range of techniques but above all else was recognised for a unique *koshi-waza*. I describe this as *tsuri-komi-uki-goshi*. I ran this past the late Roy Inman who was fanatical in the matters of Japanese nomination and he agreed – and that's good enough for me! I do not think anyone else could perform this throw as I am convinced that it was only made possible for Tony through the genetic accident of having abnormally large back muscles. He is not actually deformed, but still has in his mid-seventies, muscles that would be better suited to a bullock or carthorse.

～

Another idiosyncratic judoka is Colin Draycott 8th Dan. He is by no means forgotten; a PhD in engineering; Director of the International Judo Federation; a life Vice-President of the British Judo Association - indeed the saviour of the BJA when he stepped in with his cheque-book years back, to prevent the Association's imminent plunge into financial disaster. I had dinner with him a few years ago and he told me of the staggering amount of money his business empire had lost in the financial crisis of 2008. I was manically delighted and could not help but laugh. Our friendship is longstanding and Colin is a gentleman. He did not give me the cuff that I richly deserved – but was visibly rattled, 'It's not bloody funny' said Colin, understandably miffed. 'I lost thirty years of my life's work and had to sell my helicopter! I only bought the bloody thing to get up to Kendal.' Colin would no doubt prefer me not to mention that he was the financial force that made the famed Kendal set-up possible. He was the visionary who wanted a permanent training facility for elite judoka. Kendal was the result. He lost 300 million in the 'crash' I had no idea that such sums of money really existed! A few years ago, when I wanted to take a team of kids from my club to Japan, he offered £5000 as a contribution to the venture. So, what is my point? Well, with all of his other, often financial, contributions to judo I feel he has not been given the prominence he deserves as a fighter.

But back to the event at hand:

The competition format was as previously described; the entry split into two and the winners of each sheet to fight in the final. A simple but not very fair system; things were different then and we must not judge. My own fights were complete (I had won the senior kyu grade event beating Johnny Griffiths from Dudley in the final.) I spent the afternoon watching Underwood on one tatami and Draycott on the other. Tony, with consummate flair and some ease reached the final of the Dan grade open-weight and Colin, who had doubled up, found himself in both this final and the light-heavyweight where he would fight John Oliver of Leicester. It was not the first time I had seen this pairing. He had fought Oliver in the light-heavyweight Dan grade final of the previous year, a quite brutal fight, and now they were to meet again.

Pat Roach, one of the early members of the 'Tin Hut' Budokan had entered the competition. This is as good a place as any to throw in two associated tales. Pat was, without doubt an excellent heavyweight judoka. This future star of the TV series 'Auf Weidersehn Pet', villain of the 'Indiana Jones' movies and many more, was heavyweight Champion of the Amateur Judo Association. This was an undoubted achievement, but I have no idea how he would have fared against the British Judo Association heavyweights at the time. No matter, I only mention this because, under AJA rules, professional wrestling was considered entertainment, not sport, and so he was eligible to fight. For some reason he had entered this event which provoked interest amongst crowd and competitors. I had known him since I was a small child and in a manner of speaking, he was among my heroes. I was pleased to see him and surprised; he no longer did any judo training, instead travelling around the country and abroad on the pro-wrestling circuit when he wasn't filming.

'Hello Pat! What are you doing here!'

'Same as you, young Danny. Just fancied a knock.' I will describe his voice as 'professional Brummie' – nothing like the peculiar West-Country drawl he used as 'Bomber' in the television series. To this day I have no idea why he turned up to fight. As a television personality he could only gain publicity if he won and would lose face and standing if he lost. Maybe he just fancied a fight? Well, lose he did. He was well and truly dumped (*o-goshi*) in his first-round fight by a guy called Alan Pitt from the Black-Country. He left without saying good-bye and I did not see him again for a few years.

And by way of a break from the events at De Montfort Hall, here is my second tale concerning Pat. His film and television career were doing well, and he was now the proud owner of a fitness centre in central Birmingham – the Piccadilly Gym. I called in for no other reason than to say hello. I had a parcel which I had collected from a city centre tailors and it contained my hired graduation gown and mortarboard for the approaching ceremony. He was curious when I explained the contents of the package and he insisted that he be shown. With delight he donned the cap and gown and paraded, strutting up and down his office. 'What do you think Danny, does it suit me?'

'Of course, it does Pat. But the gown looks small.' Pat was normally six feet four and weighed in at about nineteen stone.

'I've been beefing up a bit that's why. I'm playing a villain in the next Superman movie. But I do like this get up. He examined himself in a full-length mirror which lined his office wall. 'You look fit – still doing the judo?'

'Yes, still grinding away...' He chipped in with some force and slapped his hand hard on a nearby table. His face was contorted with distaste.

'Absolute mugs game! No money in it and never will be. You're a college kid and supposed to be smart – turn to pro-wrestling and I'll put a grand, one thousand pounds in your hand next week. I'll manage you. You need more muscle but the 'Smarties' will sort that. You'll travel the world, have more money than you can spend and a different girl every night if that's your taste. If not...' I cut into his tirade.

'Whoa Pat. It's not my thing. Sorry but...' He was in full flow and not to be silenced.

'I've just thought of it! No-one else on the circuit is doing anything like it. You'll be a great hit!' He held a finger up as if he had received inspiration. 'The Professor! You'll step into the ring in this cap and gown carrying a big black book. Whenever you're stuck, or in a hold-down, one of the seconds will pass you the book and you 'look up' the escape or your next move. Imagine it! A thousand women screaming, 'Book! Book! Book!' You're staggering around the ring, out on your feet – you turn the page of the book and find the perfect next move. You can even smack your opponent with the it for added effect. It's a sure-fire winner Danny! You can address all the old biddies in that posh voice you've started to use, and they'll love you. What do you say?'

'I'm going to be a psychologist Pat.'

'Another mug's game – unless you're planning to move to the States.'

In both cases Pat might have had a point. I went to his funeral a few years back with my good friend Dave Law from the Budokan 'Tin Hut' days. Jimmy Nail sang and we drank beer with the actor Tim Healy, who it turns out was also a judo player.

⌢

A strange thing occurred that day. The preliminaries ran on time and at four o'clock the auditorium was cleared leaving only one mat in readiness for the Dan grade finals which were to happen at five o'clock. Unheard of! Judo events always took hours longer than planned. That was the natural order of things and for this not to occur was unsettling.

The main events in which I had interest were the finals of the Dan grade open-weight between Tony Underwood and Colin Draycott; Oliver and Draycott in the light heavyweight division; the middle-weight clash between Bob Trevis and Keith 'Tiger' Brown. Roy Muller was fighting a Scot, Danny Cassidy in the light-middleweights; the lightweight favourite was a BJA guy called Bernard Visgandis who had excited the crowd all day with fast attacking judo and a string of big *ippons*.

The De Montfort Hall was a famous venue, mainly for boxing and wrestling. Therefore, it is not surprising that mounted on the stage was a permanently fixed boxing ring. Obviously, the posts and ropes had been removed. An eighteen-foot square Milom's sponge judo mat had been laid on top of the boxing dais which itself was on top of the stage at least five feet high. For the sake of easy calculation, the organisers thought it reasonable that a succession of judo bouts were to be held on a platform about nine feet above the auditorium floor. Obviously, you say, there would be safety matting, foam crash mats and the like? Well, there were none. The ringside seats were reserved for dignitaries and their guests. As far as I am aware there were no protests regarding the safety of the event, indeed a lot of favourable comment was muttered about the excellence of the view.

The trophies, which were to be presented at the end of the evening by the Earl of Lanesborough, were neatly laid on a venerable Steinway grand piano below the stage. An eminently sensible arrangement. Hurrah! What could go wrong?

The first injury sustained should have provided fair warning but did not. You need to remember that the nineteen-sixties and seventies were the heyday of British professional wrestling and the likes of Jackie Mr 'TV' Pallo, Big Daddy, Judo Pat Roach, Honey Boy Zimba, and so forth, were huge television celebrities. The sight of bodies being hurled out of wrestling rings was prime-time entertainment, and much loved by all. The higher and more dangerous the fall the more wrestling was adored. So, when a finalist in the women's light-weight division was thrown to land off the mat, which in this case also meant off the boxing plinth, bounced and fell the further five feet onto the auditorium floor, the gymnastics involved were greeted with considerable enthusiasm and approval. When the unlucky judoka climbed back onto the stage and further ascended the steps onto the mat, she did so to great applause. That she could not continue the fight due to a broken collarbone was deemed a pity. She received a well-deserved rowdy ovation, but the crowd's appetite for further injuries was well and truly whetted.

During following contests many players were tumbled over one edge or both. When one player was concussed through landing on his head the sympathetic and appreciative applause reached the highest volume. Nonetheless some aged official was prompted to ferret around in an unlocked store cupboard and found a half-dozen coir gym mats which were laid at the foot of the stage. Anyone who can remember these bristling ginger monstrosities will remember also that they had no protective function and served only to make people itch. The injury ridden event continued its hazardous way.

The lightweight final was spectacular in its conclusion. Bernard Visgandis dispatched his opposition in seconds with a perfect *tsuri-komi-goshi*. His left hand made a rope of the skirt of his opponent's jackets and the throw completed with a low fast spin. The grip has since been banned but was common at the time. The throw received deserved applause.

Roy Muller beat Danny Cassidy, his Scottish opponent, equally as quickly with a business-like ankle sweep. He attacked with his right foot, momentarily relaxed, but kept his foot in contact with his opponent's – and then attacked again. Simple stuff! *Ippon!*

Bob Trevis and Keith Brown were up next, but some keen official noticed that Colin Draycott was in two finals and hence would fight the light-heavyweight and the open weight back-to-back. The middleweight event was moved to the penultimate slot.

John Oliver and Colin Draycott stood at their respective mat edges waiting to be called onto the *tatami*. The lights failed and De Montfort Hall was plunged into total darkness! The audience responded with sounds of minor worried concern and a chorus of whistles. After a restless few seconds two spotlights blazed and the combatants were picked out in glaring circles of bright light. What a spectacle! Judo was unused to such razz-a-mat-azz! (In truth it should have stayed so unused. The lighting engineer, Alf Cummings, was bored. He'd been asked to come into work but had been given no instructions. He was familiar with the professional wrestling performances and thought the judo dull and in need of livening up.) The crowd applauded this unexpected light show as the two players walked onto the mat and prepared to fight.

Draycott looked every inch the athlete; a shade over six feet tall with a body builder's physique, thick wavy black hair and film-star suave looks. He was good and he knew it; he had no problem playing to the crowd. His white *judo-gi* gleamed in the spotlights as he and Oliver stood on the stage facing each other waiting to fight. John Oliver was the reverse of Colin in most respects; short and squat, with mousey short haired that was slightly receding. His round face was hardly handsome. He was a ferocious opponent gifted with bull-like strength and a superb *harai-goshi*. *Hajime* was called and Colin opened his arms wide and adopted the pose made famous by Geesink at the Tokyo Olympics, emulating the statue of Christ the Redeemer above Rio di Janeiro. The contest became a war of attrition. *Hiza-garuma* is not supposed to be a kick at the opponent's knee cap. The first time Oliver so attacked, Draycott winced; the second time he let out an audible grunt of pain. The third time he dropped almost to one knee in agony. Oliver continued his flurry of attacks with an *o-soto-gari* and attacking Draycott's injured leg scored a *waza-ari*.

Where was the referee in all of this you might ask? Not for the first time I can only reply that times were different. There were fewer rules and referees interfered less. More than once I witnessed top-class players lose their tempers and resort to hitting each other. Referees tended to frown on this sort of behaviour and would calm the players down before re-starting the contest. However, disqualification, *hansoku-make*, was rare.

At the re-start Draycott grimly limped across the mat and attacked with a tremendous *ashi-garuma* which knocked his opponent flat on his face. Oliver immediately held his own lapels to guard against a *ground-work* attack. Ignoring the cloth Draycott drove his right hand under Oliver's neck attempting a naked strangle. There was no submission and when the referee stood them up blood was dripping from John Oliver's mouth. In return Oliver's teeth left bite indentations on Colin Draycott's arm which would have pleased any dentist. Injury honours were even! Both players achieved knock downs and Draycott evened the score with a massive *seoi-nage* that was debatably an *ippon*. The crowd were noisily ecstatic in their approval of the combativity of both players. Draycott's superior fitness showed. In the last-minute Oliver did nothing – except stay on his feet. No mean achievement considering the power of Draycott's attacks. Once again he hit with a big left *o-soto* which surely must score – but no. Oliver somehow spun to land face down. In modern judo Oliver's passivity would have resulted in disqualification. Not then! The prevailing judo ethos was that a contest was a fight, pure and simple, with the referee to assure fair play but other than that keep out of the way. It was not the referee's job to penalise defensive play, rather the attacker's job to overcome it. But there I will leave this account. After sixty years I have no intention of glorifying who won – judo excellence was the winner! (However, the trophy was rightly awarded to Colin Draycott.)

⌣

Robert Murray Trevis had the nickname 'Rocky' long before the Sylvester Stallone cinematographic boxing fantasies of the same name. He was of medium height with a Herculean frame; heavily muscled broad shoulders, a narrow waist and powerful legs. He had phenomenal natural strength hardly augmented through weight training. He had a combative judo style and a ferocious determination to win, helped or hindered by a fiery temperament. His skin was sallow in colour and with black curly hair he looked more Mediterranean French than English. He was handsome in the style of a Sicilian assassin, that is if you like that sort of thing. He had the reputation of being a 'hard knock', a brawler if you will, but this was an incomplete and insufficient description as *Sensei* Kevin Murphy vociferously noted:

'Anyone who says Trevis is just a hard knock scrapper is an idiot.' Kevin was never unsure of an opinion. He never sat on any fence; his world was full of certainties. 'Trevis is a great judo player, his body positioning in attack is damn near perfect. He is the only player I know that still uses *hane-goshi* as a main throw – and you can't do that unless your speed in attack, *tsukuri and kuzushi* are spot on. You can't beat the likes of Roy Inman by being just a mauler, it's not possible.'

His opponent in the final of the middle-weight division was to be Keith 'Tiger' Brown, a northerner with an equal reputation as a judo player and a hard man. The derivation of his nickname was obvious. Emblazoned on his chest was the head of a tiger – an excellent example of the tattooist's art.

The reputations of both men preceded them, and the crowd quietened as they stepped onto the mat. They faced each with the referee between, poised to start the fight. Alf Cummings, the lighting operator, monetarily dimmed the auditorium, excepting the powerful super-trooper which picked out the three-central figure. He was pleased with the artistic effect thus created. The referee, an eccentric from Scarborough named Norman Grundy, was startled and shaded his eyes. 'Oi, thee up there!' bawled Norman. 'Stop mucking round wi' the bloody lights. This is a judo contest not Sunday Night at the London Palladium.' Alf Cummings was hurt and felt unappreciated but returned the lighting to normal. Thus resumed, *hajime* was called and the contest began. It was bad-tempered from the off. Trevis kicked Brown and the complement was returned. Heads clashed accidentally and then clashed again with purposeful intent. Norman Grundy felt it necessary to have a chat and called *matte!* With reluctance both players stopped. 'Now, thee boys. This is supposed to be a judo contest not a street fight. Any more foul play and I'll send one of thee 'ome to bed. Understand!'

Trevis attacked with a powerful *soto-makikomi,* a favoured technique and scored *waza-ari.* This seemed to further energise Tiger Brown who rattled Rocky Trevis with a powerful *uchi-mata.* Many felt that a score was justified but none was given. Both players adopted *jigotai* postures and continued fighting literally head-to-head. And then something happened...

I am not sure who hit whom first, but both players released hold and presumably frustrated with judo, decided to box. Trevis threw a creditable left hook to the side of Tiger Brown's head which Keith countered with a swinging right to Bob's ribs – a damn good punch which made Rocky wince. Roy Muller was standing next to me and shouted, 'Use your judo on him Bob,' which I thought both clever and quick witted. Norman Grundy, a commando during the war, pulled the warriors apart. Other officials came onto the mat and in short order normality was restored - only to be lost again seconds later when Trevis was disqualified for head butting. Chaos ruled and Bob became very keen to start round two of their boxing match.

(Author's Note: I asked Bob what had started the ruckus. Apparently during the head rubbing episode Keith had said something like 'don't lose your hair Trevis' which was possibly an attempt to calm things. Bob, who was thinning, took it otherwise – something like that anyway. It was fifty years ago and memories dim.)

༄

I do not play nor have ever played cricket but believe that the one-day game is more popular than the older five-day county match. In one-day cricket there is more action; the pace is faster, and more risks are taken; balls are slogged and missed. But five-day cricket brings into play different skills and strategies. I think anyone can watch with interest players hitting a ball with a bat, but it takes the cricketing enthusiast to savour the niceties of the longer format.

And sometimes it is the same with judo...

The ultimate fight between Underwood and Draycott was intriguing to the afficionado but less so the casual watcher. Colin started the contest, as usual, with his arms held cruciform wide. Tony started, as usual, with the look of someone disinterested and half asleep. Grip fighting was less minimal and soon they were clamped together, forehead to forehead. And there they stayed. Both men were immensely strong and experts in maintaining their own balance; every action was resisted by an exact reaction, every force exerted one way was countered by its exact opposite. The resultant stalemate was inspirational stuff to those who knew what was going on. Just as the massive forces generated in a tug-of-war can result in muscle burning, aching inaction, this static fight was dramatically tense. Who would give first? Who would lose concentration or suffer a destroying build-up of lactic acid that would render those massive muscles useless?

A brief flurry occurred when Underwood staggered Draycott at the mat edge with such momentum that both players fell first from the ring, and then from the stage, landing, to the great approval of the crowd, onto the grand piano. The trophies displayed on it were scattered far and wide. After extra time, and ten minutes of fighting, (those days of yore being before *shidos* and golden score), a decision had to be made. The referee and two corner officials each judged who was the winner, the latter by raising a red or white bat to signify their choice, and the referee having the casting vote in the event of a tie.

Colin Draycott was the victor, a close call, disputed by some spectators but completely accepted by Tony Underwood, gentleman that he is, steeped in the manners of Japanese etiquette. It is an amusing irony that the trophy Draycott received had been squashed nearly flat by their earlier fall. 'Tough luck Tony,' I commiserated as we sat together in the changing rooms.

'It doesn't matter,' he said. 'It's just a scrap. It does annoy me though that the refs made the decision. Why not just let the fight go on? There would have been a score sooner or later so why not just leave it for the fighters to sort out? What's the rush to finish the fight anyway? Was Morecombe and wise on the telly, or something?'

⌒

In those days no coach journey home would have been complete without the inevitable 'sing-song.' Communal singing had been the mainstay of Victorian and Edwardian music hall and was still alive and well. The songs were known by all and had little musical merit excepting that they were simple, repetitive and could be performed by all regardless of voice. 'My old man said follow the van' was written in 1916 but was still sung in pubs and at parties. In comparison to some of the songs which we sang it was complex, having both a tune and a story. No, we were happier with such ditties as:

Ten green bottles hanging on the wall
Ten green bottles hanging on the wall
And if one green bottle should accidentally fall
There'd be nine green bottles hanging on the wall etc...
Or
Ten men went to mow, went to mow a meadow
Ten men, nine men, eight men, seven men, six men, five men, four men, three men, two men, one man and his dog,
Went to mow a meadow...

Simple pleasures I suppose for simpler days. The raucous singing of these endless songs speeded the passage of time. Peter Donnelly was, as expected, on the back seat swathed by two pretty girls but he was subdued and periodically rubbed his abdomen. The journey home passed quickly as the coach driver had predicted:

'Now listen here you lot! Quiet at the back! It's gone eight already and I'm an hour late. Any later and I'd have gone without you. So, there'll be no stopping on the way back. If anyone wants a 'Jimmy Riddle' have it now - or you'll have to use a bottle. No mess either! And I'll have no larking about...'

Some nineteen hours after its arrival outside the Grand Cinema, the Bowen's coach returned to the same spot. The November weather had not improved, and a fine rain fell as forty or more tired judo players and friends alighted, hastening for the cover of the cinema's awning. Lights above the advertising hoarding showed that the feature film was 'Carry on Cowboy' complete with the grinning faces of Sid James and Kenneth Williams. Good-byes were called and people scurried off through the rain. Kevin spoke to Mr. Donnelly through the open window of his little car apprising him of his son's injury. Peter's dad had been waiting for two hours but was unconcerned. In those days, before ever-present instant communication, lateness was accepted without much panic. I grabbed my kitbag and readied myself for the two-hundred-yard walk to my parental home. In the distance I heard the Rosary Church clock chime the few notes of the 'Ave Maria,' which it did preceding its every hourly ring.

'Hang on Danny,' called Kevin, 'I'll come with you and check on mom and dad.'

⌐

Chapter Four
Went the Day Well?

Life's rhythms are not ours to order; its entrances and exits
are not ours to command.
How long does the journey take? I wonder.
And when will this children's game finally end?
(Michael John Murphy 1923)

⤳

IN 1847 THE Irish potato crop failed, and the people starved. The population of the 'Emerald Isle' halved through death, disease and emigration. 'Coffin ships' sailed to America and further, packed with poor people hoping for life in a new country. But many simply 'crossed the water' to Britain to work as labourers in the booming industrial cities of London, Manchester, Glasgow and Birmingham. The Irish diaspora was at its height.

In 1923 Father John arrived in Alum Rock, Birmingham to minister his disordered flock. John Power had always been destined for the priesthood but willingly accepted this finality. He was the younger son of Michael 'Whiskey' Power owner of the same named Dublin distillery. That he would become a priest was just the way of it. He had no problem with this; life was easy and he believed he had a calling – but first he needed a church. On a patch of waste ground opposite the splendid gothic edifice of St Peter's, an Anglican training college for teachers, stood a dilapidated hut. The college had been built in leafy lanes but was now marooned, out of time and place, in its industrial setting. The hut had once had a purpose but no longer.

It was full of discarded detritus long forgotten, that no one had had the good sense to burn. John Power found that he could rent it, from the college as it happened, for three pounds per week.

'It's a lot of money for an old hut with a roof that leaks and has no windows,' said Father John. 'Surely you can come down a bit on the price – after all we're in the same trade so to speak.'

'We are in the same business – that's true,' said the Dean of the college, 'but more as competitors don't you think?' He was, however, a kindly soul; at a price of one pound ten shillings, the deal was agreed and sealed with a glass of sherry. Father John walked down College Road, pleased with himself and the day. His next call was to Wyatt's the hardware shop on the busy shopping strip which was the Alum Rock Road.

'I need a small tin of black paint and a paint brush, also small, suitable for lettering.'

'Doing a spot of sign-writing are you Father?' said Tom Wyatt observing the priest's collar.

'I am that - a sign for the new church. It will be called 'The Church of the Rosary and Saint Therese.' I'm the new priest, John Power – it's my first a day. Pleased to meet you. You're not a Catholic by any chance are you Mr Wyatt?'

'I am not Father. I'm Methodist. Mr Bodfish is our Minister, good man that he is. Have you met him?'

'Sure, I have not but I'm guessing that I will. Now about the paint and the brush. I don't have much...' the priest took off his back homburg, held it to his chest and scratched his head with his free hand., '...actually, I don't have any money at the moment. I was wondering if I could pay you after Mass on Sunday? There's bound to be a bob or two on the plate. What do you say?' John Power's blue eyes sparkled with his Dublin born cheek.

'I say that I'm glad I'm a Methodist. You'll need some turps to wash out the brush. Shall I put that on the bill?'

'That would be grand! What a man! I thank you and Our Lord thanks you as well. Now you haven't got a bit of old board you don't want. Any bit will do – that's good enough for a sign.'

'Will the Lord thank me for that as well?'

'He will! He most certainly bloody-well will! He was a carpenter you know so I'm sure making a sign for his church would be just the thing he would appreciate.'

'Do you have a hammer Father?'

'I do not. You have me there I'm afraid'

'Nails?'

'No – I'm pretty sure I don't have any nails, but my motto is 'Have faith in the Lord and He will provide.'

'Do you know how to sign-write Father?' The smiling young priest once again shook his head.

'I do not – but it can't be that hard surely? Mind you, I would not want the sign to be a mess now...'

Tommy Wyatt looked at the young priest, blue-eyed, fresh faced and sandy haired and decided he liked him. 'I'll do your sign Father, and put it up - be less fuss in the long run. What do you want on it?'

'Mr Wyatt, an angel smiles a blessing to you from heaven. Thank you. Just the name of the church and perhaps mass times?'

''Times' you say. How many masses will there be?' Father John thought for a moment. He had the intention of getting every Irish soul in Alum Rock to mass – even if he had to drag them into his little church kicking and screaming.

'Six, I think. It's a very small hut - six should be fine. Five on Sunday morning and one in the evening.'

'Good God! That's a helluva lot of praying Father. Where will you get enough people for six masses?'

'That should be the easy bit. Tonight, and every night I will call in at the pubs in and remind the drunks to go to mass. If I know Irishmen, they'll turn up on Sunday just so I won't get in the way of their evenings' drinking.' He thought for a moment. 'I think you'd better add to the sign that there will be a six o'clock week-day morning mass for the pious or penitent to call in before they go off to work. How can I ever repay you Mr Wyatt?'

'You could give me money I suppose.' But Tommy Wyatt lacked avarice and his eyes were laughing.

John Power was as good as his word and he haunted the pubs of Alum Rock from the 'Tilt Hammer' to the 'Saltley Gate.' He was quite partial himself to a pint of Guinness or a whiskey, maybe two, and his presence was not resented. He worked hard to build his church and expected his parishioners to work hard also. The wooden hut prospered and improved. The scrounged scaffolding planks resting on oil drums soon gave way to oaken pews. The neighbouring Anglican college found and donated a superfluous lectern which he placed on a packing case. Father John knew his flock and berated them from this temporary pulpit. 'I know why you're by the door Rafferty and you Tommy McGuigan. You make sure when the plate comes around that the price of a pint is on it. Remember boys, Jesus is in your round!'

The Country Girl, the nearest pub, did marvellous trade on Sunday. Before the end of midday Mass, Finbar O'Toole the publican, poured forty pints of Guinness, ready to be topped-up in preparation for 'the Sunday Gallop' as he called the invasion of Irishmen released from the nearby church. Lined up to settle without haste, the glasses stretched the length of the long bar, each one soon to be gratefully taken.

Ten years later the wooden hut was demolished, no longer needed as Father John had indeed convinced the working Irish of his 'patch' that 'Jesus was worth the price of a pint.' The newly built church and school for the children of the parish were truly magnificent. He had not stinted with their money!

Tommy Wyatt's sign was saved and rested in perpetuity on the vestry wall.

⌒

Bernard Marsh was, surprisingly, not a Catholic but was very good at his job as the Headmaster of the Rosary School. It was early, before the start of the school day and he had been disturbed by a noisy commotion in the playground below. He looked out of his study window and saw a circle of excited boys with two more in the centre – the unmistakeable signs of a schoolboy fight. Generally, he felt it best to let these events run their course. After a few ineffective punches one or other of the participants gave in and handshakes exchanged. He then noticed that one of the pugilists was Eric Cadman who was a thug, and prophesised Mr Marsh, destined for Borstal as a prelude to prison. He would keep an eye on events in case things got out of hand.

Eric had been brutalised by his violent, drunkard father – a diminutive Glaswegian Scot who took his razor strop to the boys and his cowed wife with daily monotony. He was indiscriminate with his lashings which made them the more terrifying, arriving as they did without rhyme nor reason. He bullied whomsoever he could bully. This long list excluded Bernard Marsh. He had once burst into the headmaster's office full of whisky and stupidity. Bernard, also a Scot, floored him with a fine left-hook and sent him home to sober up. And that was the end of the matter, no police, no social workers, no enquiry. It was just a part of the rough life of Father John Power's excellent but inner-city school.

～

Cast you mind back now to your own school days. Remember the crazes which had brief overwhelming popularity. You might recall gyrating with a hula-hoop, playing conkers or hop-scotch or Polly-on-the-mop-stick. The current fad at the Rosary School was to play marbles. This simple game required each participant to throw or roll a small glass ball into a little hole found or made in the playground tarmac. The first player to get a marble into the hole could then take a pot-shot at other marbles that had missed their mark. If the shot was successful, the player acquired that marble. A simple game but for some reason one at which Kevin Murphy excelled. He was playing and repeatedly beating Eric Cadman who became annoyed at his mounting losses.

'You're cheating Kevin – that's why you're winning.'

'Cheating? Don't be daft Eric. How can I cheat? If I hit your marble, I win it. If I miss - I don't. How can I cheat?' The conversation became heated and other boys began to gather.

'Well how come you keep winning then?'

'Because I'm a better shot than you, and I've got a lucky marble, this red one.' He held it up between thumb and forefinger to display the pure red glass ball. Eric spotted a gap in Kevin's argument.

'Lucky, you say? If you've got a lucky marble, that's cheating. I want it – give it to me!'

'Not a chance Eric. Get your own lucky marble...'

'Fair exchange is no robbery,' chanted Eric. 'I'll give you ten marbles for it.'

'No Eric. I don't want to swop. It's my marble and I'm keeping it!'

'I'll fight you for it!'

Now we all know (at least I think we do) that there is no such thing as a lucky anything, be it a marble, penny or four-leaf clover. Lucky or not young Kevin was not going to be bullied and stood firm. The mention of a fight did change the situation though, and a circle formed around the two boys with the eager spectators repeatedly shouting 'Fight!'

Kevin Murphy did not want to provide this entertainment. Eric was two years older, much bigger and would be leaving the Rosary in a matter of weeks. He was the 'cock-of-the-school' and his ability to pummel smaller boys was his only scholastic achievement. Nevertheless, Kevin would fight – the alternative being unacceptable humiliation, perhaps thereinafter being known as a 'yellow-belly.' He expected to take a beating and decided as his strategy to get in the first punch. School-boy fights usually start with shoving and escalate into blows. Kevin Murphy ignored this unwritten protocol and smashed Eric Cadman in the nose with every ounce of his thirteen-year-old's power. Blood gushed and the ensuing pain had the effect of motivating the bleeding boy into a furious onslaught which removed Kevin's upper left pre-molar and internally split his lip. Kevin fell to the ground where he lay as Eric Cadman knelt astride him delivering blow after blow to the recumbent's head. Kevin was spared further punishment as Eric flew upwards propelled thus by the strong arms of Mr Marsh, the hands of which gripped Cadman firmly around the throat.

'Enough boys! Enough now! I think it's time to call these happy festivities to a halt!'

Kevin rose unsteadily to his feet and stood facing the glowering, bloody Cadman. Mr Marsh spoke. 'Boys. It is good that you are taking healthy exercise, but the school playground is not the place for boxing. Now we will have no more of it do you hear?' Both boys remained mute as he looked from one to the other. 'Anyway, by the look of you the match was a draw, and I am the referee. Do you understand boys.' Both nodded. 'But I am curious to know – who started this contest of pugilistic skill?' Neither boy spoke but an anonymous voice called from the far secrecy of the circling throng.

'Cadman Sir – he wanted Murphy's marbles!'

'Is this true Murphy?' asked the inquisitive Mr Marsh. Kevin James Murphy, stood wordless and still, exploring the unfamiliar gap in his teeth with his tongue. 'Well as neither of you have anything to say, off to class!' Kevin and Eric sloped off, but from about eight feet distant Kevin stopped and turned. He took the red marble out of his pocket and threw it unerringly into the hole. Without glancing back, he continued to begin his school day.

꘎

My brother Kevin and I walked from the Grand Picture house and waved to the now empty coach as it chugged down the road and disappeared into the gloom. 'Stevie Pops', the Cypriot chip shop owner, cut a lonely figure as he cleaned his empty shop. We ambled past, slowly walking the few hundred yards to our parent's home, chatting about the day's judo on the way. Kevin still had a key which he used to open the green painted front door and we hurried inside both glad to be out of the November rain. Immediately we knew there was a problem. The house was grave quiet and shadow dark excepting the crack of light under the living room door. I dropped my judo duffel-bag onto the hallway floor and went into the room to see Alice Murphy, mom, sitting alone smoking a cigarette; the saucer next to her was full of ash and stained filter tips. She looked pale and worried. An explanation was hardly needed, Kevin and I both knew the cause of her distress. She intoned the familiar words. 'Your dad hasn't come home yet and I'm ever so worried. We both looked at the pendulum clock which hung in the fireside alcove and saw it was eleven-thirty. In those days pubs shut an hour before that – unless the pub had an illegal 'lock-in' and many did.

'Don't worry mom,' said Kevin. 'We'll get him.' With no further ado he turned on his heels and left. I mumbled something to mom and followed in his wake.

⌒

Cassidy, the manager of the Rock pub was a good enough sort - but of his type. He kept an orderly house, and his beer was never sour. He was a Dublin trained barman who cleaned his pumps and pipes thoroughly and threw the end of evening slops away. He was never tempted to add them to any of the barrels resting in his cellar. He dressed well in black trousers, white shirt and black tie. His high collar was always clean and if he stained it during an evening's work, he would change it for a fresh one as soon as he was able. He knew appearances were important. In some quarters he was well liked. The beat bobby, Jimmy Rimmer liked him, in part due to the weekly bottle and one-hundred cigarettes he received from Cassidy as 'a consideration.' Norman Hooper, the local councillor liked him, thanks to the ten pounds he received from Cassidy each Friday – also as 'a consideration.' Norman was on the licencing committee of the council and Cassidy's renewal was never in doubt. Eric Cadman liked him in a way. Well, at least he liked the twenty pounds that Cassidy regularly slipped him to ensure good order in his pub. His clientele were by and large Irish labourers who liked to let off steam after a hard week working 'on the building.' But Eric could handle anything that came his way – violence suited him; he had found his vocation. By and large everything ran smoothly. He made good money, the Friday and Saturday 'lock-ins' being particularly profitable. Cassidy charged more for the beer, but this was only fair as all knew that Cadman, the constable and others had to be paid off - good order had its price. The manager looked out over the bar into the back room of his pub, designated for 'Gents Only' – the G.O. as it was better known. Mick Murphy was paralytic drunk and unconscious, sleeping on his arm which rested wetly on the copper topped table awash with spilled beer. 'I hope the stupid bastard sobers up enough to get out into the street,' he thought. But that wouldn't be for three hours as it was only just gone eleven o'clock – plenty of time...

He heard a loud banging accompanied by the rattling up of the heavy brass door-latch.

'Open up Cassidy – or you'll have no door to bloody open. It's Kevin Murphy and I'm here to get Dad.' The barman opened the hatch and weaved his way between crowded tables and unbolted the door.

'Kevin, Kevin, Kevin! How good it is to see you. I'm afraid your dad has taken a bit of a turn for the worse. I was just wondering how to get him home. I'm glad you're here, and young Danny too, I see.' I followed my brother into the smoke-filled room. He stood above our unconscious parent and took a cigarette from a packet of Park Drive which lay open on the table. He lit one with slow deliberation, but I could see a slight tremor in his hands.

'I told you not to serve him past his quota Cassidy.'

'Ah Kevin now, be reasonable. How can I refuse a man a drink which he pays for with his own money? Come on now – he's a grown man after all. I'm no nurse maid, to be sure I'm not.' Kevin felt into Dad's top pocket to find it empty.

'Now there's the thing of it Cassidy. It was not his money to spend – Mom's housekeeping is gone.' The barman lost patience.

'Well, there's nothing I can do about it. Get the old drunk out of here and have done with it. It's not my problem.' Kevin let the cigarette fall from his lips where it lay on the tiled floor still burning.

'It is your problem Cassidy and here is how you'll fix it. Get two men who are sober enough to walk to carry him home and put a quid in his top pocket and I'll call it quits – or I'll wreck the joint and that'll cost you a damn sight more than a pound.' Kevin spoke softly but the room was now still, and every word was laden with threat. In response Cassidy shouted across the bar

'Eric! Get in here. Get in here now!'

⌇

Eric Cadman was now a mature man of six foot and sixteen stone of muscle. He kept himself fit at Saltley Boxing Club which was quite famous in its way having produced a few local champions. He entered the room from the front bar and stood with his arms hanging loosely at his sides. He wore a bespoke dark blue, three-piece suit - unusual as waistcoats were out of fashion. He liked his as it displayed a fine gold chain, one end of which secured a Waltham full hunter pocketwatch. This rested in his right-hand waistcoat pocket, and balance was achieved by a fob tucked into his left. His blue pin-striped shirt was complemented by a fashionable slim black tie and diamond pin. A white handkerchief was folded ruler straight in his top pocket.

Eric had missed service in the war as he was incarcerated in Winson Green gaol at the time, serving four years for grievous bodily harm. He did not know the word 'ironic' but felt it funny that he was in prison for violence while the armies of the world were efficiently killing each other by the million. He felt he could have made a useful contribution to the war effort in that respect. He was a staunch monarchist and would have done anything for the old king and now the young queen, except obey the laws of the Kingdom. He fidgeted with his gold watchchain - a prized possession. He had acquired it in the course of his day job as a 'Debt Recovery Executive.' He had coined this job description himself and thought it suited. George Silk, the illegal bookmaker and loan shark cut him in for twenty per cent of the money he recovered from hapless gamblers and the poor to whom George had loaned money at exorbitant rates. The watch and chain he had accepted in payment for some trivial amount owed. The fob he had provided himself. He continued to stand still while Cassidy ranted, his unwavering eyes fixed upon Kevin Murphy.

'Eric, Kevin Murphy here thinks that it's my fault that his useless sot of a father is blind drunk. I've never heard the like of it Eric!' He spoke, his smirking face showed he was enjoying this momentary triumph. 'And do you know what the eejit wants me to do?' Eric made no reply but continued to stare. Cassidy had paused in the expectation of Cadman's response but when none came, he shrugged and continued. 'No matter Eric. I'll tell you. He wants me to get two fellows to carry the drunk home and put a pound in his top pocket!'

He slammed his hand down hard on a table every man in the room still mute. 'What do you think of that, Eric? Tell me now, what do you think of that! Is that not a great joke?' There was a long pause, the room silent but eager to hear the reply. Finally, Eric spoke.

'Well, I think Shaughnessy and Finnegan are sober enough to do the carrying.' He walked behind the bar and rang up 'No Sale' on the till. 'How much was it for your dad's top pocket Kevin? Five quid?' Cassidy's mouth sagged open in surprise. He made no reply but staggered to a vacant seat. Eric Cadman pulled out the fob from his waistcoat pocket – a gold eagle's claw clutching a red marble.

'Do you recognise this Kevin?'

'I do Eric. Has it brought you any luck?' Eric Cadman held his other hand in front of him and see-sawed it from side to side.

'About fifty-fifty, Kevin. Fifty-fifty - no more.'

ᔐ

We left the pub walking slowly in the night-time light drizzle which formed halos around the burning gas streetlamps – electrification was late coming to Alum Rock. Shaughnessy and Finnegan followed, weighed down by their soporific burden. In the distance the Rosary Church carillon chimed the 'Ave Maria' and then proceeded to sound its dreary midnight dozen. I spoke to Kevin.

'It's been a strange day Kev, don't you think - the judo championship and now this?'

'Well as we used to say during the war, aboard the old 'Indyfat', we've seen one day end and a new one start. In truth it doesn't get much better than that.'

ᔐ

Chapter Five
A Noble Quest to the Palace of Crystal

PETER DONNELLY AND myself sat propped up in the grimy shop doorway, top and tailed in poor sleeping bags. In the main we were sheltered from the misty rain which fell, creating a pretty corona around the yellow sodium streetlights that pierced the dark. The day had started out optimistically. We hitched our first lift from outside the Birmingham City football ground and were taken the full distance of the Coventry Road, dropped off at Stonebridge island, which was the perfect spot from which to hitch-hike to London. Judo suits and rubber zoris had been neatly laid flat inside our respective bags and then tightly rolled and tied into a bedroll to be slung across our shoulders. We scrounged sandwiches from harassed mothers and headed off on that Friday afternoon to make our way to Crystal Palace for the BJA U21 Championships. Not for the first time, Peter played truant from school and I ditched lectures from university. That was the full extent of our planning and in those far-off generous times, it seemed enough. I say 'our' planning which was an exaggeration as Peter had done nothing except to tell his parents that he was staying with me for the night which, as he pointed out, was true. In these digital days such a subterfuge would be unlikely; in the Sixties phones were a rarity except in wealthier homes and we were free to roam uninterrupted. Our second lift had taken us to London; we alighted somewhere close to Euston Station.

Two young girls, dressed similarly in ridiculously short mini-skirts, high shoes and fluffy 'bolero' cardigans, looked down at us as we slunk, wrapped up but not warm, in the farthest recess of the litter strewn doorway.

'Ere you two! You can't stay there! We're working here. Sod off! You'll upset the punters!' The admonishment was repeated, and Peter and I looked at each other, unsure of how to meet this unforeseen event.

⌒

We had set off before dawn and walked two miles to our starting pitch. The bags of sandwiches had proven woefully inadequate and were eaten long before we got our first lift. As Peter pointed out this was a good thing as it meant we had less to carry.

'Where are you going lads?' asked the driver of the Commer van who pulled up in front of us in answer to our held-out thumbs. He was about thirty years old with the tanned face of an outdoor worker. His dark hair was cut conventionally short and he sported a neat moustache. His leather jerkin was unbuttoned, and the jumper underneath appeared to be streaked with tar. It turned out he was named Ash, short I presumed for Ashley.

'Well, I can take you to Stonebridge – it should be easy to get a lift down the M1 from there. Hop in.' We climbed aboard and sat three abreast on the bench seat of the old truck.

'Which one of you is going to give me a fag?'

'Sorry mate – neither of us smoke.'

'What! I only stopped to scrounge a fag. What do you mean you don't smoke, everybody smokes? Fair's fair – come on one of you must have a fag.'

'It's the truth mate – we don't smoke. Keeping ourselves fit, that sort of thing.' The driver laughed.

'Don't give me that baloney – I support Coventry, the Sky Blues, and before every home match have a pint in the Highfield Tavern. Half the team are there having a few drinks and a ciggy before the game – and you can't tell me they're not fit, being professionals and all.'

'Sorry, we don't smoke – our *Sensei* won't let us.'

'*Sensei*? What the hell is a *Sensei* when he's at home?'

'He's our coach. Our judo coach, we're off to London for a competition. We've got to be there to weigh in at eight o'clock tomorrow morning.'

'Judo! What that Japanese nonsense, shouting and breaking stones and stuff? You don't look that tough to me. Can you float in the air and shove needles through your face – that sort of bollocks?' I kept quiet and let Peter do the talking. Most of the general public had very little idea, of what judo consisted, frequently confusing it with karate.

'It's a sport mate. You have to throw someone or hold them down or make them give in. That's all. We're fighting tomorrow - Danny here is in the under twenty-one event and I'm in the under sixteens.' Peter's explanation was a waste of time.

'Well.' He said, 'the pair of you look soft to me. Up the road there is some farmland. I'll find us a field – if your big mate here can judo throw me to the ground, I'll take you down the M1 myself. What do you say?' I was not keen on the idea.

'No, you're alright mate. Mucking around in a field seems a bit mad to me. But the lift to Stonebridge would be grand.'

'You chicken then or summat? If you can throw me, I'll take you to London. If I stay on my feet or get you to the ground, you give me five bob. Fair Enough? Peter accepted on my behalf.

'Sounds fair enough to me. I'll be the ref. No punching or kicking, just a bit of friendly fun.' I was less than impressed with Peter's confidence - the whole thing was stupid. There again teenagers are well known for being idiots.

'There's got to be a time limit,' said Ash. If you can throw me in under two minutes - you win. If I stay on my feet – I win.' He turned into a lane just behind the Stonehouse Pub and pulled up in front of a gate to an empty field. 'This'll do,' he said. We climbed over the wooden five bar gate and found a patch that was well grassed. The month was October and even though it had not rained recently the field was damp with a slight softness to the turf. Had it been a racecourse I think the 'going' would have been classed as 'good.' Peter stood us about ten feet apart and checked his watch.

'When I call *hajime*, which means begin, the time starts. OK? I'll count down, five-four-three-two-one - *hajime*!' At this Ash laughed, turned around and ran twenty yards towards the centre of the field.

'What's going on? I thought we were having a fight, a wrestle?'

'You fight in your way and I'll fight in mine,' he shouted. 'As near as I know all we agreed was that if I stay on my feet for two minutes then I win five bob.' I suppose this was technically true.

'Get him Danny!' shouted Peter. It is worth mentioning that I played rugby for the university and as a winger had a fair turn of speed, so I chased after Ash who galloped off screaming a madly repeated, 'Ye-ha!' I hurtled off in pursuit and he dodged and weaved but I was quicker and eventually managed to get behind him. With a good rugby tackle I knocked him to the ground where he lay roaring hysterically in laughter which was infectious, and I joined in. Peter ran to our side and consulted his watch. 'One minute forty-five. You win Danny. You got him down in under the two minutes!' Not for the first time Ash replied,

'Bollocks!'

'But he got you down in under the two minutes!' Peter was obviously troubled by the denial.

'Oh, he got me down alright – but that wasn't the deal. We agreed that he had to throw me – and that rugby tackle from behind most certainly does not appear anywhere in the *go-kyu*. In my book it's a draw.' I got up and holding out a hand hauled Ash to his feet.

'*Go-kyu*, you say? If you know what that is then you must be a *judoka*?'

'I never said I wasn't did I? I'm Pete Ash, second Dan from Coventry Judo Club, best club in the Midlands. Good luck tomorrow at the Palace – and by the way your arm seems to be covered with cow shit!'

⁓

It was our first meeting with the late, eccentric judo player Peter Ash; a formidable fighter and Christian evangelist. Stories abound of how he combined his judo prowess and service to Jesus Christ. I am not convinced that JC would have necessarily approved: There was the winter evening in nineteen sixty-three, a winter so cold that snow lay on the ground for three months. Pete encountered a 'tramp' (an untroubled word then) huddling in a Coventry city centre doorway. He felt called to give the man his coat.

'You'll freeze mate. It's going to be ten below zero tonight.'

'Shove off!'

'Sorry mate. The Lord has spoken to me and has told me to give you my coat.'

'Well, you, the Lord and your coat can all piss off and leave me alone – I'm trying to get some kip.' Peter Ash thought for a while and undoubtedly prayed for guidance.

'Mate, when the Lord speaks, I listen. And whether you like it or not you're having this coat.' At which he grabbed his reluctant victim of charity and hauled him to his feet. Ash was a very strong man and aided by the righteousness of his cause soon had the man wrapped nicely in an exceptionally warm Crombie overcoat. The man flopped back into his corner.

'Bless you mate,' said Ash as he wandered shivering into the night.

'Piss off' came the fond farewell.

⤿

We left Peter Ash with assurances that we would indeed visit Coventry JC – easier said than done as neither of us had a car. We waved him good-bye and positioned ourselves to continue our hitch-hike to London. We then spent fruitless hours standing by the roadside. I suppose that two big lads were not everyone's idea of company. I was getting a little concerned when our luck changed and a truck stopped. The driver said he was going all the way to centre of 'The Smoke.' (This nickname was still in usage even though the Clean Air Act had rendered the air of the capital breathable once more. The 'Great Smog' of December nineteen fifty-two killed as many as twelve thousand Londoners. The smog had been banished for a decade but the ancient slang name for London still stuck.)

'I'm heading for the freight terminal at Euston. I'm carrying a load of starter motors and dynamos from the Lucas to be shipped down to Spain.' The driver's name was Dave Smith, a burly figure of about forty-five and somewhat over-weight. His hair was army cut – short, back and sides, and when he later took off his greasy flat cap, it proved to be thinning. He had regular features and was clean shaven and probably had been good looking in the style of twenty years earlier. 'You know the trouble with this country, don't you?' Donnelly and I did not answer which turned out to be the right thing to do. 'The trouble with this country today is that there is no discipline. No discipline, and the country is going to the dogs. Look at you two – no disrespect mind, but two lads like yourselves hitch-hiking down to London. What's all that about? You should have jobs or be in the army. Mods and Rockers? What's all that about? Meeting up at the seaside to have a fight. Bloody stupid if you ask me. I had enough fighting to last me a lifetime – it was called the bloody war. If you lot are so keen on having a scrap join the army! They should never have stopped National Service. The army would sort things out and make the likes of you have a haircut!' He looked at me. 'You seem a decent enough young bloke. Why have you got your hair half-way down your back? You look like a girl. You're not one of 'those' are you?' In truth my hair was not even collar length and Peter's was cut short.

'No, I'm not homosexual, if that's what you mean' I replied tersely, 'and I just like my hair a bit longer. It's my choice and it's a free country.'

'Yes, it is a free country - thanks to good old Winnie, and the Army, Navy and Air-force. But it nearly wasn't and in nineteen-thirty-nine when I was joined up the odds were that we would all soon be under the Nazi jackboot. I wonder what would have happened to your long hair then? By the way, has one of your farted? There's a strong smell of shit.' I put my inadequately cleaned arm behind my back and changed the subject.

'You were in the army then, Dave?'

'In in the army? In the chuffin' army. Of course, I was - every bugger was! There was a war you know – something you young sods seem to forget with your Beatles, long hair and transistor radios. Smith!

Private D! 76489 Royal Warwickshire Regiment 2nd Battalion, Sir!' He took his right hand off the steering wheel and made a smart salute followed by a wistful shake of the head. 'In the chuffin' army – well I don't know!' He turned out to be very interesting and told us stories of his service in the war all the way to Euston station – 'to pass the time' he said.

'I didn't have a job in thirty-nine and it was obvious that Hitler was going to cut up rough, so I joined up with our Frank – my big brother. Two year older he was, God bless him and rest his soul. It were his idea and I just tagged along like. We joined the Warwickshire Lads, were kitted up, and after a few weeks training we were ready for war! It were like being on chuffin' holiday - a new uniform, a change of shirt and underpants twice a week and the food! My God I'd never eaten as much. The sergeant who gave out the uniforms when we joined up gave us all a size too big and said we'd grow into them and he wasn't wrong. Great chunks of corned beef, piles of spuds, bread and marg, pints of tea to wash it down. Great stuff! I put on two stone in two months. Then the war started. Hitler invaded Poland and in no time flat we were in France. Do you know what happened then lads?'

'No Dave.'

'Nothing – absolutely chuffin nothing. We were sent to the border between France and Belgium and would you Adam and Eve it, there were still the remains of the trenches and shell holes from the First World War! We used to wander along the old Front Line looking for bullets and things that had been left or lost. I found an old rifle; no use mind; it were all rusted and covered in corrosion and mud. I cleaned it up and bugger me – it was a Lee-Enfield, the same rifle that we'd all been given. Spooked me a bit that to think of what had happened to the poor sod that owned it. Something bad I bet, because the last thing you do is lose your gun. We'd go into the little bars and cafes, estaminets they were called, and buy cheap wine. It had to be wine because the beer was no good, as weak as piss. And if you wanted entertainment for the 'old man below' (he pointed at his crotch) you could get that as well – for a price.

Christmas came – still nothing happened. Winter passed and still nothing. The weather began to warm up and some of us stripped off and started swimming in the canal – clean water, not like the cuts in Brum, full of oil, filth and shit. And then out of nowhere, about the beginning of May, Jerry hit us good and hard! The 'Blitzkrieg' which means 'lightning war' had started. Stukas dive bombed us; Messerschmitt's machine gunned us, and the Panzer tanks tore through Belgium as if it wasn't there. We were in a right old pickle. We were scared shitless and if anyone tells you different, they are chuffin' lying. The Jerries chased the whole British Army all the way to Dunkirk and then, for some reason or other, stopped. I have no idea why. The whole of the British Army was there, waiting to be destroyed on the beaches and Jerry let us off! I don't know what Hitler was thinking – nobody does. We were caught like rats in a trap and for a couple of days Jerry did nothing! Some say that Hitler wanted peace with Britain, that we and the Jerries were natural allies. Fat chuffin' chance! Anyway, we lined up on the beach in great lines stretching out into the sea. Thousands of little boats ferried the men to bigger boats further out or made their own way back to Blighty. I stood in the water for eighteen hours – to begin with just paddling and then up to my waist. I've never been in the sea since! Our Captain was with us – a bloody good bloke and he kept our spirits up. He was an Irishman. I remember one of the lads passed him his watch:

'Can you make sure my mammy gets it,' he said, 'just in case I don't make it Cap?'

'Ah ye'll get through right enough O'Neill.' Said Flood. 'Ye'll not get shot. You're so bloody ugly Jerry will take you for a pig. Ye'll be fine.' - but he took the watch and buttoned it in an inside pocket.

There was a landing craft coming our way. Captain flood turned to face us and shouted as loudly as he could:

'We're nearly home lads - nearly boys, nearly there!' There's a landing craft coming, and you know what to do. When the gate drops - go forwards; no rush lads just get up the ramp to the back of the boat. The navy has done its job!' Most of us, the 14th Machine Gun Company cheered but some just clenched their teeth. It was a grim business, but the Captain did his best to keep our spirits up.

'Anything to say boys? Anything to say?'

'Is your wife still a virgin Captain?'

'Of course not! I hear McGuire here gave her a good seeing to before we came to France!'

The landing craft ploughed forwards. A shell exploded in front of it drenching us with shingle and salt water. Their Oerlikon gun rattled return fire and we were all were nearly deafened. Captain Flood screamed. 'It will ground soon boyos, and when it does just get up the ramp as fast as you can. Don't think of anything – just go! Anything else boys?'

'Have you got a sister, Cap?'

'I have, but she's too good for you. My dog is too bloody good for you Marklew. Anyway, she's promised...'

And then a bullet hit his tin helmet! 'Damn!' He shouted in alarm and then laughed. He put his finger into the hole and held it up for us to see.

'Its good luck boys!' The boat's ramp collapsed into the water, Captain Flood crouched and yelled at us to get forward. Then a second bullet hit him in the back of his head and came out through his eye. It were a terrible sight. He didn't make a sound. He just fell onto the lowered ramp. Our sergeant, Sergeant Sweeney, took over:

'Come on!' He shouted and pulled Captain Flood off the ramp; he shoved him into the sea with his boot. And then a bullet or piece of shrapnel neatly removed *his* lower jaw. I've never seen anything like it; he just stood there with eyes wide, and half a face. Then he collapsed into the water at the bottom of the boat and lay there. I think he drowned. We all stepped over him. I suppose we should have done something but none of us did. Shells and bombs exploded, erupting great volcanoes of shale and water. Dead soldiers scattered the beach and floated in the surf... it were a bloody mess.'

He stopped speaking and just stared out of the windscreen for a while; then he breathed deeply and sighed. 'Anyway, that was the end of the war for me. The landing craft took us to an offshore ship which ferried us back to England. Then I noticed that when I went for a good old Jimmy Riddle, it hurt, and blood came out. The doctor said that standing in the cold water all that time had destroyed my kidneys and I was no longer fit for active service.' He took a deep breath, another sigh. 'Funny thing – I never saw a German, not even one and only fired my gun a few times at planes strafing the beech – but I did my bit alright. Yes, I did my bit!'

When he finished there seemed nothing to say and we sat in silence until we got out at Euston Station and waved our good-byes.

⟿

The two 'ladies of the night' were not happy with our company. 'Go on, piss off. Between this doorway and that lamppost is our patch and we pay good money for it. I've got a regular at half-past eight and he'll drive straight past if he sees you two.'

It took a second or two for the penny to drop but when it did Peter's eyes lit brightly.

'Are you pulling my leg? You're saying you rent a doorway and a strip of pavement. Who from, London Council?'

'No! From a couple of nasty gangsters with knives and guns who will happily give you a beating and a few stripes if you don't piss off. Now hop it!' Peter was having fun.

'Oh, I get it you're both...' One girl answered quickly.

'Yes, that's right. What do you think we are? Undercover girls for the Salvation Army?'

'Sorry love,' I said. 'We'll move on. We just needed somewhere to rest for the night. We're headed for Crystal Palace.'

'The Palace? You're nowhere close. You need to be south of the river. Catch the tube or the bus but don't try to doss round here – it ain't safe. Why you off there anyway?'

'We're fighting in a judo competition tomorrow. We've hitch-hiked from Birmingham...'

'I used to do judo,' said one of the girls, 'I was a green belt. I won a competition – I threw the other girl with *o-soto-gari*. Why you are sleeping in a doorway?'

'No money,' said Peter. 'We're both students and broke. You haven't got sixpence for a bag of chips, have you? I'm so hungry I was thinking of looking in the bins. And you two are very pretty – you must make a lot of money.'

'You cheeky little sod. Well, I never.' Nonetheless the girl smiled. Peter persisted.

'It's true though. I thought you were models - or perhaps film-stars.'

'We've both done some modelling and been in films – if you know what I mean.' The girls sniggered.

'See, I knew it!' said Peter. 'Go on, from one judo player to another treat us to a bag of chips. A bag of chips and a kiss and we'll be on our way.'

An hour later we were sitting on the upstairs back seat of the last bus from Euston to Sydenham eating fish and chips. Peter's relentless nagging combined with flattery had resulted in half a crown – enough for double chips and one fish.

'What was the kiss like?'

'It was a great kiss, and she had some body on her.'

'It was a mad thing to do though Peter, don't you think?'

'Well, we're eating fish and chips, warm on a bus and an hour ago we were freezing in a shop doorway. Doesn't seem so mad to me.'

'We've still got the freezing to come mind. It's close to midnight and we've still got to get through the night.'

'It'll be fine – we're bound to find another doorway or bus shelter...'

And we did, a bus shelter on Sydenham Hill where we uncomfortably dozed in our sleeping bags until disturbed at six in the morning by the rattle of bottles. A milkman left two pints outside a nearby house.

'That's a stroke of luck,' said Peter. 'Breakfast!' He looked at me as we strolled along. 'Your face looks like an old brush. There're bits of hair here and there and one big yellow spot. Shall I pop it?'

We guiltily drank the two bottles as we walked to final mile to the National Stadium in plenty of time for the eight o'clock weigh in.

꩜

I have always thought Crystal Palace to be the spiritual home of competition judo. Its construction in the sixties style of bare concrete, oiled wood and glass seemed to fit. The mat area, particularly in those days, was impressive. Four contest areas lay side by side, taped out on purpose made green tatamis. This was unmatched anywhere else. We were more used to dojos that were housed in working men's clubs, war surplus Nissen huts, in cellars or above pubs with mat areas comprised of sponge, sawdust or old mattresses. It also housed a full length fifty-metre Olympic size swimming pool – perhaps the only one in the country at the time. It is impossible for me not to mention that a few years later in that very pool a senior British International judoka dived in after the swimmers in an international match. Now all that I can say is that the officials must have lived blameless, maybe even sheltered lives as they believed his explanation; that he thought lane swimming was in progress and simply made a mistake. Utter rubbish of course, but it gives me hope for mankind that there is a whole population of people who, in these difficult times, are prepared to believe a charitable explanation, no matter how ludicrous. There is a streak of madness that runs through the veins of judoka, haven't you noticed? The sport seems to have more than its fair share of eccentrics who, may not be technically insane but are not right in the head.

We made straight away for the changing rooms and when I looked in a mirror, I was appalled at the vision in front of me. I had not quite grown out of teenage acne and half a dozen spots had erupted like yellow capped volcanoes. Shit! And my facial hair grew in patches so there were tufts dotted around my cheeks and jaw. There used to be a popular cartoon series on the television called 'Scooby-Do.' I looked like Shaggy, the scruffy teenager.. Nevertheless, after some surgical squeezing, a hot shower and scrub with the provided red carbolic soap I felt fine and untroubled by the discomfort of the night. Peter joined me in the shower. Now I do not take a particular interest in these matters and any observations I make are not driven by sexual curiosity or intent, but in those days, we showered naked and thought nothing of it. I note that now lads shower with their briefs on. Why? (I know this because I accompanied my son, on the cadet and junior competition circuit and found myself legitimately in changing rooms. The lads were never naked and showered in pants. Now I repeat I have no interest in the penises of young men but am puzzled by the change in showering behaviour.)

Clad in *judo-gi* trousers we both weighed in and made our respective weights with no trouble.

'I'm hungry, Danny,' whined Peter.

'I'm hungry too. But we've got no money left except for two bob and we need to save that to catch a bus through London tonight. There's no place to hitch-hike back from here – we need to get to Hendon or the Edgeware Road.'

'Let's spend the money – we're bound to find someone who will give us a lift back or to the motorway.'

'No, Peter, no.'

'Let's buy something from the caff, eat half of it and then take it back and complain, say it was bad or something, and ask for our money back. Or buy a pie eat most of it, then put a small stone in it and pretend to break a tooth. That always works – they're scared of being sued for breaking hygiene laws.'

'You've done this before?'

'Course! I've had free chips from every chip shop in Shard End!'

'No Peter – it's dishonest.'

'You drank the milk this morning and we nicked that. Anyway, I'm starving and I'm going to get some grub. Coming?'

We made our way to the café, which was self-service, and had the plated meals ready in rows of Perspex boxes which lined the length of the counter. It was busy and we joined the queue, grazing as we went lifting lid after lid, and taking a small snack from each. I remember clearly that when we reached the payment till, Peter was still eating a slice of boiled ham. He asked for a glass of water and I paid tuppence for a cup of tea which we shared loaded with sugar.

～

Peter's event was before mine and I sat on the pull-out seats as close to the mat as possible. We had chatted and he confirmed that he did not know any of the names on the posted list nor recognise any of the competitors sitting about. He had two exceptional attacks; a massive pull-on left *o-goshi* (the first throw *Sensei* Kevin taught and made us continually practice) and a very strong *uchi-mata*. He won his first fight in the pool of sixty-four with a left *taio-toshi*. The fight took less than one minute. His second fight was the same – left *taio-toshi*. And his third and fourth...

'What gives with all these *taios* Peter? Why no *o-goshis* or *uchis*?'

'Saving them for best, aren't I. Everyone will think I'm a one trick pony. When it stops working, I'll hit 'em with the *o-goshi* – so hard that they won't get up. Whoever I fight in the final I hate and want to kill.' His eyes gleamed.

'That's a bit mad Peter, a bit steep don't you think?'

'No! Whoever it is - it's his fault. This whole weekend is his fault! Hitch-hiking here because we've got no money - his fault! You fighting Mad Ash – his fault! Listening to those bloody depressing war stories – his fault! Scrounging money off sex-workers – his fault! Sleeping in doorways – his fault! Being hungry – his fault! The whole bloody business is his fault, and I'll make him pay.'

As it happened Peter won his event and became Champion with seven successive left-handed *taio-toshis*. A strange thing to do; a talented strangeness which brought him to the attention, for the first time, of the international selectors of the BJA.

~

My progress was more pedestrian. To begin with, there were half the number of competitors in the under 81kg event and hence a maximum of five fights. I won my first two fights easily enough and scraped through the quarterfinal with a very narrow win over a lad from the north. I won as he had picked up a 'chui' for stepping out of the contest area – a poor way to win a fight over a good player. I won well in the semi-finals beating Barry Littlejohn with *ippon* from a left *o-soto-gari*, which left me to fight Les Hudspith from Solihull Judo Club. I knew Les quite well; he was a star player, already an U21 International. He came down to the Morris JC from time to time as we would visit Solihull JC for extra training, under the exceptional coach Peter Barnett.

Les had a perfect physique, he did a great deal of weight training and I knew I would be out powered. He also had a unique *tokui-waza* – a left-handed *sode-tsuri-komi-goshi* from a double end of sleeve grip.

It was a phenomenal throw and quite dangerous as both your arms were controlled and could not be used to break-fall. The real danger was that if Les failed to rotate sufficiently, you landed on the point of a shoulder. Rumour had it that he broke a few bones!

I was far from confident but there was room for hope. I had seen Les turned over a few times by Tony Underwood, Bob Trevis and once by Fred Stansbie, an army man who had a devastating right *uchi-mata*. It was his only throw but when it worked – it worked! I normally beat Fred and was in the same ballpark as Bob and Tony. As it happened it was not much of a fight. I was determined not to go over and did not – but an untidy attack ended in *ne-waza* and I was held down with a full-on *kami-shio-gatame*. There is only one thing of note to mention and it has nothing whatsoever to do with judo. Les had a great physique, every muscle was defined, and it was rumoured that he made extra money through artistic posing – something like that anyway. It was also gossiped that his male member was, well shall we say that in a horticultural event, it would easily have won the title of 'best in show.'

I spent thirty seconds of my life with my face nestled near the aforesaid appendage and I believe that, although creditable, the fabled proportions were, in fact, more modest.

⁓

We encountered Kenny Webber the coach at Shard End Judo Club quietly eating fish and chips in the Crystal Palace canteen. The meeting was hardly accidental. The day's events were done, and Peter and I were looking for someone who might give us a lift back to Birmingham to save the chore of hitch-hiking. By way of greeting Peter bounded up happily.

'Hello *Sensei,* can I have a chip?' Kenny looked up from his plate and shook his head.

'Just when I thought the worst was over... No, Peter. Buy your own chips.'

'I can't *Sensei* – I haven't got any money.'

'Well get Danny to buy some then.'

'Can't *Sensei*. He's broke as well. We haven't eaten since yesterday either...' which was not quite true. 'Go on *Sensei* – just one chip!' Kenny Webber 3rd Dan looked at me for clarification.

'Is this scrounging so-and-so telling the truth Danny, you're both broke?'

'It is Kenny – more or less. I've got two shillings, but we'll need that to catch a bus across London to Hendon. We hitch-hiked down yesterday.' Kenny Webber shook his head.

'Yesterday you say. Where did you sleep last night?' Peter was quick to answer.

'To begin with we slept in a doorway, but two 'night-ladies' told us to bugger off but...' he added meaningfully, 'they weren't mean, and did buy us some chips. Then we slept in a bus shelter.'

'Night-ladies?' I answered Kenny's implied question.

'He means 'ladies of the night.'

With further head shaking Kenny opened his wallet and took out a ten-shilling note and muttered a pretend prayer. 'Dear Lord – I don't know what I did wrong to deserve these two pestering me...' He gave me the brown banknote. 'Go and buy yourselves a meal. I watched you fight and you both did well, particularly the nipper. Call it a present.'

Kenny Webber fed us both and told me to keep the change from the ten-bob note. He also gave us a lift back to Birmingham. I always intended to pay the money back, but fifty years passed by too quickly and I never got round to it. Sorry *Sensei*.

∽

Peter Donnelly lay fast asleep in the back of Kenny Webber's small Ford Anglia as we journeyed back to Birmingham, having taken the Edgeware Road northwards and then picked up the M1 at Hendon.

'How did you start judo Kenny.' An easy question and many of the older generation of *judoka* had a similar tale to tell.

'In the army I suppose. We all had to do unarmed combat which was basically *jiu-jitsu*. I spoke to your kid about it a few years back. It was the same for him, only Kevin was in the navy.'

'Were you in the war then Kenny?'

'Depends which war you mean. The world didn't go quiet when Hitler blew his brains out in 1945 you know. World War Two ended but there were plenty of other wars going on to keep the armies, navies and air forces of the world entertained. I joined up in 1947. India was in turmoil so was most of Africa, Indochina, Malaysia, the Persian Gulf – you name it and there was fighting going on. My regiment was sent to Palestine, which was a mess, is still a mess and in my opinion will always be a mess. Anyway, to go back to your question, o-*soto-gari* saved my life which is why I took up judo.' There was nothing to do and so I kept quiet while Kenny told his story:

'The British army was supposed to keep the peace, but it was impossible. You know that war the Arabs and Jews fought last year? The 'Six Day War' they call it now. It came as no surprise at all to me I can tell you. The Arabs hate the Jews and the Jews hate them back - and they're supposed to live in the same place. Well good luck with that! When I was there in forty-seven there was no country called Israel. There was a lot of sympathy for the Jews because of Hitler murdering six million of them in the gas chambers. The United Nations voted that there should be two states in the area, Israel and Palestine. The Jews accepted this, but the Arabs did not and the rest, as they say, is history. We were posted near a small Arab village called 'Betsy Sheehan' – that wasn't its proper name of course but the Arabic name sounded the same. There was a Jewish village nearby, I can't remember what that was called just now. I tell you Danny, you couldn't tell one place from the other. About fifty little stone houses in each, a well for water a few dozen goats and sheep and nothing else. Both were stuck in the middle of a stony landscape – just desert really. Nothing there, a hard place not worth fighting over - not in my eyes. Apparently, the villages had gotten on well for hundreds of years, but all that changed when the Jews took the United Nations at its word and decided that Israel now existed and declared that its territory was the ancient lands named in the Bible.

The whole region was in chaos. There was no proper government of Israel just terrorist gangs trying to take power. One such gang committed a terrible atrocity at an Arab village called Deir Yassin, murdering about a hundred men, women and children. A week or so later the Arabs pulled all the passengers off a Jewish train and shot them in cold blood. As I say the place was a mess – and the British were supposed to keep order. Fat chance!

I had a good mate in the army, a Geordie lad from Tyneside called 'Nobby' Clarke. He was a good sort and we got on. We were off duty and had gone into 'Betsy Sheehan' for a drink. Now as it was an Arab village, and as they are all Muslims there shouldn't have been a bar because their religion forbids alcohol. Well, religion or no religion there was a bar which served good food and a local hooch called Araq, which tastes sweet and of aniseed. You drink it with water which turns milky when they're mixed. It was so bloody hot that me and Nobby sat outside under the verandah. It was a horrible posting and was getting everyone down. We sat quietly, completely brassed off. Nobby looked around at the baked, parched, dusty town square, nudged me and pointed. Two Arabs repeatedly struck a pack loaded donkey to encourage greater effort. I noticed the old scars on the animal's rump. Now Nobby was a big chap – your height Danny but hefty. He said to me in his thick Newcastle accent, 'I think I'll go and let them two Johnnies feel the whip on their own backs.'

'No, Nobby,' I said. 'One war's just ended and you want to start another.'

'I just can't stand to see a man thrash a dumb animal. If I had me gun Kenny, I'd shoot the bastards from here.' You might be surprised to know, Danny. that we were not allowed to carry weapons out of barracks. Well, Nobby took aim with a pretend rifle and clicked his fingers to fire an imaginary shot. One of the Arabs saw him and took offence. He began to wave his arms wildly in the air. He screamed at Nobby and, of course, Nobby shouted back. We didn't understand Arabic and the Arabs certainly didn't understand Geordie – but the message was clear on both sides, and it was not friendly. Well, we finished our drinks, paid up and decided to head back to camp. We were strolling down a narrow street; all the streets were narrow to block out the sun. We turned a corner and there they were – the two johnnies who had been beating the donkey. We knew it meant trouble and that they were waving knives came as no surprise. I'm not talking about flick-knives or any spiv Teddy-boy malarkey, Danny - more like machetes they were. Have you done any self-defence with Kevin?'

'I have done a bit. Every now and then Kev does a *jiu-jitsu* session – just for a change.'

'Well, you'll know the first rules – Kevin and me put the package together that's used in most of the Birmingham clubs. But there is a big difference between self-defence and unarmed combat that's taught in the army. Self-defence is all about keeping yourself safe, but army stuff is about trying to kill the other bloke as well. Nobby Clarke failed the first rule of self-defence alright. He marched towards the two Arabs shouting, in that strong Geordie accent, 'D'ya want some, bonnie lad? D'ya want some?' Over and over, he said the same thing. One bloke went for Nobby and the other came at me. I tell you Danny, I was bricking it! When you see fights on the telly or at the pictures everything seems clear. It was nothing like that at all. I could hardly think, and everything seemed confusing and mixed up. The only thing I could remember from my training was to get close. Our sergeant, Jacky Milburn, us kept saying 'Get close in a knife fight so the opponent can't slash or stab. You have one advantage - you know which arm he is going to attack you with, the one that's holding the bloody knife! Control that arm and then hip throw or back-chop, whichever seems best.' Some of the training must have stuck. Johnny Arab came at me, I got inside his slash and wrapped up his knife hand and pulled him close. I remember he smelled of lemon - I don't know what that was all about. He was shouting all the time 'Allah Wakhbar, Allah Wakhbar' – something like that. I managed to step across and throw him with the 'back chop' which is *o-soto-gari,* and he went down with an almighty wallop. The road surface was baked mud which was as hard as stone and the fella just lay there gasping. I'd landed on top of him and I was okay. He'd dropped the knife which I picked up and was going to shove it in his guts, which was what we'd been trained to do, but I couldn't. When I got a good look at his face, he was just a kid – certainly no older than me. I was relieved when he got up and scarpered. I don't know why but I examined the knife blade and was amazed to see 'Ford Motor Company' stamped into the heavy metal. I think it was homemade from the leaf-spring of a car.

It took me a few seconds to get my wits about me. When I looked round for Nobby he was sitting on a low wall with his left arm hanging loosely and pouring with blood – literally pouring down his arm and had already attracted a cloud of flies which I thought disgusting. Now I tell you what Danny, you can't spend but a few weeks in Palestine without getting a suntan - but Nobby was as white as a ghost. And then, can you believe it, I started to shake and be sick! I heaved and threw up all the araq and the lamb stew that I'd had at the bar. Nobby began to sway and I knew I needed to get a tourniquet on his bleeding arm. Then my guts started to loosen. I just managed to drop my shorts and deposit a load in the middle of the street! I had no choice - a second later and I would have been in a right old mess! To cut a long story short I cleaned myself up as best I could and took the belt out of my shorts. I wrapped it around Nobby's upper arm. My God, I'd never seen such a cut other than in a butcher's shop. I tightened it and managed to stop the bleeding. Then two other Arabs appeared from one of the mud brick houses and helped me carry Nobby to the main drag where we flagged down a jeep and two military police took him to the camp hospital...' He became silent as if recalling the day in some deep way. 'Can you believe it? Two Arabs were trying to kill us and then five minutes later another two Arabs were helping to save Nobby's life. I'll never understand what happened that day, but I know one thing for sure - *o-soto-gari* saved my life.'

Kenny became silent, seemingly brooding. I didn't know what to say but after a few minutes I asked inanely, 'What did you do with the knife?' He brightened a little.

'Still got it Danny! It's in the shed at home – comes in quite useful in the garden, for pruning and the like.'

⌒

The dark miles clicked by. Kenny recovered his good humour and started to talk about the events of the day. 'I saw two great players today...' I was momentarily elated until he continued, 'the nipper in the back and that London lad, Parisi.' I was a little hurt and blurted out, 'what about me?' Kenny laughed.

'You'll do all right Danny – a silver in the nationals ain't bad, but you'd lost against Hudspith before you went on the mat.' I completely respected *Sensei* Kenny Webber, but really did not want to hear any criticism of my performance. Kenny was either unaware or did not care about my finer feelings. 'You need three things to become a true champion Danny and you've got one of them.

'That's a start then Kenny.' I said this with a touch of bitterness which was completely ignored.

'It's a start, fair enough – it's a start. You've got good judo skills, mind you your ground-work is pretty rubbish. But you're smart and will learn. What you haven't got is the body to do the job and the mindset of a champion. You need all three – Body, mind and skills. But the one aspect that really lets you down is the easiest to put right. You need to get into much better physical condition.'

'I need to be stronger?'

'You do, much stronger. Then you need to apply the strength correctly. The extra power will give you more control – it's not just strength for its own sake. Imagine this. If I tied a paintbrush to your arm and told you to hold your arm out straight and write your name on a wall, could you do it?'

'I suppose so – if there was paint on the brush...'

'Don't be smart! Now if I rested a ten-kilo weight on your arm, then could you do it?'

'I might be able to, but my writing would be all over the shop.'

'Exactly! But if you were much stronger you could still do it. More control! The correct application of strength.'

'How about the 'mindset of a champion?' Kenny shrugged.

'Get the first two right and the third often follows.'

'What about Peter? You think he's got what it takes? Kenny shrugged again.

'Look at what he did today. Why do you think he threw everyone with the same bloody throw?' Kenny did not wait for a reply.

'He put down a marker, that's what he did. He made people take notice. Reminds me of Abbe when he used to name the technique he was going to throw with.'

(Abbe again! Why were so many of the 'old timers' obsessed with Kenshiro Abbe?)

'Was he really that good Kenny? Kevin goes on about him so does Colin Draycott. How do you think he compares with the likes of Jacks or Starbrook?'

'He's the best *judoka* I've ever seen. I went on a few courses of his before he went back to Japan. That's why I joined the BJC – I was so impressed. As for how he would get on with today's top players, I really don't have a clue. Modern judo is very different. Abbe would have been at his best thirty years ago when judo was almost completely a Japanese sport. It was practised differently and the philosophy of Jigaro Kano was very important. Judo has changed in the last ten years. It's much more westernised. Anyway Danny, you can make up your own mind about Abbe. A few of us have been writing to him and he's coming back to Britain next year. There's a treat for you and Peter!'

꩜

Just before midnight Kenny Webber's little car stopped outside Peter Donnelly's house in Buckland End Avenue. Peter was now awake and refreshed from his two-hour nap. I stood on the street-lighted pavement holding the car door as he squeezed from the back seat and crawled out on all fours.

'You can stay here tonight; my mom won't mind.' Without much thought I rejected this offer. I knew that after his nap he would be hyperactive and manic. I was tired.

'No thanks Peter. I fancy my own bed. I'll catch the night service from the Clock Garage.' I leaned to speak to Kenny through the open car window. 'Are you going that way Kenny? It's only a mile – I can walk if you're not.' In pretend annoyance *Sensei* Kenny Webber replied.

'Get back in Danny. The sooner you're in, the quicker I can get rid of you.'

Peter and I stood in the still of the cold night. 'How does it feel to be the best Espoir judo player in Britain?'

'It doesn't feel anything much. It was a good week-end though, wasn't it?'

'It was that brother – a good week-end.' We hugged tightly, said our good-byes and I climbed stiffly back into Kenny Webber's cramped little car.

Chapter Six
The Training Tilts

THERE COMES A time in the development of every aspiring judo player when the weekly training sessions at your local club are simply not enough. They become too familiar and lack challenge. Kevin spotted this and advised the solution. 'It's about time you and Donnelly started travelling around the clubs. You need new players to fight and new coaches to learn from. It's doing you no good bashing away here and at the Morris week after week.' He was right of course. Transportation was an initial problem but Tony Underwood, Dave Law, Roy Muller amongst others had cars and Peter Donnelly was good at scrounging lifts:

〜

'Yow um a bostin big chap' said Stan Rouse the coach at Dudley Judo Club. His black country accent was as thick as groaty pudding. Sixty years ago, there were parts of the Black Country where spoken English was a set of word-like sounds hammered and welded together in a manner incomprehensible to all except natives. Young boys born in Netherton, hence sufficiently close to Birmingham to understand more regular speech, made a few pennies here and there as translators; for tuppence could be bought guidebooks with simple renditions of everyday phrases. They were often sold by the straw hatted men in striped aprons who went round pubs with wicker baskets selling local cooked delicacies such as tripe, blood-puddings, brains, intestines, testicles and the like. (I jest of course. These fine foods were usually for supper. The men actually sold cockles, winkles, mussels, whelks and deep-fried pigskin.)

'Yow um a bostin big chap,' he repeated this muttered observation and poked and prodded me squeezing shoulders and biceps. He carried on, 'Yower mam's bin feedin' yow up - now yow just hang on a bit. I'm going to slip my arm around your waist like – nice and tight and then pull you in a bit...' At this he threw his hips in deep and fast and launched me onto the mat with a powerful, thumping *o-goshi*. 'Now, yow daint expect that now did ya?' I was perplexed and made this clear.

'No, of course I didn't! We were talking to each other! Why would I expect to be thrown?'

'Yow 've got to be ready in this game young chap! I've showed ya summat there and I won't charge you for the lesson – although you can buy me a pint later. You got to be ready for the unexpected.' Stan was a fine coach, a good judo player and eccentric.

Jigaro Kano could never have envisaged any such judo club. It would have been better suited as the lair of a Black Country Fagin, where his pack of feral street urchins, wearing battered top hats, drinking hot gin and smoking long clay pipes, would nightly bringing their ill-gotten gains for evaluation by the hook-nosed villain. Instead, it was a judo club housed in the loft of an eighteenth-century inn, which would have originally stored hay for the coach-horses stabled below. Little had changed in the hundred or so years since it had ceased to be a coaching halt but the filth and grime still evident in every crack or corner showed that the building had a later industrial heritage. A combination of soot, soil, and swarf held together by grease had long since set like volcanic lava. It left a peculiar all-pervasive smell which I can only liken to the whiff of a burnt-out building. I doubt this helps, unless you have been in one with everything charred and dripping with water. If you have, you'll know what I mean. The walls of this glorified barn had at some time been whitewashed, but damp and time had long since reduced this poor paint to powder which flaked and crumbled and lay as grey dust on the floor. Access to the dojo was a complicated affair. From the street the pub was entered through the front door of the public bar. A gauntlet of disapproving eyes, indoor shaded by inevitable flat caps, followed you as you left through the rear exit into the enclosed courtyard. The bays for the coaches and stables for the horses were still present complete with the remains of straw bales and cracked leather harness which had not been required for fifty years or more. The courtyard was paved with blue engineering bricks which provided a flat surface – particularly fortuitous in the winter as there was no light. A hurricane lamp sometimes burned at the foot of a ladder but other than that only the faintest illumination came from the hole above into which the ladder protruded. Fifteen precarious rungs led upwards into the dojo – a place of hobgoblins, demons and dark shadows. One electric light dangled from a nail driven into a low roof-timber. The place was packed with cavorting, madly driven black-country men intent upon rough judo which owed as much to the heavy industrial history of the area as it did to Japan. The dojo was the province of tough men with work strong arms, giving out and taking hard knocks.

If there was any springiness in the dojo floor it was due to rot and not design. In the pub below, over a later pint of excellent Batham's mild, Stan explained with pride the construction of the mat. I had moaned that it was rock hard and had no give in it at all – I had the bruises to prove it. 'It's a bostin' mat! Really fast to wuk on. You'um saft, Danny.' It seems they got the canvas from a haulier, slipped someone a few quid to turn a blind eye so to speak. Underneath they raked twenty bags of sawdust from the wood yard. This worked well for a few weeks but then it compressed and set hard. They took it up every year or so to break up the lumps and add a few more bags of sawdust.

'Bostin' mat!' repeated Stan. 'But where d'yow think the wood guz as it nids a few mow're bags every year?'

'It's being eaten Stan! It's obvious! With all the sweat and damp in the mat there will be a million woodlice and other insects and grubs having a five-star dinner every night!' He and others nudged each other and laughed at my explanation which they thought humorous. I could not convince them of my serious intent and the more I tried the funnier they found my explanations. They slapped their thighs and me on the back and said I would do well on the music hall stage.

The club members were complicit in one trick which was played on every visitor thought worthy of the jape. Now the essence of a good prank is not to force it; to let it happen in its own time. In our case circumstances prevailed that it happened on our first visit. Tony Underwood spoke to Stan Rouse. 'Excuse me Stan, I need a leak. I there a toilet?'

'Goo through that door there and miyund the step there's a bit of a drop.' Tony and I were practising together with Peter doing battle elsewhere. He broke off, bowed and said he would be 'back in a bit.' I stopped grateful for a rest and took the opportunity to adjust my kit and tighten my belt. I could not help but notice the air of anticipation that had gripped the room, and all eyes were on Tony Underwood. One of the Dan grades, Roy Whitacre, had casually walked to the door and stood close as Tony opened it outwards. It is important here to know that Tony had been well brought up by his mom and dad, and it is to their credit that his language is seldom coarse – he hardly ever swears.

'Oh Shit!' he screamed in terror as he stepped forward into oblivion. There was no floor. Whitacre grabbed him and hauled him back to safety to the great laughter and some applause of the watching club. The door was there for the specific purpose of hauling bags of grain into the loft. and now had no other use than to create terror and hence the associated amusement of the *judoka* of Dudley. Stan Rouse explained:

'It's s'posed to be the fire-escape, but yow'ud brek yow'er legs if you jumped out - and we ain't got no rope.'

'It's dangerous Stan – somebody could get killed!'

'It tay yungun – doh be saft.'

'It is Stan and so is the hole you have to climb through to get into the dojo. I nearly fell down it twice. In fact, Roy Whitacre kept shoving me towards it and then attacking as I stepped away from the edge!' Stan winked and turned his head sideways in appreciation.

'Ar, ee's a crafty one is Roy; any road up, yow day fall dowun t'ole, so no 'arm.'

There was no point in trying to make any of them see sense – they had their view of the world and I had mine. Tony drew me to one side, and we discussed the evening as the rest finished their pints in good humour and laughing – no doubt at our or at least my expense. Tony was well known by reputation and had turned everyone over with his pet throw. 'How did you get on with Whitacre?' Tony, Peter and myself sat together in the downstairs bar analysing our performance.

'He threw me once with that double dig *ko-soto-gake* that he does. Great throw! I landed flat on my back and had the stuffing knocked out of me. He only did it the once though and other than that we were about even. I rolled him once.' Peter and Tony nodded their understanding.

'Roy's a great fighter.' Commented Tony. 'He takes everyone with the *ko-soto*. How did you get on with Harry Hobbs?

'Didn't fight him...'

'Good – the mans the best there is. As strong and as tough as Trevis but with an amazing *morote-seoi-nage.*

On subsequent visits Dudley JC remained odd but never again had such a mysterious air reminiscent of a bygone age. Modernity has its place of course - but don't we all savour those islands of originality that are rooted in a simpler past?

⤿

One of the very first judo clubs in Birmingham was the Birmingham School of Judo, otherwise known as Kyrle Hall. The building, a grand 1920s monolith was established by the Pinsent family for the social good of Birmingham's poor. There was a hostel for young men, play activities for children and all manner of sporting facilities. Squash must not have been popular in the early 1950s as the court was given up to judo. It was fully matted with padded walls. The first instructor was Frank Ryder who like a lot of the early pioneers knew a thing or two. Not unusually he also proved to be an odd-ball. He took to using the title Professor but was no charlatan and Birmingham judo owes a lot to him. Early members of the club were my brother Kevin Murphy, cousin Jimmy White, and myself as a seven-year-old. I well remember the frenzy caused when Kenshiro Abbe descended on the club for a week of tuition and demonstrations. Abbe was achieving god-like status at the time, and there is no doubt that the admiration with which he is regarded continues to this day amongst his ageing and diminishing band of followers.

It was 1955. The atmosphere at the club was one of great excitement, and the squash court dojo was packed. The training session with Kenshiro Abbe 8th Dan, recently from Japan and acclaimed by some as the greatest judo player ever, had to be split. Judoka were rotated on and off the mat every half hour. When off the mat players crammed with me into the high spectators' gallery to watch this legendary man. Kenshiro Abbe did not look the part, with his round thick set face and a flaring nose. He was of average height, perhaps less, of medium build almost bald and old. (In fact, he was only forty but from the perspective of my tender years he seemed ancient.) Nonetheless he was afforded complete, god-like respect. The dojo was silent. The assemblage faced Abbe, kneeling in parallel straight lines, and all bowed in obeisance at his call of 'Rei.'

Throughout the day he demonstrated technique after technique and the consensus was that his application was perfect. He took considerable delight in throwing his partners with casual ease as he took turns with everyone during 'moving practice.' There were murmurs of appreciation at the timing of his *ashi-waza* and gasps of almost wonder as he effortlessly threw much bigger players. He was the epitome of movement and grace. I was a mere child but well understood the aura encircling him as he walked around the mat advising and correcting, occasionally just watching and nodding approval with his thumbs hooked into his red and white belt. The high spot of the day came with his challenge to the club that he would fight everyone in turn and beat them with the throw which he would nominate. From my vantage in the viewing gallery I watched, nervous that he might fail. He progressed through his 'line-up' of maybe thirty players throwing the lower ranked kyu grades with ease. But the high end of the line consisted of six or seven black belts, and the final player was the mighty Fatso Jinx.

To begin with he threw using mainly foot sweeps; with some opponents he show-boated pretending himself to be in danger before winning with his chosen technique. He had one lad hopping around the mat on one foot before turning him mat-wards with *uki-otoshi*. '*Kuzushi* important - big circle important!' he announced to the applauding crowd before continuing his performance with my brother Brian. 'You tall – I throw you with *ko-uchi gake*!' Abbe feigned a right *ippon-seoi-nage* attack and when Brian resisted, Abbe quickly turned the attack into the rear throw. The technique was faultless, but my brother's landing was not. He struggled to his feet, bowed and smiled bravely but was clearly winded.

He came to Kevin, his penultimate opponent. 'What best throw in judo?' Kevin looked perplexed and uncomfortable.

'Sorry *Sensei*. I do not think there is a best throw. The best throw is the one that is best to do at the time.'

'Good answer! You good boy. I no throw you! Go back, back!' Kevin bowed and made his way back into the line of judoka and knelt down.' Abbe's face broke into a wide grin. 'I make good joke. Of course, I throw you now – with most important throw. No best but *o-goshi* important, like *kyu-shin-do*!' Kevin returned to the centre of the mat to be duly thrown. Finally, the climax came. Fatso Jinx stood waiting to fight Kenshiro Abbe and I would guess the former outweighed the latter by sixty kilograms. At six-four and at least one-thirty kilos the big man was literally twice the size of his Japanese opponent. 'You big boy – like *sumo-ka*. I *sumo* champion at school.' In the event there was no magnificent climax – no spectacular throw by Abbe. Jinx certainly made a better fist of things than anyone else but after about a minute Abbe attacked with his nominated foot-sweep. Jinx skidded high to one side but did not quite fall. A small bone or ligament in Fatso's foot snapped; the contest was over. Abbe received a tumultuous accolade of applause, but his face was set sternly either because of the applause or that he had not thrown Jinx – maybe both.

⤳

This heyday had long since passed, but the club had re-opened in the smaller gymnasium of the main building. It was not a competitive club at all, but it did have an associated and excellent social side. Peter Donnelly, Tony Underwood and many of the judo crowd became regulars; a place to have an 'easy knock' and a bit of fun afterwards. Kyrle Hall was now under new management and was a hostel for young men and women in particular foreign exchange students. I had a crush upon one girl, Mara Ivers, a petite flaxen haired girl from Latvia. I had contrived conversations with her but felt awkward and did not have the confidence to pursue matters. There was the basement 'Crypt Coffee Bar' where the tables were coffins and the décor ghoulish, complete with zombies, skeletons and such stuff all glowing under the ever-present ultra-violet light. The larger gym was now a music venue which put on shows by many famous bands of the time – The Kinks, The Who and The Crazy World of Arthur Brown come to mind. The Crypt was also the venue for my eighteenth birthday party...

⮑

I don't think I was a virgin and had not been for almost a year – in truth I was not exactly sure: Judo displays were popular at summer fetes and the like, and Kevin was always willing to volunteer us to prance around in school halls, rectory gardens, shopping centres and once at half-time at a first division football match. This present occasion was in the grounds of a country parsonage in Coleshill, a leafy venue unchanged for the past four hundred years. The vicar was a kind soul with the odd name of Fenchurch Smythe – his father being a steam train enthusiast. It was a vibrant summer's day and fifteen-year-old Peter and seventeen-year-old me impressed the crowd with a 'fight' which was billed as a 'best out of three' challenge, giving us ample scope to throw each other, on and off the mat, stumble and crash into mat-side spectators – all good stuff.

The Reverend Fenchurch had two-sixteen-year-old daughters; identical twins named Abigail and Rebecca. Their father had the values, hopes, dreams and outlook of a country cleric of the 1850's. His daughters were most certainly a product of the 'swinging Sixties' and they inevitably clashed. Matters were made worse, as far as the Reverend was concerned, by the fact that the girls were extremely pretty in the 'dolly-bird' manner that was fashionable at the time. He was paranoid that one, or the other, or both would get pregnant and was scared to let them out of his sight.

At the end of our display the twins made a beeline for Peter who, in turn, brought them over to me, and before long the four of us were wandering around, sampling the delights of the fayre. I won a cocoanut by knocking down a set of cans with a wooden ball. The girls bounced up and down, excitedly clapping their hands in happy unison. I felt very proud. Peter won a goldfish by throwing a ping-pong ball into a jam jar. The girls were less enthusiastic about his feat – which pleased me.

'It's a shame for the poor thing.' Said Abigail (or Rebecca) and Rebecca (or Abigail) agreed. I pointedly agreed with them. 'You should let it go,' said the girls in harmony. Peter quite rightly said that freeing a goldfish in a country field was no easy matter. 'Let's take it to the river,' the twins suggested, a course of action upon which we united. Soon we four were wandering along an idyllic country lane, leafily shaded from the evening sun. The girls climbed, and we heroically vaulted over a style, and then we flirted through a recently harvested wheat-field, at the bottom of which flowed the river Cole. Peter held the jam jar containing the goldfish, (now named Ringo,) in one hand and held Abigail (or Rebecca) in the other. I tenderly grasped the spare twin. 'Love Among the Haystacks' is a beautiful short story by D.H. Lawrence. In the mid-sixties love was still going strong but hay was now compressed into less picturesque rectangular bales. From the riverbank we said good-bye to Ringo and wished him well. The girls were pleased, and one or the other of the sweet things wiped a tear from her eye. Peter suggested that with a little re-arrangement the bales of straw dotted about could be fashioned into a den – a sort of square igloo. It seemed a grand plan.

'Better make two,' suggested Peter, 'for privacy.'

When wheat is cut, the stubble left is sharp spikey stuff – not at all comfortable upon which to lie. I took off my denim jacket and spread it out the best that I could. Abigail (or Rebecca) helpfully suggested that her short leather skirt unbuttoned completely and would provide extra protection from the straw. 'Anyway,' she said, 'it will only get in the way. We lay in our grassy cocoon and passionately kissed and fondled – I was in heaven until she gasped, 'Have you got a Durex?' This was terrible news! She expected me to go 'all the way!' Even worse I did have a contraceptive. It had lain unused in the back-pocket of my jeans for months. I only carried it out of bravado and now I was faced with an impossible dilemma. If I said 'yes' I would have to go through with the act and beyond the obvious mechanics I had no idea what to do. I was frightened. If I said 'no' I would miss the opportunity for which I had literally prayed. I told myself to stay calm and take deep breaths. I made the fateful decision.

'Yes, it's in my back pocket – I'll get it.'

'Do you want me to put it on?' For a moment I panicked. Had I got it wrong – surely not? I quickly realised what she meant and thought this was a considerate offer.

'Yes please.'

To the best of my knowledge the only people who had touched my penis other than myself were my mother and a doctor. The sensation when she held me was ecstatically thrilling and I only managed to maintain self-control by thinking of the Headmistress of my primary school, Sister Joseph – a severe looking nun who sported a moustache. Abigail (etc..) had removed her panties and I clambered between her legs internally reciting the Lord's Prayer for guidance and composure. The entrance bale of straw began to move.

'Abigail, Rebecca – are you in there?' The cultured voice of the Reverend Fenchurch Smythe simultaneously collapsed and prematurely satisfied my ardour. So, if I was still a virgin it was not by much – perhaps a centimetre at most.

⌐

A year later, I missed a large part of my eighteenth birthday party at the 'Crypt', but I am told that my absence was not noticed and that everyone had a good time.

'I've got a present for you Murph.' Said Dave Law.

'That's great Dave but you needn't have bothered.' Nonetheless I looked expectantly waiting for a parcel or something like.

'It's not here,' said Dave, 'It's in one of the rooms at the hostel. Come on I'll take you.' I walked with him up a flight of steps to the accommodation floor where he tapped upon a door. A young female voice answered - almost certainly not English.

'Come in.' I was puzzled and looked at Dave for explanation.

'Good luck Murph, and happy birthday.' At which he bundled me inside.

I like Ska music, and the song 'House of Fun' by Madness makes me smile and feel fondly nostalgic.

⌒

Malcolm Collins stood before me. I was sitting on the mat in the Budokan 'Tin Hut', catching my breath. He kicked my feet 'Do you fancy a pull, Danny?'

'Not really Malcolm, I'm knackered.' This was not true - I just didn't like fighting him. He was at least ten years older than me but as fast as a whippet and spent a lot of time doing something annoying around my feet. He had remarkably good *ashi-waza* and when you were unsettled threw in a fast *taio-toshi* with which he rolled me more than once. If I threw him it did not seem to count. He would simply bounce up and carry on irritating my legs until the next time he caught me with some bizarre, lightweight jiggery-pokery. He was a good player who won the AJA Midland Area several times and was a representative in the 1964 multi associational Olympic trials.

Malcolm and I always had a good 'knock' and honours were about even. I was much bigger and stronger, and I could normally take him with *uchi-mata*. He didn't care providing he rolled me once or twice. There was a commotion at the far end of the club near the door.

An Irish lad, let's call him Jerry, had entered. He was not long 'off the boat' as they say and working on the building sites, there was a lot of construction going on in those days. Kevin had advertised the judo club in the local papers and the arrival of Jerry was one result. He was in his working clothes, which were filthy from his day's labour. His accent was thicker than Irish butter. He was of medium height and powerfully built; imagine the richest Irish brogue you have heard and then add a bit. He stood at the entrance door and spoke to any and everyone.

'I thought I'd give this judo thing a bit of a go. Which one of youse fellas in pyjamas is the man?' His entrance was ignored until he put a muddy boot onto the canvas.

'Get your feet off the mat!' Kevin roared this order from the far end of the dojo and quickly followed his command to stand next to the Irishman. There was the inevitable belligerent reply.

'I'll stand where the feck I like and there's none of youse eejits to tell me otherwise.' At which Kevin struck him gently in the throat and then applied a wristlock with which to escort the luckless man outside. This caused less fuss than you might think. Kevin loudly explained a few rules, his wristlock still applied:

'Never step onto the mat without permission and never with you shoes on; never come into my club dressed like a tramp; never come into the club with beer on your breath – and have a bloody wash and use plenty of carbolic! Do you understand! You'd better or I'll break your wrist! Understand?'

'Yessir! Jaysus me arm's had it!'

'Now away home – and if you want to try the 'judo thing' come again on Thursday.'

Jerry Martin turned out to be a decent guy. He arrived for the next session the cleanest man in the dojo, scrubbed and smelling of some God-awful fragrance, wearing a terrible but new polyester suit. We were surprised to see him, less so Kevin, I think. Jerry explained, 'By God I thought, I've been given a pasting with no effort at all. This judo is the game for me alright.' He never became a great player but with enormous strength and a few techniques he did well enough and picked up a few Kyu grade medals. As for Kevin, Jerry thought of him as little short of God himself. He followed his advice in every matter sometimes too literally.

'If you're ever involved with the police, don't fight or shout your mouth off, that will only make things worse. Just stand your ground and be polite – the less you say the better.' Jerry arrived at the club one Monday night, cleanly dressed as always but limping and bent over in an awkward manner. He winced as he walked and let out an audible sigh of pain as he sat down.

'You won't be training tonight then Jerry. What's happened?'

'It's nothing *Sensei* Kevin – I have had worse from a bad-tempered horse on the farm back in Sligo, indeed I have. But I did as you told me *Sensei* and they were wise words, so they were!'

'Well, what happened?' Kevin and a half-dozen of us clustered round to hear the tale.

'Oh, nothing much. It was a fine evening on Saturday, and I was coming home from the Irish Centre and waiting for the bus – I'd been to see a showband. I'd had a couple of pints but no more - on that I swear. The evening was grand, and I felt happy and said 'good night' to a couple of police as they passed, nothing more - just a polite few words. They started to give me the third degree: 'Where have you been? What's in your pockets?' They called me an Irish bastard and worse. They drew their truncheons and began to jab and prod and said I was under arrest. I hadn't done anything, so I wrapped my arms around the bus-stop. They began to beat me, but I wouldn't let go. They hit my arms back and legs - everywhere but my head but I would not let go, no sir! Finally, the bus came, and the police laughed.

'On ya bus Paddy.' They walked off and the driver, an old fella from Cork, helped me onto a seat. Kevin took him into the changing room and later confided that the price for saying 'Good-night' to constables of the law appeared to be a few dozen bruises and a couple of broken ribs.

'Jerry's black and blue all over, he won't be on the mat for at least a month.' In fact, he never trained again and went back home to Sligo.

⮌

The 'Tin Hut Budokan' was the sister club to the Budokan Victory Hall. Although Kevin was the coach neither Peter nor myself were regulars due to distance and other commitments. It did have some good players and a unique history:

Charlie White, my uncle Charlie, was a crook; why he was I don't know. Before he turned to crime, he was a motor-bike mechanic, self-taught but nonetheless proficient. In the late 1920s he was a keen and apparently excellent motorcyclist and cut a dash. He was quite the ladies' man and married one of them. It didn't last and they drifted apart physically as well as emotionally. She took residence with a farmer in Stratford and Charlie lost the lower part of his right leg in a motor-bike pile-up – to the best of my knowledge the events were not connected. In a sense he was lucky. Surgeons had gained a lot of practice in the removal of mangled limbs in the First World War, which was a recent memory. Also, the manufacture of false legs was now a fine art and Charlie learned to walk and ride his beloved Francis-Barnett motorbike mostly un-hindered by his new aluminium prosthesis.

"'Ow's the leg Charlie?' A neighbour might call.'

'Pretty bloody good.' He would say while whacking himself below the knee with the screwdriver he habitually carried in the pocket of his brown cow-gown. The clank made him, and any appreciative audience laugh. 'Only trouble is, it sometimes locks when I try to kick start the bike!'

'He's a one, that Charlie White, a right case.' And I suppose he was. He met Bertha Penkman at a dance held weekly at Saltley Baths. Charlie danced very well, if a little stiffly and he and Bertha fell in love; well at least far enough to have two children.

⌐

'I do care about him Alice,' she said, explaining her obvious swelling to my mother, her sister. 'But we can't get married – there are 'reasons.' And I do wish he didn't smell of grease and petrol.' They rented a little house in Handsworth and were happy enough. For convenience sake she adopted his name, and life carried on in its way. She looked after their home and little Jimmy; soon baby Peter came along. Charlie White fixed up motorbikes in his garden shed and serviced the odd car or truck. He did a good job and charged less than a regular garage. He was also willing to take any article of value to cover the cost of repairs if his customer was broke.

Times were very hard – it was the era of the Great Depression. He needed some money so decided the best thing was to rob the local post office. He had never been dishonest, yet strangely his first thought was to turn to crime, more than that even – armed robbery. He had a gun, given to him by Eddie Bonser, his very old next-door neighbour, a veteran of the Boer Wars. Charlie had fixed the clutch on Eddie's Austin Seven and the old revolver seemed fair payment.

'I don't need it Charlie. I only keep it to shoot anyone who breaks in – but the way I feel nowadays I'm more likely to shoot myself. Be careful though, it ain't a toy and I've looked after it. The trigger is very slick and there are three bullets in the chamber, that's all I've got.'

So, one bright sunny day in April 1936 Charlie White donned his blue overalls, goggles, black helmet, and with a Webley service revolver in his pocket set off to rob Queenshead Road post office. 'I'll be back in a bit,' he called to Bertha, 'just going for some fags.' He parked the machine carefully and with a red kerchief pulled up over his mouth entered the building and waited in the short queue until it was his turn. 'Allo, Charlie,' said Siddy Wilkes, 'long time no see. Got toothache 'av ya?'

'I ain't Charlie – I'm somebody else.'

'Don't be daft Charlie. I knew it was you as soon as you walked in. Who else round here has got a tin leg and smells like a garage?'

'I ain't Charlie, and I'm robbing the place. If you think I ain't, have a look at this!' He took out the pistol and vaguely pointed it.

'That's enough mucking about Charlie. Put the bloody thing away before you get yourself in trouble. That's Eddie Bonser's gun ain't it? He said he'd given it to you for fixing his jalopy.'

'Last time Siddy! I mean it!'

'Well, if you ain't Charlie, how come you know my name?' Charlie White realised he was beaten and left the post office to the sound of the alarm ringing. He jumped onto the Franny-B and his aluminium leg promptly locked at the knee preventing him from using the kick start or hobbling away. Unfortunately, the police station was only a hundred yards distant and when two officers arrested him, he was astride his bike calmly smoking a cigarette.

Bertha Penkman died of TB while he was doing a ten year stretch in Winson Green prison for armed robbery. His children, Jimmy and Peter were brought up by my mother

～

Kevin had continued his Jiu-Jitsu training in the navy. After the war became a merchant seaman and practiced in dojos around the world. I recall him talking of Kandi in Sri Lanka (then Ceylon), San Francisco and Rio di Janeiro. Nevertheless, this was very bitty, and he did not settle to judo until his time at Kyrle Hall. Kevin and Jimmy were early Dan grades. But judo was expanding, and Jimmy or Kevin decided another club should be started in Handsworth. Charlie White was out of gaol, and had rented, a very large but decrepit house with a garden to match. It was situated in, of all places, Queenshead Road, the setting of his failed career as a Birmingham mobster. The post office was still there but Charlie never used it.

'The place gives me the heebie-jeebies, just the look of it. Siddy Wilkes is still there even though he's about seventy. He came to visit me in 'The Green.' I said to him, 'Why did you set the bloody alarm off Siddy – you know I wouldn't have shot you.'

'Dunno really – it just seemed the thing to do.'

'We were good mates before the robbery but now I won't look at the man. If I see him in the road I cross over. Eight years locked up because of him.' I never bothered to argue the point that it was really because he'd tried to commit robbery with a loaded revolver.

Charlie's son Jimmy was very talented. He was a self-taught musician and could play the piano, guitar and trumpet to a high standard. He had a fine ear and could tune a carburettor so that an engine would purr. His oil paintings were excellent, both his originals and copies of famous works. He was also a ladies' man like his father, and soon he hastily married Sylvia before the birth of his first son. But it was a good wedding and a happy marriage; another son being born a year or so later. Sadly, Jimmy White was also a crook – but a likeable villain. His criminal career was more artistic than that of his dad and did not involve guns. It did involve a robbery partnered by another judo player mentioned in these pages. True to his family's tradition it was a failure but resulted in only two years of servitude – a mere nothing. Jimmy kept his mouth shut and his accomplice was never caught, in fact he did very well in life and became famous. Jimmy got through the next forty years with only minor convictions including one for the provision of a certain herb as a cure for gout – at least that's what he said in court. Oh yes, he also styled himself as 'Professor White' and claimed to be a homeopathic chiropodist.

⤻

He and Kevin had started a coal business, 'Murite Coals' and had bought a pre-war coal lorry on finance called in those days 'the never-never.' (This turned out to be true. And a year or so later the coal business failed and the payments on the lorry fell into arrears. The old lorry was re-possessed, and the court ordered that the fifty pounds owed be paid off at half-a-crown per week. This was also not paid. Bailiffs came round in due course, but it turned out that the pair of them came to Kevin for Jiu-Jitsu lessons and so the matter was somehow forgotten.)

Jimmy and Kevin sat in the kitchen of Charlie White's house making plans. Jimmy was reading a copy of 'Exchange and Mart' which was a paper that advertised all manner of second-hand goods. It was locally called 'The Burglar's Weekly' as it gave the criminal fraternity an idea as to where to go shopping. He looked up and announced, 'We could start a judo club over here.'

'Good idea Jimmy – all we need is a dojo, mats and people – money to rent a place 'til the club gets going.' Jimmy put the paper down on the stained table.

'There's an army surplus auction at Hednesford Racecourse on Saturday. They're auctioning fifty Nissen huts and a thousand army mattresses. We could put the hut up in the garden.' This description was an exaggeration - the sparsely vegetated black patch could never be regarded as a garden. He spoke to his father, 'You wouldn't mind would you Charlie?' His father shrugged and carried on surveying the Racing Post. 'We could go up in the coal-lorry and bring the stuff back on the flat bed. Auction on Saturday, put the hut up on Sunday, start the club during the week!' It was a lousy plan, but it worked out exactly. Forty-nine of the Nissen huts 'Guaranteed Complete' were sold for reasonable prices. Lot number fifty 'Parts Missing' was unsold until Jimmy slipped the auctioneer a five pound 'back hander.' The forty mattresses, 'used with some stains,' were legitimate purchases at one shilling each. Jimmy, Kevin and Pat Roach, who had tagged along to help, loaded the curved, corrugated panels and the stained palliasses onto the back of the coal-lorry and tied the load down as best they could.

'There are no nuts and bolts to put it together.' Said Pat.

'Not to worry,' said Jimmy, 'Charlie will have loads in his shed.' Pat Roach continued his observations.

'There aren't any doors. Charlie will have a pair of those as well will he?' Finally, they set off.

'It's heavier than I thought,' said Kevin, 'much heavier!' Crunching and straining through the gears the valiant lorry made its slow progress back to Birmingham, protesting at every hill and demanding frequent halts to cool and take on water. The forty-mile journey took four hours, even so the hut and mattresses were unloaded before dark, the latter stored in Charlie's kitchen in case of rain. The erection of the hut became the topic of night-time conversation.

'We ought to dig some sort of foundation I suppose?' Charlie looked up from his inevitable paper – now the Evening Despatch and answered Kevin.

'You don't need no foundation Kevin. The whole garden is a foundation! This house was built on the land of 'The Soho Works' a great factory was here. Scrape away the muck and underneath there's two foot of concrete, the foundation for a bloody great rolling mill. That's why nothing ever grows. The whole back garden is solid! It was easier to leave it be than get rid of the concrete when they knocked down the factory. Foundation indeed!'

The next day in fine weather the frame of the hut was assembled. Jimmy White figured it all out without benefit a plan or construction guide. The job would have been excellent too had they had sufficient nuts and bolts. Charlie did as well as he could but could only scavenge about half the necessary number. 'It'll be alright.' said Jimmy. 'The corrugated sheets will hold everything together and we can put more bolts in later.' In a way he was proven correct. The hut never fell down although it did sway in high winds and was never weatherproof. In the severe winters of the early sixties the mat was cleared of snow before training. 'later' never came regarding the additional nuts and bolts. The hut was just about serviceable, and everyone became used to its peculiarities. Over the years the gaps between the galvanised sheets were repeatedly stuffed with wads of Charlie's Racing Post and a variety of containers were kept by to catch drips in times of rain. A couple of doors were stolen from a nearby derelict house and made to fit. Jimmy White had done his two years national service in the Royal Electrical and Mechanical Engineers and knew well the dangers of the cable he rigged up to tap into the electricity supply of Charlie's kitchen. But the hut had light! A small domestic gas fire was screwed to a wall, and gas piped from the house in a hundred foot of water heater hose stolen from Austin Motors at Longbridge. 'Strong stuff.' said Jimmy. 'It's reinforced!' In very quick order Jimmy used his artistic gift to paint a Japanese 'Rising Sun' depiction on the rear dojo wall. The sun and its rays were 'Signal Red' - a popular colour for the BMC Mini being produced at the time.

The 'Tin Hut' Budokan prospered and in the late 50s into the 60s became the training ground for many fine players such as Pat Roach, Dave Law and Malcolm Collins. I went on the mat with Pat hundreds of times but at six foot five and one hundred and thirty kilograms of well-trained muscle I could get nowhere near him. He threw me many times with a very old fashioned *hane-goshi*; his *kuzushi* had me hanging in mid-air and the rest of the throw was just window dressing. Pat Roach was a very fine judoka. How well would he have fared with the top players of the day? I really don't know. I think he would have acquitted himself well enough but not with the likes of Parisi or Starbrook. This is speculation, but what is not is that he made his name and fortune on the big and little screen in part due to the hours of practice put in at the old Tin Hut.

Chapter Seven
Fields of Battle

I NEVER QUITE enjoyed visiting Solihull Judo Club – why would I? It was full of dangerous men all intent upon doing me bodily harm. I knew most of the Solihull crowd individually from championships and when one or two paid a call at the Morris. 'En masse', as the French have it, they were a fearsome bunch: Dave Walker, Dave Southall, Les Hudspith, Keith Cannaby, Chris Adams, Tony Weaver, Geoff Hobbs, Ronnie Knight, Roy Muller and many others, all champions and or International players. A night on the mat at Solihull was like an evening in a war zone. The first time I went was with Roy and Peter; Roy suggested this one Thursday at the Morris. 'Can't get there Roy – I haven't got a car and neither has Pete.' He thought for a while.

'I'll pick you up, where do you live?'

'I live just round the corner from here and Pete lives in Shard End.' Arrangements were made which I have to say were complicated with a considerable distance between the locations but we were young and Roy did not seem to mind driving the additional thirty miles. In those days most people did not have cars. The vehicles they did have were usually 'knackers. Engineering quality was poor and the lack of proper metal treatment meant that a five-year-old vehicle was often full of rust and mechanical problems. The Hillman Imp van which Roy drove was six years old and would have been welcomed at any scrap yard. I got in and a half-hour later we collected Peter waiting in the car park of the Harlequin pub. He got in the back without complaint and as we drove asked if the van windows could be closed as he was cold.

'Not really,' said Roy. 'the exhaust leaks a bit and if I shut the window the fumes will kill us.' We arrived at Tudor Grange Sports Complex with Peter coughing and swearing that he was sitting in front on the way home. Roy drove through the car-park and over the grass of the playing field to a secluded section of the building and gave an explanation. 'There's a loose window in the toilets. If we go in through the front door you have to pay two shillings. So, we climb in through the window, get changed and then join the class.' I was less than happy.

'What, you want us to break into a judo club?' Roy explained that it was a night school class and that the coach, Pete Barnett, got paid a fixed rate so it really was alright. By this time Donnelly was through the window. Unfortunately, we met the centre manager when we left the toilets and headed to the dojo.

''Ave you three paid? Let's see your tickets.' Roy said we were late and should be on the mat and would show them after the class. 'Make sure you do – I'll be checking!'

'If that bloke annoys me again.' Said Roy, 'one way or another I'll twat him. He gets on my tits.'

⤶

Pete Barnett ran a familiar training session. I had heard that he was heavily influenced by Geoff Gleeson the BJA National Coach who had written a popular book called 'Judo for the West.' The big difference that I noticed about Pete Barnett's sessions was that he conducted training to music and that the *randori* sessions were longer and harder – I have mentioned before that what was expected in *randori* was open to a variety of interpretations. Anyway, come the last three-quarters of an hour free practice was indicated and I looked around to see who to ignore first. Peter was in his element and straight away teamed up with Geoff Hobbs and was happily scrapping. I found myself on with a chap called Ian Thompson, about my height but heavier and more powerful. He seemed to take a dislike to me and came at me strongly, kicks disguised as *ashi-waza* and the odd dig – that sort of thing. Nothing much happened. Next up I had a pull with Dave Southall for a rest. He was six-feet seven and over twenty stones; a British International so in truth there was not a lot I could do and we took it easy. Anyway, I liked Dave, and we got on. Our chat was interrupted when there was a commotion at the end of the dojo. Tony Weaver was holding Ian Thompson lovingly by the throat and stretching him up against the rear wall. Their conversation was elevated as was Ian, balanced precariously on tip-toes. The words passed between them were somewhat coarse and so I will translate:

Tony: 'If you attempt to participate in rough tactics again, you will be the loser. I will ensure that your vital signs expire. You will flatline.'

Ian: 'I wish you to lower me so that I may stand firmly on my feet. You are a female genital orifice.'

Tony: 'You are excrement Thompson; a miserable portion of faeces and your penis is diminutive.'

This happy banter was interrupted by Pete Barnett who hauled them apart and told them to cool down. It might be of interest to point out that Ian was no lightweight and no slouch on the mat. He weighed in at over ninety kilos and was the winner of many competitions and a soon to be silver medallist in the British Open. I suppose they were well matched as 'Weave' was an elite player and would also go on to win a British Open silver. Tony had an almost identical build to myself – about six-foot two and ninety kilos but made mostly of gristle, muscle and bone held together with vulcanised rubber bands. He had large powerful hands and his grip was almost impossible to break. (Whenever he arrived to train at the Morris, I was never pleased to see him. He wore expensive clothes and drove a Jaguar. Worst of all he was good looking and the girl with whom I was hoping to become intimately acquainted drooled over him. I found this an annoyance. We had a 'pull round' later but I fared badly. He threw me twice with *harai-goshi* and I got nowhere.)

'The attitude in the club is very competitive,' I thought as Roy Muller and Chris Adams hurtled past and bounced off the dojo wall. I must have been speaking my thoughts as Weave, leaning against the wall next to me, answered.

'Thompson isn't competitive, he's deranged.' (He actually said 'mad trucker' or something like that.) I pulled him out of the way as Adams and Muller continued to bounce around the dojo. Chris threw in a big hip-throw which might have taken Roy had not the wall once again intervened. It was obvious in the way that they took hold that tempers were wearing thin. Adams attacked with a strong right, *o-uchi-gari,* Muller countered with a *de-ashi-harai* which resulted in a stumble. Both players attacked and collided with the doors of the dojo which though locked, flew open to the sound of splintering wood. Once again Peter Barnett had to intervene to calm both players down.

'Is it always like this Tony?'

'Not really – this is your lucky night!'

⏎

The session ended and after we bowed off and showered, arrangements were made to meet in the pub. Roy said we should climb out of the toilet widow so that we did not have to go past the manager on the front desk on the way out.

'Come with me Pete,' said Roy. 'There's a fire hose in the corridor. I'll run it out and use it to tie the handles of the double-doors together then he can't come down to check on us.' What could go wrong? Royston reached the doors with the unrolled hose at exactly the time the manager arrived on the other side. Peter thought the only reasonable thing to do was to open the stop-cock which delivered water at high pressure down the hose and then full force into the ample stomach of the surprised leisure centre official. There was nothing for it but to gather our bags and run, leaving the poor chap soaking wet and wrestling with the snaking hosepipe!

Of course, there was hell to play but Pete Barnett smoothed everything over explaining that the people concerned had psychiatric difficulties, and were part of a mental health programme designed to restore their faculties through hard exercise.

⏎

We walked into the pub; Muller quite wet from the shenanigans with the hose pipe. He bought myself and Donnelly a pint of shandy which, considering everything seemed, only fair. I sat next to Dave Walker who did not drink and sipped a mug of hot chocolate.

'Sorry we didn't get to have a better knock Dave.'

'Don't worry, I'm coming to the Morris on Thursday – I'll beat you up then!'

'I look forward to it David – but can you go easy on the head-butting ritual. Every time I go on the mat with you, I end up with a bruised head.' He smiled.

'Trevis started it...' Dave was right. It had become a bit of a custom to head-butt visitors. But this form of humour was not to my taste, and I use this word purposefully as a clash of heads was considered funny. 'I forgot you're a bit of a posh boy Danny. What's a 'Toff' like you doing in judo anyway? Shouldn't you be playing cricket or 'crocket'- something like that?' This banter continued for a while and that is all it was, good natured nonsense.

'Posh! What me? I was raised in the slums of Devon Street until we moved to Alum Rock, and you know what a shit-heap that is! Posh my arse!'

'Well how come you speak so posh then?' And his question was as fair as the answer was complicated, to do with social mobility and psychological theories of self-identity. But it was true that I had won a scholarship to a good school and then on to a first-class university. Along the way I decided that my 'Brummie' accent was a liability and ditched it for something more educated and middle-class. A bit pathetic I suppose, but there you go. 'You're always scrounging, Danny. Do you want to earn a few quid?' Dave Walker put down his hot chocolate and waited for my response.

'I'm not always scrounging, but I am always broke...'

'Same thing. Anyway, I've got a job on and I need a bit of a lift. I've got some logs to stack and get covered so they dry out over the winter.' I could indeed do with earning a bit of cash and stacking a few logs didn't seem that bad.

'How many logs? How much are you paying?'

'How about five bob per ton?' There was a problem. I had no idea how much, how many logs constituted a ton. Twenty bags of coal were a ton, each bag being a hundred-weight but logs would weigh lighter. I took a guess; a ton of logs would be about forty bags.

'How much wood is there to stack?'

'About fifteen ton.' I did another quick estimate.

'That's a lot of wood Dave. How long will that take?'

'And I thought you were supposed to be smart. That depends on how fast you work, don't it? Anyway, if you want the job be at my yard at seven tomorrow morning. If you're late don't bother. Seven it is – on the dot. You know where the yard is?' I did - I'd been there before.

'Cradley Heath?'

'Yes, that's it. Just a thought. How will you get there, as you don't have a car?'

'I do have a car; I just can't afford to run it at the moment. I've got my bike. The pedal will warm me up.'

❧

One of us underestimated. Mountains of cut and split logs scattered Dave Walker's substantial yard. 'We'll never get that done in a day Dave.'

'Never said nothing about a day, did I? And enough of the 'we' – I'm going to make some concrete posts and then I'm off with the Stihl saw to cut more logs!'

'Where do you want them stacked?'

'Double row along the fence. No higher than six-foot or it will fall down.' This was an added complication. He read my mind and pointed. 'Fill the trailer and then pull the trailer over to the fence.'

'Bloody hell Dave. The trailer on its own must weigh a half-ton!'

'Get away with ya! Aluminium trailer, easy work – watch!' He fished out a home-made harness which attached to the trailer using a couple of eye-bolts He slipped the padded ropes around his broad shoulders and began to pull – and then jog. 'I do a half-hour with this every day. Great training for the legs. Anyway, enough of this gab – I've got work to do!'

Two hours later I had stacked the first load and my hands were a mess.

'Have you got any gloves Dave?' He looked up from his task. He had 'knocked up' a mound of concrete by hand and was shovelling it into moulds and adding reinforcement bars.

'What for?' I showed him my hands. 'You don't need gloves. You need to toughen up!'

'That might be true, but they're not going to toughen up today. They'll just get worse.'

'Piss on them.'

'What!'

'You heard. It toughens up the skin. It's what they use to tan leather.'

'I'd prefer gloves Dave. Have you got any?'

'No!' He looked at his watch. 'It's breakfast time Danny. Go and get four bacon and egg sandwiches from the café on the high street. There's a hardware shop further down – you can get work gloves there. And get a shift on – there's a lot to do!' He shook his head, gave me a pound note and carried on making concrete posts. As I left the yard a white Transit van pulled into the gateway. Three men were crammed into the front bench-seat. One leaned out of the window and called to me. He spoke in a strange accent and manner – almost Irish, but not quite.

'You the feckin' boss-man?' He was dark skinned, roughly dressed and wearing a greasy cap.

'No, I'm not, but he's inside. Can I help?' It seemed the reasonable thing to say.

'Well, if you're not the feckin' boss – I'm wastin' breath talking.' I shrugged and walked on, more concerned with getting breakfast and a pair of gloves. Coarse behaviour meant little to me - I'd grown up with it.

⌣

I returned to a gory scene and a story of mayhem. Dave Walker was sitting on the recently stacked logs, his back leaning against the fence of old, creosoted railway sleepers. His face was smeared with blood and his right hand caressed his ribs. 'Christ! Dave, what's happened?' Dave recounted what had occurred. The lads, 'Tinkers,' had been intent on making trouble:

Dave had seen them enter his yard but carried on with his task while they approached. 'You're the boss-man then? We're doing a bit of buying and selling. What have you got?' The first of the threesome picked up the Stihl chainsaw which Dave had ready for his next job. 'This saw must be worth a few bob. I'll give you a quid for it. What do you say?'

'I say put the saw down and get out of the yard. I've nothing to sell to you boys.' In response the leader of the mob pulled the start cord and the saw roared into life – Dave kept his equipment in good order.

'It works well enough. A quid or lose a few fingers; your choice now – be smart.' Without straightening Dave hit him with all his well-trained might. The edge of his shovel bit deeply into the man's calf, gouging bone and slicing muscle. With a scream of pain, he dropped the chainsaw and fell to the ground clutching his leg in agony. The second assailant attacked with the crow-bar hidden in his coat and the third with a pick-axe handle similarly secreted. Dave wrested the bar from the tinker's grip but not before he received a half-dozen blows from the wooden stave across his ribs and one to the head. He held the crow-bar attacker's arm under his armpit and with a strong *ude-gatame* snapped this limb at the elbow. The third assailant was slammed into the disordered log pile with an impromptu *te-garuma*.

The gang struggled to leave Dave Walker's yard. I saw the Transit van roar off when I returned with sandwiches and gloves. They were unlucky of course, to attempt the intimidation of an international judo player, a future veterans double world champion no less. Ah well – that's life; you can't always get what you want – but sometimes you get what you deserve.

Dave chewed on a sandwich but I could see his hand shaking. He had wiped the blood of his face with some nearby sacking. 'You need to get to hospital Dave.'

'Why?'

'Why? You've got a bloody great gash in your head that needs stitches - I can see that from here. Probably broken ribs too!'

'There's some electricians tape in the shed, that'll sort my head out. As for my ribs, even if they are cracked there's nothing to be done. We both know that.' This at least was true. Every judo player knows that cracked ribs are a nuisance but something that has simply to be left to heal. 'Anyway,' said Dave Walker, 'this is nothing. I've had worse.' And sitting there together, amongst piles of wood and the detritus of a Black-Country builders' yard, he told me of the abuse he had suffered as a child:

'The old man was a violent bastard who beat me up regularly for any reason – and if there was no reason, he beat me just for fun. Mom was no use – they were both drunks. He knocked her about as well, but mainly me.

When I was little, I used to cry of course – but by the time I was eight or nine I stopped and took whatever he gave out. It was defiance I suppose. One day I remember he used me as a punch-bag but I wouldn't cry or shout out I just stood still and let him hit me. I was very calm. He kept shouting at me, "Cry you bastard!" but I didn't and never did again. It's funny really the punches stopped hurting. I think he knocked me out a couple of times – I'm not sure. I can remember being on the floor, getting to my feet and then being on the floor again. When he stopped being able to hurt me with his fists, he turned nasty, really nasty and hurt me up here.' Dave tapped his head with a finger. 'Just up your street Danny, you training to be a 'shrink' and all. I'd found a couple of young rabbits in the woods and brought them back and kept them in a cage that I made in the back yard. I looked after them and fed them, stroked them and they became very tame. I liked the feel of them, warm and soft. I would hold them to my face and cuddle them... He killed them in front of me.'

'Jesus Dave, That's awful.' He looked so crestfallen. I did not know what to say. I found in later life as a psychotherapist that sometimes there is nothing to say; sometimes there are no best words.

'It didn't stop there. I was just a kid and started living in the woods rather than go home. It's all a bit of a blur now. I can see everything that happened but it's like remembering different pieces of a jig-saw rather than the whole picture. Over the next few years, I had two other pets - both dogs. He drowned Bruce in the water butt and then smashed Suki's teeth to bits. That's when I snapped. I was fourteen... The police were called by a neighbour.' He became still lost in memories perhaps.

'What happened?'

'I didn't kill him – but I nearly did. I left home and never went back.' Once again, I struggled to know what to say.

'How did you manage? You were fourteen – how did you live?'

'To begin with I lived rough, in the woods, in sheds and the like. I went to school occasionally to get a free dinner – did a lot of scrounging, a bit like you Danny.' We both laughed but without force or humour. 'And then a bloke in the area took me in and looked after me – at first he did... and then it became clear why he'd taken me in...' For the third time I was struggling for words.

'Oh, Dave ...' He gave a shrug and stood up, grimacing with pain.

'I've got concrete to mix and posts to make. Where's me shovel? And you'll be here for a week unless you get on with stacking those logs.' He held my hands quite gently. 'Gloves indeed!'

༄

There is a bit more to say about the head-butting ritual – a few instances come to mind. I have many faults, chief amongst which is that I am too trusting. No, I am too trusting of my friends and even more precisely, too trusting of Peter Donnelly and Royston Muller. They are a 'double act' not quite in the league of Morecombe and Wise or Laurel and Hardy, but close. However, their routines differ in that they have only one purpose and that is to make themselves laugh.

I recall at another visit to Solihull JC, confiding to them that I wanted to kill Tony Weaver, preferably on the mat using judo but failing that with a baseball bat up a dark alley. 'He gets the better of me every time we fight.' I whinged.

'Psychology!' spurted out Muller. 'You're the psychologist. He's easy to rattle – be a bit arrogant with him, a bit cocky. He hates that and loses concentration. When you're on the mat with him whisper into his ear 'This is the leg I'm going to throw you with Tony, this is the leg.' Peter who was standing close butted in. 'I do the same. I just say 'This is the leg' – he bottles, and I throw him. No trouble! I guarantee it – just say 'This is the leg' and bang! Attack and he's over.'

When you're head-butted with great force it is not correct to say that you see stars. No, not at all. It is more like a blinding flash of light followed by darkness. Also, there is very little pain. Once again, I was 'having a pull' with Weave and getting nowhere. The Muller-Donnelly strategy came to mind and before I gave it sufficient thought, I slapped my left leg and muttered in his ear, 'This is the leg Tony.' I did not expect his reply.

'This is the head Danny,' at which he slammed his forehead into my face and I floated gently to the ground. As I mentioned it hardly hurt and being unconscious for a while is not that bad really. Donnelly and Muller found this amusing and both smiled with the satisfaction of a job well done. When the red mist cleared Tony Weaver was affectionately apologetic and the only harm done was a black eye (mine) and nightmares (also mine) in which I follow Weave into an unlit alley armed with a baseball bat which, at the crucial moment, turns out to me made of sponge. Weave transforms into one enormous evil head and I wake up bathed in sweat screaming 'It's not my leg!' Of course, there is a back story to the whole incident and here it is:

⤿

Peter Barnett was very proud of his club and with good reason. Through his efforts it had become perhaps the most competitive club in the midlands and home to a host of international players. When he decided that his squad needed a change, he organised that another club should visit - an extremely competitive club based in London. I am not going to give a name – you will have to guess or do your own detective work. The visit was arranged and the Solihull mob looked forward to a pleasant evening. Spirits were high fuelled by the adrenaline of expectation.

Peter Donnelly, Geoff Hobbs, Tony Weaver and the rest were enjoying themselves fighting the elite and international visitors that graced the mat. But young men are notoriously volatile...

By and large judo is conducted in a good spirit. There is very little of the 'gamesmanship' that exists in other sports. There is the stereotype that athletes should be the epitome of good manners and behaviour, quite unrealistic and not always adhered to. (Muhammed Ali styled himself 'The Greatest' and it turned out that he probably was. Nevertheless, his verbal shenanigans were disapproved of by commentators, older boxers, his challengers and the general public, at least in his early career. Ali didn't seem to care.)

So, when Tony Weaver was scrapping with one young visitor, a player of precocious talent, and getting the worst of it, most took notice. The London youngster began to showboat. 'This is the leg!' he repeatedly said before attacking the luckless Tony, who, in the end, had enough of it and replied.

'This is the head,' and flattened his tormentor with what was known in those days as a 'Glasgow Kiss.' All hell broke loose of course with players on both sides intervening before older, calmer heads prevailed and the situation quietened.

What happened to these stallions? No - stags is a better metaphor? Well, one prospered in business and lives well with his lovely wife and has a son of whom he is very proud. The other prospered differently and became one of the truly 'world greats' of judo. He also has a son of whom he is proud.

⤸

Every now and then a judo club gets the reputation as a place to go for a good hard training night and that will draw the top players in an area to it like iron-filings to a magnet. Thus, a club may attain a reputation which might last a few years or a few decades. Solihull was such a club; the Morris Commercial had its day and later the *Karu-Kyoshi-Kan*.

Tony Underwood took to the 3Ks – it was his sort of place. It was full of good judoka blessed or cursed with his brand of humour. In that respect Malcolm Collins was the best – or worst, have it as you will. Possibly for our benefit, Malcolm called a free mat and left us to our own devices. My first knock was against Mick Smith, a hard talented player. He put me over with a foot-sweep and I returned the compliment with a left *ko-soto-gake* – but he complained. 'You stood on my foot!' This was true: I stood on his right foot with my left, and when he attempted to release it, I attacked and he went over.

'Sorry Mick,' I apologised – but didn't mean it. I did the same trick a few minutes later but this time attacked with *uchi-mata.*

'You can't do that!' He was genuinely annoyed 'it's against the rules!'

'Well, I've never read a rule against it.' This was true, but I'd never read the rules and so I didn't really know. Forty years later when I met Mick at the opening of judo's Centre of Excellence he was still complaining about the technique, and I still didn't know if it was against the rules of the game.

Next up was Bryan Drew. He threw me a few times and I did nothing in return. He was my nightmare opponent. At about five-foot nine he was hardly short, and at eighteen stone he was hardly light. He was as strong as the proverbial ox and fast on his feet. I don't think any of my attacks troubled him – even slightly. A few years later Bryan became British Open-weight champion and a finalist in the 'Britain's Strongest Man' competition. This has since cheered me, and put my performance into context.

Malcolm and the bunch loved their judo so much that they took it on holiday – twice to America:

~

I quite enjoyed the funeral of Malcolm Collins, or more correctly Dr Malcolm Colins PhD; BEd which is not to say I did not mourn his passing. I had literally known him since my childhood. I recall him sitting with my brother Kevin, each in a dilapidated fireside armchair, at my parent's home. They drank endless cups of tea and talked about judo and nothing else – over the years this same scene was repeated a thousand times – albeit at a variety of locations. With great affection

I remember the hours on the mat with Malcolm; at the old Tin Hut Budokan and then later at his own club, also of the Nissen variety. The 3Ks hut was of much superior construction having being erected during the war by professional soldiers. It's still there, as is the judo club.

I looked around, examining the packed congregation for familiar faces and there were many; Densign White and Kerrith Brown, former Olympians and Chairmen of the BJA both; Dennis Stewart an early club member, British Champion and Olympic bronze medallist; Colin Draycott Senior Vice-President of the Association; Mac Abbott coach of the Wolverhampton Judo Club during its 'wonder years' and many more of the judo fraternity. Malcolm was well liked and well respected. Tony Underwood and Bryan Drew gave funny, personal and sentimental eulogies. Densign White's was more formal. Malcolm's wife Joan, alternately laughed and cried.

After the service I sat with Tony, Peter Donnelly, Roy Muller and Colin Draycott, telling stories which, in one way or another, honoured Dr Collins.

'He turned out some great players over the years did Malcolm. Who do you think was the best?' Roy Muller used this opening gambit to tell us once again, how he had thrown Dennis Stewart.

'Do you remember the time Danny, when we visited? Malcolm said he had a good player with great potential. He shouted over to me, 'Watch him Roy – he's good!' Well as soon as we took hold I attacked with sweeping ankle and Dennis must have gone four foot into the air! Do you remember that Danny? Do you?' I replied as Roy expected me to answer.

'I do Roy – great throw. Remind me again – how old was Dennis at the time?'

'About fifteen, but that's not the point! I got the first one in.'

'OK – so how many times did Dennis throw you after that?' Roy smiled.

'Never, not once! Do I look stupid? No, I bowed off and left him to beat up the other players in the club. I never had a scrap with him again.' A wise decision really; Dennis Stewart is awesome and has the widest shoulders of anyone in judo including those of Colin Draycott who was sitting opposite. Colin spoke to me. 'It's been a few years Danny - how many?

'Not so long Colin – we met at Malcolm's club a while back.'

'At the 3Ks?' He looked at me with a quizzical expression on his face.

'Yes, you and Paul Radburn turned up when you were training for the veterans' World Championships.'

'Oh yes. I forgot.' Well, I didn't forget. With nothing to do, I had turned up unannounced simply to sniff the air, drift around the mat and have a chat. When Paul and Colin walked in it was a great and pleasant surprise. Billy Webb was coaching assisted by his son Jack. Billy had been a great player; trained in Japan and winner of the Australian Open. He was past his prime now but at fifty-years old still in phenomenal physical condition. Colin was heavier than in his competition days but who doesn't put on a bit of lumber in their mid-sixties? Inevitably the 'gentle pull' between Billy and Colin became less gentle, and then a full-blown scrap. I stood by watching with Moscow Olympian Paul 'Radders' Radburn.

'Madness!' he said. I muttered some words of agreement. They say 'old soldiers never die', and old *judoka* never stop wanting to fight.

⤳

Tony Underwood is a very light drinker and the few pints we'd had to toast Malcolm's passing had loosened his tongue. 'Did I ever tell you how Malcolm and me met Elvis?' I had heard Tony's version of events and Malcolm's. They were similar but diverged in certain important ways. Malcolm said they were invited to Elvis Presley's private dojo in the penthouse suite of the Las Vegas Hilton. Tony said that the invitation was accepted and that they practiced a few techniques with the great man. 'I really liked the 3Ks' said Tony. In the early years Malcolm organised a few judo holidays. The first was to California – and it was absolutely mad from start to finish...' I interrupted.

'Get on with it! Tell us about the Elvis incident Tony – and the truth this time!'

'I always tell the truth! Every version I tell is exactly as I remember it! Well, Malcolm had arranged for us to visit different judo clubs and the Yanks made us very welcome. The Orange County judo club was of a good standard – the coach had studied in Japan and won an award in the 1950s as the 'best foreign' judo player. Hal Sharp was his name – an excellent man and is still going strong in California. But there was one guy at the club who thought too much of himself. He was county champion but that didn't mean a lot. Come the end of the night – you know how the Yanks like a bit of razzamatazz – it was suggested that we have an 'international' match. I was last in the five-man team and had to fight this champion loud-mouth. While Nigel Parsons was fighting, Hal Sharp came over and whispered in my ear.

'I'll give you fifty dollars if you dump him. He's a big-headed son-of-a-bitch who needs taking down a peg or two.' In the event when I fought him, I threw him in about ten seconds, and landed on top of him to make sure he knew he'd been thrown. He was winded and took it badly – serves him right. Later Hal Sharp came over with a cloth bag. 'Great throw Tony,' he said. 'Here's the fifty bucks. In fact, Tony they're casino chips but you're going to Las Vegas so really it's the same thing.'

A week later we were in Las Vegas, the last night of the trip, and me and Malcolm were spending *my* fifty dollars in the slot machines at the Hilton Hotel. There must have been at least a thousand of them on the ground floor. Every now and then we won – but overall, we were losing. At about seven o'clock there was a great commotion with people crowding to look out of the windows. I asked one of the stewards what was going on and was told that it was 'just Elvis's helicopter landing on the roof.' As cool as ice Malcolm said, 'well you'd better take us to him – we're his judo coaches from England!' He pointed to the judo badges and the words 'Judo' and 'Great Britain' on the track-suit tops we were wearing. To tell you the truth I was completely surprised when the steward said 'Yes Sir', told us to follow him and radioed that he had Elvis's 'judo guys from England.' He took us to a private lift which shot us to the top of the building in seconds – I've never been in such a fast lift. We were both very pleased with ourselves – which changed immediately when the doors opened. We were looking at ten of Elvis's guards, all pointing guns at us. They were all dressed in the same suits - like in that film 'Men in Black.'

'Good evening boys,' said an older guy at the front who was pointing a shotgun at my chest. 'I hope you've had a good day – because if you make one wrong move it will surely be your last.' He had grizzled grey hair and the sort of face that told you he was as hard as iron and probably ate concrete and milk for breakfast. Malcolm stayed very calm.

'There must be some mistake. We're judo players from England and know Elvis is into martial arts – so we thought we would introduce ourselves.'

'How very kind – I'll pass the message on. Now hold your hands in the air, turn around and place them against the lift wall. I'm gonna count to 'one.' If I reach 'two' you'll be dead.' A voice called out from behind the mob.

'What's going on there Chuck? Is there a problem?'

'No problem Sir. Just a couple of guys from England trying to muscle in – they say they're something to do with judo.'

'The hell you say. Judo not Karate? Let me see them.' The crowd split apart and there, dressed in a white track-suit with a towel around his neck, was Elvis Presley. He smiled at us. 'Uh, huh, you're judo men? Really? You're not photographers or autograph hunters?' Malcolm carried on being cool and collected.

'No Sir. Just judo players. We're sorry...' Elvis cut in and held up a hand to silence the apology.

'I've got a small dojo in my suite. I usually do a karate kata or two before a show - it helps me relax. Do you want to come through and show me some hot judo?'

And that's what happened. We showed him some moves – he was very keen on my pet throw. We talked about the relative merits of judo and karate, he was convinced that karate was the best fighting art, but Malcolm put him right.

'Elvis – there is no 'best' martial art. They all have their place – I suppose the 'best' one is the one you like the most.' Elvis was not happy with this.

'I get it guys! I get it! But in a fight don't you think a good *karate-ka* would beat a good *judo-ka* everything else being equal?'

'No – not at all! If you're close enough to strike, then you're close enough for me to throw. And when you're on the deck – game over! Karate has no ground-work skills.'

Elvis remained unconvinced. After about a half-hour Elvis said he had to get ready for his show but was still puzzling over the karate versus judo debate. 'Have you ever been in a fight Malcolm – I mean a proper fight?'

'Once or twice. One time I was attacked by six blokes with machetes all trying to kill me.' Elvis was aghast.

'Jesus Christ Malcolm. Was that in the ghetto? It must have been one helluva bad part of the 'hood. Was judo effective?'

'No. Not at all. But the sub-machine gun I was carrying worked a treat! It was in forty-eight and I was in the British Army fighting the communists in Malaysia.'

'Christ!' said Elvis. 'Who won?' Malcolm just repeated two proud words.

'British Army!'

'And that was that. Elvis had to get ready for his show and we were escorted back down to the ground floor. Before we left Elvis asked if we wanted him to sing any particular song. We briefly discussed it and chose 'Blue Suede Shoes.' He was as good as his word, and that was the song he opened his show with.

Peter Donnelly shook his head. 'I still don't believe you Tony – it's a good story but heavy on the old bull-shit.' Tony pretended to be hurt.

'It's true Peter! Every word – ask Malcolm.'

⌇

Some coaches and players work well together, and Peter Donnelly worked well with Kenny Webber the founder and coach at the Ren-*do-kan* In his competition days Kenny was known as a ferocious fighter with a tremendous hip-throw. But his fighting days were cut short owing to a set of broken vertebrae in his lower back picked up when he crashed his motor-bike. This injury caused him difficulty throughout his long life and he often wore a back support.

The club was close to where Peter lived and he started to visit regularly; my attendance was less frequent. Peter's competition performance, already good, blossomed under *Sensei* Kenny's guidance. I asked him why this was. 'There was not much difference between Kenny and Kevin – they both insisted that the most important part of judo was to get the basics right. But Kenny made the importance of *tsukuri* and *kuzushi* come alive. He was very picky – he didn't want your body positioning nearly right, he wanted it exactly right. I remember he once told me to imagine a perfectly balanced see-saw with a ninety-kilo weight on each end. Put a marble on one end and it will tip up. 'Be perfect Peter – small things make a difference.' He was fanatical about the correct application of force to break your opponent's balance; Kevin said the same things but Kenny made it come alive. And he would make me work until my arms were dropping off. Kenny had a bit of toughness in him that I don't think Kevin had.'

⌒

One October evening in 1968 *Sensei* Kenny seemed very pleased. We lined up for the start of a training session with him kneeling at one side of the mat and about thirty of us on the other. He was holding a sheet of paper. 'I have some very good news. Kenshiro Abbe has agreed to come back to England and has also said that he will do a series of week-end courses around the country and our club will be top of his list!'

My elder brother Brian died a few years back, and thankfully so; his mind lost to the horror confusion which is Alzheimer's. I well remember my last conversations with him.

'You do judo, don't you?' He would ask with an uncertain look on his face.

'I do Brian.' His face would brighten.

'Have you ever heard of Abbe? He was good - the best there was! Abbe, yes that was his name, Abbe. The best there was. Do you do judo?'

'I do...' Getting into his stride Brian would continue.

'Have you never heard of Abbe? He was good - the best there was. Abbe, yes that was his name, Abbe. The best there was. Do you do judo?' And this repetitive loop would continue, and continue. The funny thing was that Brian had only dabbled in judo for a year or two in the nineteen-fifties. Abbe had certainly made a lasting impression. My brother's lifelong sporting passion was golf, but he never once mentioned Jack Nicklaus.

Kenny Webber was one of Abbe's early followers and had been amongst those who had canvassed that he should return to England. The Japanese master had mesmerised a generation of British judoka in the 1950s – a spell that still lingers. He founded the British Judo Council to promote traditional judo driven by his philosophy of 'Kyu-Shin-Do.' But his personal life was hardly that of the calm Zen-Buddhist or Shinto master. It was punctuated throughout by disharmony and fragmentation. Abbe returned to Japan in 1964 to watch the Tokyo Olympics. Many of his followers, amongst them Kenny Webber, subsequently wrote urging him to return to England which he did in 1969 - but he was not the same Kenshiro Abbe...

Chapter Eight
Kenshiro Abbe - Samurai

THE YEAR WAS 2019 and I had not seen Peter for a while and decided to visit him. Judo has always been my sporting passion of course, but after two hip-replacements I had decided that cycling was a smoother option. I pulled my bike out of the shed, gave it a quick 'once over', put a few bits and pieces in the paniers and set off to pedal to my friend's house. There's nothing much to do on a bike except think; I thought a lot about judo in general and much about Kenshiro Abbe. There was one incident that I wished to clarify – and the only person who could provide illumination was Peter Donnelly. I brooded and then cast my mind back sixty years:

꙰

In the manner of boys, I was trying to impress upon Billy Little and Micky Gill, my best friends, just how great Kenshiro Abbe was. They did not do judo and in 1958 neither did anyone else in my school. I was eleven years old and my verbal skills lacked force so, there and then, I created my own Abbe mythology:

'Yes, he lined all the men in the club up and said he would defeat them in turn using a different throw each time and he would do it all in less than ten minutes.' This seemed a believable if superhuman feat to me but not to Micky or Bill.

'How many people were in the line?' This was a reasonable enough question. When this event had happened at the Birmingham School of Judo, Abbe had taken a 'line up' and defeated each player with a nominated throw. I suppose there may have been thirty-five or forty players in all. I thought for a few seconds and the question was repeated. 'How many people did he beat?' I had no alternative but to impressively lie.

'About one hundred – I didn't count exactly, but there were four rows of men and about twenty-five in each row...' Micky Gill was very good at mental arithmetic.

'Nonsense! That meant he had to beat a player every six seconds and that's not counting the time it would take for the players to changeover.' I squirmed and had to rescue the situation.

'*Sensei* Ryder, the referee, had a stopwatch and only counted the time they were actually fighting. I'm not sure the back rows were full so it may have been a few less than one hundred...'

'How many throws are there in judo?' challenged Billy Little. This was a nuisance as I did not know.

'I think there are one hundred and ten throws – but a lot of them are secret and only taught to black-belts. Some of the top throws are only known by Japanese masters and it takes ten years of training to learn how to do them. There is one throw that is so mysterious only the top judo master in the world can do it – it's called the '*fuji-yama*' which means 'death throw' but can only be used if the master's life is threatened. If the master uses it at any other time, he must commit ritual suicide which is call 'Harry Kurry.' The lads seemed to relax their interrogation.

'Did he throw everyone?' I decided to make my fiction more believable.

'Actually, he didn't. The last person in the line-up was called Fatso Jinx. He is the biggest person you'll ever see and a black belt. Fatso's about six-foot six and thirty stone. *Sensei* Abbe nearly threw him with a special hip throw called 'Harry Gosh' but Jinx was too heavy. So, he tried a foot sweep called a 'Dashy Barry' which broke Fatso's ankle and he couldn't carry on. *Sensei* Abbe did some secret Japanese healing on his foot and the pain went away. My friends must have decided to believe, at least in part, my fantastical stories of the almost superhuman powers of Kenshiro Abbe. They hardly raised protest when I said he could fall on his back off a roof and do himself no injury as there was a special way of landing called 'Yu Keemi.'

I explained with care that this was a 'mind over matter' technique which involved 'the dis-articulation of bones.' I had no idea what this meant. I stole the phrase from a veterinary book and think it has something to do with snakes.

⌇

As I pedalled along, I recalled some of the stories I had heard about Abbe over the years, stories which gave a clue as to his eccentric nature, the yearnings of his followers – or both: In the 1950s he had become the stuff of legend and a mythology grew espousing his feats, beliefs and abilities:

Sensei Abbe believed that black belt judoka should be able to fight without the benefit of judo mats. He called this 'real fighting' and instructed that the tatami should be removed so that *randori* and *shiai* be conducted on the concrete floor. This would toughen up the players, make them improve their defensive skills and improve their break-fall techniques.

Another time, at a judo summer course held on a farm, he decided to instruct the participants in how to ride a horse bare back. (I have heard the same story where the animal was a cow.)

'I now show you how to ride horse!' At this Abbe vaulted onto the horse's back and holding the reins lightly and the horse firmly between his legs gave his lesson.

'If you want horse go right, pull reins right and push right heel into horse.' The horse calmly and obediently followed *Sensei*'s instructions.

'To go left, pull left and push with left heel.' The horse once again did as commanded.

'To go forward, pull both reins and kick heels.' But this time the horse refused to move, and *Sensei* Abbe tried again – but the horse still would not move! Abbe jumped off the horse and walked to face the animal eye to eye.

'You very stupid horse! Naughty horse – you not learn lesson!' At which *Sensei* broke into laughter and wandered away!

Kenshiro Abbe was also a compassionate man and something of a healer. Once his car was delayed in a London traffic jam. He got out of the car to find the cause and saw a crowd of people surrounding a large Alsatian dog that had been run over. It was yelping in great pain, its hind legs crushed. Abbe calmed the animal using a pressure point, and then gently used another to make the animal die peacefully.

He could also cure bad backs and was a whiz with headaches. His prowess with the *kendo* sword was also legendary: whilst demonstrating a *kendo kata*, Abbe delivered a sword stroke with such precision that the razor-sharp sword shaved his opponent's hair without drawing a drop of blood. When asked if he had been afraid his opponent said, 'Why should I be afraid? I am with Master Kenshiro Abbe!'

There was the time when Abbe was taught a lesson by a venerable old master: Abbe was on a train, a judo champion in Japan which was much the same in those days as being Champion of the World. He was feeling proud of himself and took offence when a wizened old codger, also in the carriage, began to stare.

'Why you stare at me old man? Avert your eyes! Do you not know who I am?'

'Of course, I know you! You are Kenshiro Abbe, champion *judoka* – a young man who does not know how much he has to learn!'

'You insult me old man. If you were not so ancient, I would teach you a lesson.' The ancient one got up, slowly hobbled to Abbe and touched him on the chest with one finger. Abbe found himself hardly able to move and grabbed the old man's hand. In an instant Abbe was flying through the air to land heavily on the carriage floor.

'You have much to learn, and the first thing is to be humble,' said the old man. 'I am Master Ueshiba.'

Abbe then prostrated himself and begged Master Ueshiba to accept him as a student.

But Abbe was no pacifist: In London he was accosted by three thugs in a midnight dark alley. They demanded his wallet which he took out of his pocket and dropped on the floor in the space between them. 'Here is my wallet but I am prepared to die for it – are you?' Abbe focussed on the vagabonds with steely, unafraid eyes and the youths sloped off!

I pondered that all these stories could well have been true. But could not help but note that they had a mystical ring to them that would not have been out of place if talked about the Jedi of Star Wars.

$\backsim$

Kenshiro Abbe was born in a village on the island of Shikoku, Japan in the cold winter of 1915. He was the son of Toshizo Abe, who was the local headmaster and a kendo instructor. When Abbe was not yet four years old, his father drowned in a flash flood while training in the mountains. A young schoolteacher, Manpei Hino, subsequently became a father figure for the young boy and introduced him to the martial arts, including sumo at which Abbe went on to become a local school champion. In 1929, Abbe began learning judo from Kazohira Nakamoto, a former police officer. That same year, he was promoted to the rank of 1st Dan in the art and, unusually, he reached 2nd Dan the next year, and 3rd the year after that. Thus, at the age of sixteen, he became the youngest judo student ever promoted to 3rd Dan. His progress continued to be rapid. (Third dan at sixteen and then 6th Dan by twenty-two would be literally impossible today.)

Abbe's early life was at a time when Japanese culture was completely dissimilar to that of Western Europe. The film, 'The Last Samurai' staring little Tom Cruise does a good job of pointing this out. (I really like the film, even though I think Tiny Tom is an idiot. What sort of a muppet headed fool could believe in Scientology?) The film does present a reasonable idea of 'Bushido – the way of the warrior,' which had had a great resurgence in early twentieth century Japan. The country once more became obsessed with this martial code of conduct, so much so that academics refer to this time as the 'Bushido Boom.' Japan was still quite mediaeval. The ruling Emperor was regarded as a living god, and only a few percent of the population could vote - most certainly not women. Bushido was an ingrained part of Japanese culture, particularly so amongst the military, police and martial artists. Kenshiro Abbe fell into all these categories. The virtues of Bushido were a part of his being. There are many such virtues perhaps paramount in the list being 'Honour.'

In early twentieth-century Japan the sense of shame was one of the major controls used in children's education. The following expressions are still used today, to appeal to the minds and hearts of youths in order to manage their behaviour: 'You will be laughed at;' 'It will disgrace you;' and 'Are you not ashamed?' Samurais, in defence of their honour (or avoiding shame), would even go so far as to take their own lives (i.e., *seppuku*, ritual disembowelment).

Kenshiro Abbe, a product of Bushido, was not British! His ways were not our ways!

$\backsim$

As I pedalled along my thoughts turned to my closest friend:

Peter Myles Donnelly was born in December 1951. His parents were a lovely couple of the old school. His mother was Mrs Donnelly who did motherly things. Dad did what fathers did in the 50s and left the running of their home to his wife. (Of course, I never found out their forenames – why would I? They were 'Mr and Mrs' to me, and Mom and Dad to Peter.) There was also a sister and a dog called McGregor, a useless terrier like effort with no teeth. The house in which they lived was one of a hundred or more stretched out in a long featureless crescent. Shard End had been mapped out well and no doubt looked very efficient and elegant from the air. Inside the household was immaculate. I visited his parental house to help Peter with homework – he was not doing well at school.

There are many reasons for scholastic success and failure. One of them is intelligence and all the others are not. In Peter's case his IQ most certainly was not his 'problem.' I will state that it will be 140 give or take. In truth Peter did not have a problem with education, rather the other way round. He missed a lot of schooling with chronic bronchitis and found the lessons dull – a lethal combination not recommended for the passing of exams. Despite, or because of, my best efforts as a tutor Peter and education parted company, mutually relieved, after eleven years of conflict, misunderstanding and confusion. Peter took with him a GCE in Art. (It is worth mentioning that fifty years down the line he is passionate about art, painting in particular and has made a considerable study of French Impressionism, Post-Impressionism and abstract art exemplified by Jackson Pollack. He also had a very successful and lucrative career in banking and Financial Services which might have surprised the teachers and examiners who failed him at mathematics. He studies the peculiarities of quantum mechanics for relaxation.)

'Rough and tough' – two similar rhyming words but in the context of the social development of a neighbourhood have quite different connotations. The slums in which I was raised were 'rough', but stable, cohesive and safe. Families had lived together for generations and most of the sharp edges had been worn away. In contrast the new estates, like Shard End, were yet to find an equilibrium. Anxiety pervaded and an ever-present manifestation of this was a fragility which could easily shatter into hostility or aggression. Societies are governed by two types of rules; the laws of the land and the informal 'street rules' which require no Act of Parliament. These are not written down but are intuitively known to all who live in the group to which they apply. In uneasy streets there is no room for miscommunications.

I am not a great fan of physical aggression, but it must be said that is as old as the human species and shows no sign of becoming unfashionable. It is probably Homo Sapiens oldest, most primitive, and most immediate form of communication. Many of the great figures of psychology believe it to be a fundamental part of the human psyche. It has without doubt played an important part in human development and the societies in which people live. It is also very plain that people enjoy violence; wars are still immensely popular in spite of their very evident horrors. The biggest, most financially rewarded sports on the planet are ritualised battles between two tribes. Violent personal combat sports result in death less often than in Roman times but will still have crowds baying for blood in rings, octagons or even on judo mats world-wide.

I have noticed that judo players, particularly the good ones, are for the most part, very just people. I am convinced that there is something distinct about judo, perhaps because it has a history steeped in Japanese culture and the philosophy of Jigaro Kano. It is the antithesis of bullying. The young Peter Donnelly had a highly developed sense of fair play.

⌒

I needed a rest. I found a secluded lane, stepped off my faithful Pinarello (the perfect racing bike of its day, now long past) and decided to make a cup of tea. The best camping stove by far is a Trangia – a simple device that burns methylated spirits. It boils water quickly and I was soon drinking hot, sweet tea laced with hip-flask whiskey. As I sat on the grass, I recalled one event of my youth:

We were getting changed after training one December night when Fred Stansbie suggested we went up to the 'Hunters Moon' which held a discotheque every night until eleven o'clock. This was unusual. Fred was ten years or more older than most of us having spent a decade in the army as a physical training instructor. I think he was having some sort of mid-life crisis. We were not keen, but he persisted, so Fred, myself, Peter got into his black Ford Consul. Tony Underwood drove a falling-to-bits 3.4 Jaguar which he could not afford to run and would try to scrounge a few pennies towards the petrol from anyone to whom he gave a lift – which is why we went with Fred.

The disco was crowded and in full swing when we arrived. A large but flabby bouncer let us in. He had a nick-name – 'Kibosh' and was six feet of black-suited, bullying stupidity. Peter sauntered off to join some friends which left myself and Fred to push our way to the bar. Fred wore what he always wore, a sharp mohair suit, white shirt and black tie. I remember his shirt and shoulder dandruff flecks glowing brightly under the ultra-violet lights which seemed compulsory in discotheques at the time. I was puzzled as we edged to the bar in that people kept calling us 'Sid.' Time and again this name was muttered lowly or spluttered in pretence of a cough. At the bar we ordered two pints for which payment was refused. 'On the house lads.' I found this troublesome. Why on earth were we being given free beer? It then became clear when the manager took us to one side.

'You can check round lads, but I'm telling you the place is clean. There were a couple of young pieces of shit trying to sell speed and

Mandies but they've been barred. The place is clean lads. No need to unsettle anyone.'

'Sid,' of course meant CID. In truth Fred looked more like a member of Special Branch than a man out for a wild night of disco dancing. I suppose he was the plain-clothes sergeant and I his young bomber jacketed sidekick. The rumour must have circulated that we were the police as we were afforded a ring of clear space in the otherwise crowded room. I was disappointed at this turn of events because I had met a girl on a previous visit who was unbelievably beautiful and had shown some interest in my advances. This was promising. I normally felt somewhat lost at discos and the like as I had no ready patter and no real interest in either dancing or popular music. I was mooching around, hoping to see her and try my clumsy luck again, but without success. I had joined Fred back at the bar, when then trouble started at the entrance to the club.

↩

'Kibosh' the fat 'bouncer' held some insignificant youth against the exit door and repeatedly punched him in the face. Even in the dimmed light of the discotheque, that blood was flowing could easily be seen. The manager threw the 'kill switch' which simultaneously cancelled the music and switched on the main lighting.

'Time for you to earn that free pint I suppose' he said. Which was both a fair and inaccurate point. Fred put down his drink and walked across the room. I followed in time to see Peter pull Kibosh away.

'Leave him, Kibosh – you're killing him. He's had enough.'

'I'll say when he's had enough! Screamed the bouncer and once again punched the face of his near unconscious victim. Peter held the doorman's arm.

'I said leave him!' The bouncer never finished the famous two-word reply. 'Off' had not left his lips when Peter flattened him with a powerful *o-soto-gari* followed immediately into *kesa-gatame* then converted into *kata-gatame* when the now pinned Kibosh attempted to shove him away. Fred stood above them, his presence keeping excited youngsters distant who might otherwise have aimed a gratuitous kick. Peter cranked up the *kata-gatame* and Kibosh's howls diminished into moans of pain.

'Let me go – I've had enough.' The pleading words fell onto deaf ears.

'I'll tell you when you've had enough.' echoed Peter. For some reason, perhaps sub-consciously remembering *Sensei* Kevin's story of his wartime altercation with 'Tojo', Peter relaxed his grip and licked his own forefinger. 'Keep still now Kibosh – or I'll shove my finger up your nose and scratch your brain.' The bouncer's moaning became a snotty whimper. Calm was quickly restored – and the manager sacked 'Kibosh.'

We left the pub and met Tony Underwood, belatedly arriving; his thirsty car had run out of petrol.

'Are you lot going already?'

'Nothing's happening Tony,' said Peter, – there's no point in staying!'

We got into Fred's Consul and took Peter to his nearby home. He was completely unruffled by the events of the night.

⤴

I climbed back onto my bike and mused that cycling is the best form of unhurried transport ever invented – its benefits are numerous. Bikes run on almost any sort of fuel; cake is good. The exhaust emissions are negligible (excluding the after effects of a lunch-time Guinness); bikes are fast enough to get you about and slow enough to allow you to enjoy the scenery. Yes, I loved my bike. Some people give their bikes pet names, but they are silly. I have not given my bike a name – even though she is very pretty.

For some reason, cramming for exams I think, I was unable to attend the Abbe training course which Kenny Webber had arranged at the *Ren-do*-Kan years earlier, but I recalled it as being greatly anticipated and I was disappointed not to go. My brother Kevin and Kenny were old friends and Kevin had co-operated in organising and promoting the Abbe week-end. At various times I had spoken to both on the events that had happened - but not yet Peter:

'Right from the start things did not go well,' said Kevin. 'Kenny had scrounged an extra set of tatamis so three mat areas were laid at the Ren-do-Kan. The whole of the school gym was covered but Kenny had filled an aisle with school chairs at the side for spectators. Before the start a few lads, who were watching had climbed to the top of the wall bars for a better view. Abbe, in bad humour, said to Kenny 'no monkeys, no monkeys!' and Kenny fetched them down. Fair enough, but an unnecessary distraction.

There were about forty judokas lined up on one side of the mat with Kenny, myself and Abbe on the other. Abbe decided that he should take the bow alone and brusquely ushered us away. Again, no big deal, but the atmosphere felt tense. Abbe began to ramble on and on and on. His English was never good but had certainly gotten worse in the five years he had just spent in Japan. It was very hard to understand him and after the first ten minutes the natives were beginning to get restless. Finally, Abbe got the session going with a demonstration of *hane-goshi* with repeated commands that 'all movement like cart-wheel. BIG circle only - *kyu-shin-do*. Always *kyu-shin-do!*' He seemed to relax a little when the class was working and in fairness his demonstrations were good. But his techniques were mainstream now and he had nothing different to put on the table. He spent too much time talking and people were getting bored. He was most certainly not the Kenshiro Abbe that I had first seen at Kyrle Hall, Frank Ryder's club – mind you that was fourteen years past!'

↫

I remembered the Birmingham School of Judo event well, even though I was only seven years old at the time. I had been taken along to watch by Kevin with whom I was temporarily living. Our father, a chronic alcoholic, had once again fallen off the 'wagon' and my older brothers and sisters decided that I should be farmed out to one or the other of them while he worked through this period of drunken debauchery. I was a practicing psychologist long before it dawned on me that he was probably suffering from post-traumatic stress disorder as a result of his experiences in the Ypres trenches of World War One.

I had watched Abbe perform his magic from the gallery above the squash court which housed the judo club. It was obvious to me, young boy that I was, that the day had been a great success. There was an atmosphere of festive jubilation which continued into the night – Abbe being feted at a local restaurant.

I was taken to the evening festivities. I do not know whether this was simply because Kevin wanted me to tag along or because it was the easiest thing to do with me. I felt very proud to be with my two big brothers and my cousin. The upstairs room at the nearby 'Shah Jahan' was filled with forty or more hungry judoka with *Sensei* Abbe seated at the top of the high table. It was the first time I had been into a restaurant or even a café.

It was a palace of its type; every table covered with a crisp, white cloth, and place settings adorned with elegantly folded linen napkins. The highly polished ornate cutlery sparkled, reflecting light from crystal chandeliers. At home there was newspaper to protect the table, and plates, knives and forks were any ill assortment of cheap bone handled table-ware.

The air was filled with aromas, exciting and so unfamiliar. I had never eaten curry before though I knew of it from the writings of Rudyard Kipling and the stories told by my father who had spent four army years in India and Afghanistan. He told me how he had watched shrouded tribes-women make simple dough pancakes patted thin between workworn hands and set them to cook on smooth stones at the edge of a roaring camp fire. I had never tasted one of course. Kevin ordered for both of us. 'One and a half chicken Bombay, off the bone, two papadums, two Bombay duck, one and a half-boiled rice, two chapati. The atmosphere was joyful. A happy crowd of young men and women laughing, joking, smoking, talking about the events of the day - judo in general and Abbe in particular.

'Do you think he's the best in the world? He beat Joe Robinson in London and he's supposed to be the Professional World Heavyweight Champion!'

Kevin responded. 'Says who? As near as I know there isn't a professional judo world championship.' (The three Robinson brothers all claimed to be World Champions of one sort or another.)

'There's an article in this month's 'Black-belt' magazine which says Joe Robinson won by one point!' Kevin scornfully responded.

'Rubbish! What does 'one point' in judo mean anyway? I read that account - for a start it was written by Jack Robinson. He's the father of the bunch and he's got delusions – he's started to call himself 'Professor,' utter bullshit! I think I'll call myself 'Professor Kevin' – what do you think Danny?' He turned to me and I felt honoured to be a part of this adult conversation. In the manner of children, I overstepped the mark a little.

'Bullshit, Kevin – utter bullshit.' Kevin momentarily glowered.

'Oi! Watch your language or you'll feel the back of my hand.' I felt ashamed and lowered my head but everyone laughed and Kevin ruffled my hair. All was good.

The food arrived and many bottles had appeared on the tables – beer I think, there was very little wine drunk in 1950s England. Stacks of papadums (delicious) were passed around along with slivers of dried fish which turned out to be 'Bombay duck' (horrible). A bed of rice was made on my plate and Kevin spooned out the thick brownish yellow sauce with chunks of succulent chicken. Food had never tasted as good! Every mouthful a spice filled confusion of unfamiliar flavours. Copying the others, I scooped chunks of meat into my mouth with the chapati and unselfconsciously licked my fingers clean. I have since dined at Maxims in Paris and paid £400 per head for the privilege. The two-shilling curry from the Shah Jahan lives on in my memory and all I recall of the meal at the famous Parisian restaurant is that the chef had made a picture on the plate out of gravy - and I left still hungry.

Speeches were made and time and again Kenshiro Abbe was thanked by people I have long since forgotten. 'For he's a jolly good fellow' was orchestrated by Frank Ryder (who later also took to calling himself Professor!) and in return Abbe sang something in Japanese for which he received resounding applause. The evening was done. I fell asleep on the homeward bus and Kevin must have carried me from the bus-stop as I woke up next morning on my bed at his house, fully clothed and covered with his big overcoat.

There was no celebration at the Ren-do-kan course fourteen years later:

I recalled sitting drinking coffee with Kenny Webber in a roof-top cafe near Sofia Gardens, Cardiff. The British Schools Judo Association was holding its annual championship and I was accompanying a bunch of kids who were being coached by Dave Law and myself. I bumped into Kenny and conversation drifted to old times. I was keen to know his version of what had happened at the Abbe week-end:

'It was one of the saddest times of my life in judo,' said Kenny. 'There was nothing to celebrate whatsoever.' He paused in recollection. 'Saturday was a pretty poor show. Abbe seemed distracted and spent a lot of time trying to explain his philosophy but it was all a bit of a ramble. Then he became totally distracted when a black-belt in Kendo turned up complete with sword and armour. I think the guy just wanted to see Abbe - something like that. Anyway, Abbe seemed more interested in the Kendo than the judo. Me and your Kevin kept things going but it was a bit of a mess.

On Sunday only about half the people turned up which I think offended Abbe – whatever the reason he was in a poor mood. Once again it was all a bit lack-lustre, boring to be honest. I was in a difficult position as was, your kid, Kevin. We couldn't take over out of respect for Abbe. The brown stuff came out of the air conditioning when he said he would take a line up and beat everyone to show them the power of *kyu-shin-do*. I lined the class up and then we all knelt. I explained this was to be a demonstration – Abbe butted in with 'No! No! Fight!' I counted thirteen in the line-up but the last three were Fred Stansbie, young Peter Donnelly and Bob Trevis all good players! Abbe went through the kyu grades easily enough, there was nobody who could fight anyhow. The first Dan grade was little Ray Jewell who Abbe countered with ura-*nage* but it was obvious that Ray knew the score and went over. Then came Fred who simply went along with the show and made it look like he was attacking Abbe but getting nowhere. Fred could have thrown him easily. I remember at one championship when Fred dumped Les Hudspith so hard that Les had to be carried off the mat! In the end Abbe threw Fred with a counter but it was clear that Fred jumped and was just playing along. With Peter it was different. To begin with they walked around but Peter caught Abbe with a dolly foot-sweep and the old man nearly went down – he would have gone too but Peter held him up. Abbe was very annoyed at this and started muttering under his breath. I have no idea what he was saying but then Donnelly turned in with a left *taio-toshi* and rolled, a *maki-komi* if you like. Abbe thumped into the mat and carried on rolling into the chairs. Then the shit did hit the fan! He went absolutely mucking mad. He got up ranting and shouting in Japanese and then started screaming at Peter, 'Naughty boy! You very naughty boy! Naughty boy, naughty boy!' Over and over again he ranted and then changed to 'Go! Go! Off tatami. Go! You no *judoka*, you no *kyu-shin-do*. Naughty boy go home!' Peter shrugged but said nothing and started to leave the mat. Kevin called for him to wait and took his hand. They then bowed and walked off the mat together.

‍

Cycling is the best form of transportation - for short journeys - ever invented. For longer trips it helps to be fit. The parts of your body which suffer if you are not are; thighs, neck, shoulders, back and the perineum - the bit where your body meets the saddle – yes, that can hurt a lot. It also helps to plan a journey properly. Hills are a nuisance too; as is rain and too much sun. Cycling in traffic can vary from being unpleasant to the cause of actual terror. Insects flying into your mouth and eyes are horrible - as are the ones that bite. A wasp caught up in your cycling vest can be life-threatening. I was glad my journey was almost over.

‍

In 1805 the United Kingdom was at war with Napoleonic France and doing quite well in the conflict. Thousands of French prisoners were taken and it became a problem as to where to put them. At first, they were housed in old rotting ships that were no longer capable of sailing. These 'hulks' as they were known, were pretty terrible; full of rats, vermin, diseases of every variety and of course wildly insanitary. Conditions must have been bad because the British government decided they were too extreme, even for the French, and commissioned a new gaol to be built in the wilderness that was Dartmoor. It is still a bleak and dangerous place - a good setting for a prison and also for Sir Arthur's famous story about a very big dog.

Most people are unaware that Great Britain has fought two wars against the Americans. The first was the War of Independence which the colonists won and celebrate in noisy ways every fourth of July. The second was a draw. This happened in the Napoleonic War of 1812 - the former colonials took umbrage when Great Britain decided to stop them trading with France, and instituted a naval blockade of east-coast America. In the following fracas the British invaded Washington D.C. and in 1814 burned down the first White House, along with much of the city. The Americans were unhappy about this of course, but really it was only fair as years earlier, John Paul Jones, the American hero, burned down Whitehaven a neat little fishing port on the west coast of Cumbria. As near as I know the people of Whitehaven had never done harm to anything – excepting fish. In the 1812 war many thousands of American prisoners were taken and a goodly few dumped in the new gaol that was H.M.P Dartmoor.

⤸

Which might be why the best pint of beer I have had in my life, by a long chalk, was spoiled in small part by having an American spelling!

I jest. The first pint of 'Jail Ale' was so welcome that it went down 'without touching the sides' as they say. Isn't beer good? Beer is why God invented thirst! Do you recall the final scene in the immortal film 'Ice Cold in Alex' where John Mills stares at the glass on the bar in front of him filled with near frozen beer? He delays drinking for a moment to heighten his pleasure. The pint of Jail Ale that Peter had waiting was so wanted, so desired, so needed, that I didn't do any of that staring nonsense. I gulped it, guzzled it, swilled it, and quaffed it gratefully down.

'Better?' asked Peter. It was, it most certainly was. My cycle trip was over - thank God! My ride from Worcester to Topsham – a beautiful village on the estuary of the river Exe had taken two days. I was pleased as I had expected it to take three. We sat outside the Passage Inn, fresh pints to hand and looked out over the river bathed rose gold in the late evening sunlight. A single bank of cloud hung motionless over the slow water, now glowing orange, later vermillion, in the rays of the ageing sun. A small fleet of moored small craft, earlier a myriad of colours – yellows, green, blues, red, - had lost their bright hues in the fading light. The evening was warm and the world was good. A waitress arrived and placed two trencherman sized plates on the weathered oak table. 'I thought you'd be hungry,' said Peter, 'so I ordered dinner – and the food is good.' The mound of buttery mashed potatoes laden with liver, bacon and onions cooked with red wine and garlic, stifled conversation for a while. 'What do you think,' asked Peter.

'I've died, and against all the odds and expectations, haven't ended up with my backside being roasted.' I took a twenty pound note out of my wallet. 'Get a couple more pints Peter – my legs are shot. I don't think I can walk.'

'Talking about backsides, never offer me money again or you know where it will go. As for your legs, it serves you right. Any bloke your age who decides to ride a push-bike a hundred and sixty miles deserves to be in pain.'

'Age? I'm only seventy!'

'Seventy-two,' he corrected. 'You're seventy-two.'

⌒

I lit a celebratory cigar, a Romeo y Julietta corona. I was indeed pleased with my achievement. We talked of this and that, of 'fools and kings' as they say. I realised that I was not sure how to raise the subject of what had happened between him and Kenshiro Abbe almost a half-century earlier. In the end I had no strategy:

'Peter, for the record, I need to get your side of the nonsense with Abbe at the Ren-do-kan course.' He took a long draught of the excellent ale.

'There's not a lot to say Danny. I dumped Abbe, he went crackers and threw me off the mat. Kevin came with me. A deep thing to do by the way - very meaningful. He was my first *Sensei* and he stood by me.'

'But why did you dump him? He was getting on after all?'

'I never intended to throw him. At first, I just went along with the show, same as Fred. But then I put in an easy foot sweep and he nearly went – I had to hold him up. After that he lost the plot muttering to me "Bad judo! Judo no good! No *kyu-shin-do*" so I attacked with a gentle *taio-toshi*, that old-fashioned 'in and out, step across spin' technique that Dave Porter used, – I think they call it the 'tornado.' He went over like a ton of bricks and then carried on rolling into the chairs. I did think to myself, 'was that *'kyu-shin-do'* enough for you?' Anyway, I don't care anymore – but for a while I did. A lot of the old guys thought I'd committed a great sin; that he'd lost face – the code of the bushido and all that. But I tell you Danny, I'm a seventh Dan - British champion, European medallist and Olympian in my time. I've lived and trained in Japan and know a bit about Japanese culture and bushido. There were so many other things within the 'warrior' code that he could have done. Laugh, for example or be pleased!' We became silent. I puffed at my cigar and Peter softly hummed and then sang: *"What's done is done, what's won is won, what's lost is lost and gone forever"* He quietly sang the mournful words written about the city of Derry and the Irish 'Troubles,' – he had a sweet voice.

A cooling breeze wafted in from the sea carrying with it that indefinable rock-pool scent that makes sea-farers of us all. There is a universal look amongst Irishmen, the turning of the head with chin lowered, one eye wide the other half closed. If a look can be ironic, it was.

'The man might have been a genius when he was young - but he seemed old and bitter. Leave it now Danny – let it rest.' Peter whispered the words as he stood to fetch more drinks.

The estuary was peacefully streaked with silver from the faded day. The sun was gone and had left but a faint roseate glow in the west as a keepsake. A cormorant, almost lost in dusk shadows stood on a rib timber of a long-lost ketch, wings spread facing the dying light perhaps to garner last heat before the approaching cool of night.

David Starbrook – British Champion

Chapter Nine
David Starbrook - First Contact

THE YOUNG MAN who faced me across the tatami did not seem to be a god or even demi-god. He was shorter than me by at least two inches which for some reason gave me a little re-assurance. He had rounded features, rather than granite chiselled and his black, untidy, curly hair, did not appear heroic – it was the end of the sixties when legends sported a longer cut. He did look broad across the shoulders however, and his face was expressionless, neither confident nor unconfident - if anything uncaring; he certainly showed no signs of anxiety. He looked younger than me which also lifted my spirits. The Crystal Palace crowd was noisy and seemed to increase in volume as the referee motioned us to our respective marks where we bowed.

'*Hajime*,' was called and the fight was on. I had recently won a few local competitions and had notched up some creditable second places; to Hudspith a year gone and Terry Watt (an Irish legend who later went on to be five times Olympian). My brother Kevin had boosted my confidence by assuring me that my opponent was open to a left *uchi-mata*. This was coincidentally fortunate as this was the best in my small arsenal of throws. I was not quite a one throw merchant, my *o-soto-gari* and *taio-toshi* were reasonable but my *uchi-mata* was by far my best throw and I had turned over some good players. In those days there was less grip fighting and I had little difficulty in getting my favourite hold; a double lapel grip with my right fingers making a pocket of the cloth under my opponents arm-pit. He took a conventional grip, at least I think he did. In truth it is all a bit of a blur – shock does funny things to a man. I threw in an early big attack and found it to be a little like attempting to throw a garden shed. I am hazy as to what happened next but am reliably informed that he hooked his left heel behind my left knee and drove me backwards into the mat with the force of a train.

I am a serious person by and large, and do not like cartoons and other such childish diversions. I now view Tom and Jerry with greater respect; I hit the mat with atomic force and exploded. My body shattered into a hundred pieces which spread out across the *tatami*. Slowly, this jig-saw of destruction pieced itself back together. I lay stunned looking up at the vaulted roof of the Crystal Palace arena. I had learned in my first-year studies at university that generally boys lose the ability to cry with pain as they grow older. They scream and shout but can only cry tears for emotional reasons; snotty wet crying through pain is lost as the boy develops. This probably has some evolutionary function. Well, evolution be damned - I wanted to cry! My whole being had been destroyed and were it any other time and place I would have just laid there and bawled, blarted or sobbed - some such childish display anyway. I pulled myself together, and I realised I could not breathe. I struggled to my feet and awaited the referee to award *ippon* to my opponent. Angelo Parisi came across the tatami, shook my hand and gave me a friendly hug. I slid from the contest area and wished there was a nearby slime hole in which to live for a month or two.

'Never mind mate,' said a soft spoken, unseen voice - probably London but certainly not Cockney. 'You rocked him with the *uchi* and not many can do that.' I turned to look to see Dave Starbrook who was to fight next. He had the look of a person quarried, not mortally born. His angular face was impassive, timeless and formidable. Angelo Parisi, (future Olympic Champion) had left the mat to be replaced by David Starbrook (future World Bronze and Olympic Silver and Bronze Medallist). It dawned on me that I was in the company of the 'big boys' and that perhaps competitive judo at this level was best to be avoided. I had not the talent for it, the body for it nor the mental ability to compete. Don't get me wrong. I liked being battered and hurt and spending half my life injured as well as the next *judoka* – but there are limits. I would be better off without top level judo and it could certainly do without me. I watched as Starbrook walked across the mat; he had the appearance of a man that did *uchi-komi* practice with a tractor. His opponent was to be Bob Trevis my clubmate from the Morris Commercial JC. Bob was a formidable scrapper; many times, AJA champion and also concurrently AJA, BJA and BJC area champion. I have no doubt that had he ever committed himself to judo full time he would have made the very top flight.

The fight started well enough for Bob with no score after two minutes and then, almost unbelievably he rolled Starbrook over with a left-handed *maki-komi* and scored a *waza-ari*!

This was, however was Bob's undoing. I remember speaking to Peter Donnelly years later when he was at his Olympic best. He gave me this piece of advice which makes complete sense if you give it a moment's thought.

'If you want to improve your standing judo - make sure your *ne-waza* is excellent.' Starbrook's ground-work was world class. A reverse arm-roll took Trevis onto his back followed by a slick transition into *juji-gatame*. The *ippon* inevitably followed as Bob's arm straightened and locked. In contrast to the nonsense seen on the professional wrestling circuit when an arm is locked out, two choices remain – submit or dislocation. Bob wisely submitted, and rubbed his elbow for weeks afterwards.

↬

The final of the under eighty kilogramme division of the 1969 British Judo Championship was between Brian Jacks and David Starbrook – the two greatest names in British judo at the time. Not just great players within Britain but formidable on the world stage. To be precise it was the 'de facto' final as this stage of the event was run as a pool and they had accumulated the same number of wins – neither had lost a pool fight. This contest would decide the championship. The players bowed onto the tatami and took their places ready to start. They stood in marked contrast. Starbrook much the taller, surely too tall to fight at under eighty? He was devoid of any fat, every muscle lean and defined. He had a craggy angular jawline reminiscent of any superhero in the popular D.C. comics; Batman or Superman come to mind. He possessed legendary fitness and strength and was becoming known as the 'Iron Man' of judo.

Brian Jacks was also a judo legend and had acquired this status early. As a sixteen-year-old he had represented Great Britain at the 1964 Tokyo Olympics. He had twice been European Junior Champion and as a senior had already won two European Bronze Medals and one Silver. If anything, he was perhaps more revered by the judo community than Starbrook. He was also renowned for almost super-human fitness and had a more classical physique suited to the eighty-kilo player. He was blessed with blond hair and boyish good looks; newspapers, unsurprisingly, had dubbed him the 'golden boy.'

These two great players, destined for further greatness, faced each other with eyes locked and waited for the referee call '*Hajime.*'

⌒

I watched the contest from mat-side but after fifty years the details are unclear. However, the real surprise is that I have spoken with both players person to person on the matter. Both know that they fought and that's about it. Neither Brian nor David has any precise memory of the scrap and really, neither cares! Now, for the proverbial ninety-nine per cent of judo players to fight for a British title would be a major event, for most the pinnacle of a career. But for these world greats it was so completely unimportant that it no longer graces either's memory! I suppose Brian and David can be forgiven this lack of recall in the light of the tremendous successes they were to achieve later – David going from success to success in world judo and Brian adding media fame and fortune to his already full cabinet of glittering prizes.

I know the result of this battle. Dave Starbrook became British Champion and the points recorded suggest that it was a decision win. I have asked the great and the good in British judo and no-one can add anything else. Kevin Crickmar, former renowned international player and archivist of everything judo confirms the win was as suggested. As mentioned, I was there, and can only recall the fight as close and engaging but not who did what. I don't think there was a scoring technique.

⌒

Peter and I walked out of Crystal Palace and were amongst the last to leave. We were in no rush as the BJA Midland Area had booked some rooms at the Queens Hotel and we were staying overnight. This was good of them because although they only paid for the favoured few an equal number muscled in to take advantage of this hospitality. I was sharing with Dave Southall. He had the mattress on the floor and I had a sleeping bag on the bed. This was a good arrangement as, at two metres tall, he needed the extra leg room.

The night was cold with the prospect of winter rain or sleet. A solitary car and a lonely figure stood in the strange orange glare of the sports centre's lights. The bonnet of a car was raised and as we walked closer a head and torso lifted out of the engine compartment and was revealed to be the Champion of Great Britain, David Starbrook.

'Know anything about cars?' he asked as we approached. Funnily enough I did! I had bought my first car earlier in the year from Pat Roach who, in addition to his wrestling career, also owned a scrap yard:

'Does it go Pat?' I asked him looking without enthusiasm at the rusted brown Mini he was trying to sell me.

'Of course, it goes Danny – I wouldn't flog you a car that didn't work, would I?' Well, the engine did run but every other part of the car had rust or some fatal mechanical disease. Had Pat cheated me? Probably not. I only gave him twenty pounds and as the saying goes 'you get what you pay for.' The result was that I had spent months taking it apart, learning along the way, and putting it back together with parts acquired from friends who 'knew someone at the Austin.' It was considered a mark of stupidity to pay list price for car parts in those days. No wonder British Leyland could never make a profit! (And, it must be said, they made terrible cars.)

'What happens when you try to start it Dave?'

'The engine catches but runs badly, backfires and then stops. It stinks of petrol now so it's probably flooded as well. It was misfiring a bit when I drove here.' I leaned under the hood and checked the obvious things; the plug leads were all on correctly, and each delivered a good spark when the engine was turned over. The next thing to check was the distributor which was held in place by a simple pinch bolt. If this became loose the timing would drift and the engine would misfire and run badly. It was pure luck of course but I checked, and it was loose. I explained that I thought this could be the problem. 'If you could turn it over Dave, I'll try to adjust the distributor. Keep your foot off the gas unless the engine fires and then rev it up.' Fortune smiled on us and the engine started! I adjusted the timing by ear until the engine was running smoothly. 'You'll have to get the distributor set properly but, in the meantime, you should be able to get home.'

'The first thing I'm going to do is take you lads for a drink!' He shook both our hands vigorously and smiled in gratitude. His voice was gentle and reassuring and had a pleasant ring. I had watched Dave Starbrook throughout the day and the emotionless look on his face was awe-inspiring – even frightening. I suspected that half of his opponents had lost before they took hold. The beaming smile relaxed his features and it was clear that 'The Iron Man' had a softer side.

'You can sit in the back Danny,' said Peter. 'I'm sick of being the 'nipper.' He meant it too and I had another realisation. 'Donnelly's grown up!'

⌐

When Dave Starbrook said he knew 'a great old pub' I believed him but did not know what to expect.

'It's a genuine Victorian pub,' said Dave. Not many of them escaped the bombing in the war. Anyway, step inside the 'Rock of Ages' and you're stepping back a hundred years. The food is good too, straight from the East End – a taste of real London.'

As befitting a Saturday, the bar was busy but not yet heaving as it would later be. Peter hauled the heavy mahogany door open clutching the shined brass handle to allow David and myself first access and the blue fug of a hundred cigarettes spumed out onto the street. Inside was a palace of plush red leather, polished wood and brassy metal gleaming gold. Chandeliers that had originally held gas mantles, oil lamps and tallow candles, gave illumination reflected a thousand times from every glass, bevelled mirror, gleaming pump spigot and church inspired stained window. Walls were clad with sumptuous glazed tiles of patterned emerald and ruby red. The high bar shelf minded four dozen highly polished straight glasses and handled jugs. The copper topped bar lustred and the scrubbed wooden floor was well sprinkled with fresh sawdust which gave a smell of pine. In the centre burned a grille guarded coal stove upon which rested a two-gallon copper urn simmering for those drinkers who liked their spirit hot with maybe a spoonful of sugar. 'Wow' said Peter, and I agreed – wow indeed! In theory he was still a year too young to drink but this had not been a problem since he was fourteen. The sixties were easy times.

'Grab that table in the corner,' said Dave 'and I'll get the drinks.' He made his way to the bar and was greeted as he did so with calls of 'Hi Dave' and affectionate back patting. It was apparent that David Starbrook was not only known but liked. He came back clutching three pints, safe in his phenomenally strong hands. 'For you two this is London Sway – proper ale not like that Watney's Red Barrel and Worthington 'E' that seems to be taking over the bloody world. I've ordered food – they only do one thing, pie and mash with liquor or gravy. I chose the liquor you can get gravy anywhere.'

'What's that you're drinking Dave?' His pint was a darker hue but it did not seem to be a mild ale.

'Guinness and cider.' He was right about the London Sway, an excellent drink, but as an Irishman I have to reserve comment about his Black Velvet. (In fact, this is correctly a mix of Guinness and champagne which renders it very expensive and, in my book, ruins the Guinness. I was in Dublin once with an Englishman who asked for the cider version. 'Can I have a Guinness and cider please?' The barman, immaculate in white shirt, black tie and trousers simply said 'No' and turned away to serve another customer.)

An exceedingly pretty waitress in a mini skirt brought over the food. Peter Donnelly, with all the fervour and appetites of a seventeen-year-old stared lustily, and preferentially at the pie, which he devoured in about one minute. I took two and the older, wiser David a sedately five. The beer was quickly dispatched, and I rose from my chair with the questioning words, 'Same again?' I was ordered by David Starbrook to sit down as we were in his pub and my money was 'no good.' How could I argue? Literally, how could I? When perhaps the hardest, toughest fittest strongest judo player in the world insists, it is only polite and sensible to give in. The man was generous to a fault. More beer and pies consumed Peter asked him the obvious question.

'What got you started in Judo Dave?' He took a sip of his drink before answering.

'It happened by accident more or less. I left school at fifteen with no idea what to do. I didn't like the lessons much except for anything physical or practical. I thought I might like to join the merchant navy and applied for my papers. I went to the Seaman's Union offices. They said they'd send them through but I never got them. Could've got lost in the post I suppose but I've always wondered if my mum got hold of them and got rid of them. She wasn't keen on the idea! I can remember feeling very restless. I'd been at a residential school, so when I left and moved to live with mum, I was new to the area. I didn't feel that I fitted in. There was a bit of bother with some of the local lads that took a dislike to me – said I was 'posh' that sort of thing. Me posh! Anyway, there was a sign in the window of Shoreditch Evening Institute advertising classes for ballroom dancing, football and judo. At school I'd been rubbish at football and didn't fancy dancing so I thought I'd give judo a bash – I liked hard physical exercise. I'd boxed a bit and was quite good. I was in the inter-counties tournament and did well enough. Well, I gave judo a go. The coaches, Pat Walker, Steve Wisdom and Harry Wynn, thought I had talent and after about eighteen-months said that I needed to go to a bigger club where there was better opposition. The Renshuden was easy to get to and Harry also coached there. It was just the ticket.'

The couple of pints of London Sway had loosened Peter's tongue and he was never, never slowing in coming forward, lubrication added or not.

'You do sound a bit posh though,' he said mischievously to the great man.' The other London lads are all "Or wight mate". Starbrook did not rise to the bait so Peter carried on. 'Is it because you went to a boarding school?' I was willing Peter to shut up – this was not the man to annoy but Starbrook took this teasing in good spirits.

'You're thinking of the wrong sort of residential school, young Donnelly. Anyway, you sound like what you sound like Peter – end of.' Peter thought about this for a second and then pointed an accusative finger at me.

'He doesn't for a start. Five years back he had a broader Brummie accent than me – now listen to him!'

'Oh, for God's sake Peter. Not again! I've told you before, and you bloody well know it, that I'm training to be a psychologist and speaking clearly is a requirement of my job. It's a tool of the trade.'

'Bullshit!' came the reply. Starbrook came to or rescue.

'I'll have to leave you children to squabble. I've got to go – I'm meeting Dave Barnard and a few of the boys from the Renshuden later. I'll drop you back at the Palace if you like?'

'No thanks, we are going into town to have a look at the bright lights and the big city – but thanks.'

'You off to celebrate your win?' Peter asked.

'Not really. We'll have a few pints maybe and then down the East End for supper – jellied eels at Tubby's.' Dave Starbrook stood and offered his mighty hand which we shook in affectionate good-bye. 'See you around lads – keep turning them over.' He faced Peter directly. 'I've watched you on the mat Donnelly and you're good – I expect we'll fight soon enough.' For once Peter looked a little shamefaced.

'I didn't win though – I fought like an idiot in the semis.' The great man shook his head.

'Not true – the other guy was just better. But how old are you – seventeen? You're at the bottom of the pile right now, but in a few years...' He left the sentence unfinished. David Starbrook, British Champion left the pub to other farewells and Peter and I sat down to drain our glasses.

'I hope I never fight him,' said Peter. 'I wouldn't stand a chance.'

'I wouldn't say that, you're still young and haven't got your full strength nor competition experience. He's seven years older than you and...' Peter interrupted.

'No, I'm not bothered about any of that. It's not what I mean.'

'What do you mean then?' Peter looked at me in a strange almost wistful way.

'He's my hero – you can never beat your heroes!'

'Well, you throw me often enough these days...'

'That's different – anyway you're not my hero. You're my brother.'

Richard Barraclough – British Freestyle Wrestling Champion

Chapter Ten
Richard Barraclough - The Gentleman Knight

I SUPPOSE I should have made the acquaintance of Richard Barraclough much sooner than I did – after all he was a lecturer in the Sports Science department of Birmingham University where I was studying Psychology. An international freestyle wrestler and British Champion no less; an international judoka running a judo club on my doorstep - I should have been hotfoot to his dojo banging on the door begging to be let in, but was not. The main reason for this looking back, was age. My age, or the age of the times led me along different paths for a while. I was a young man of about twenty, the first person in my family to go to university; the first person in our slum street and one of only a handful from my neighbourhood in general.

I had chosen to stay in Birmingham consciously so that I would not disrupt my judo training. It comes as some surprise therefore when I say, on reflection, that my priorities at university were fun, fun and more fun. Such activities came in a variety of packages: mucking around with my mates' fun; drinking Newcastle Brown Ale fun; rugby fun – which combined both activities, and not least, attempting to foist myself onto pretty young girls. This last endeavour took up a great deal of each day – in thought at least. I don't think I was very good at it. Even worse the media at the time attempted to convince the world in general that 'free love' was the daily bread for all young people, and that the 'swinging sixties' meant that a new sexual partner each week was normal, and if anything, a bit on the low side. The media portrayal of the times filled me with doubt and insecurity. At heart I was a good Irish Catholic boy who got few opportunities to resist temptation. I paid for my infrequent transgressions in guilt.

Peter Donnelly would often join me for university fun, which he took to like a duck to water and seemed to have none of the worries that plagued me. We often went to Sunday Mass after a hectic Saturday night where he would peacefully nap while I prayed. However, my prayers were unlikely to have been answered as they often were pleas to God to grant me greater success with the young ladies who were currently dominating my thoughts. I conducted one sided negotiations with Him, to enlist His aid in achieving some measure of carnal fulfilment. He seemed immune to my argument that granting some measure of sexual success would actually help me in living a more pious life. I was, of course, not the first young man to attempt this ploy made famous in the prayer of St Augustine: 'Lord make me chaste – but not yet.'

I pulled myself together in the second year. The words of encouragement I received from my eldest brother and judo coach helped.

'If you don't stop mucking about and get down to some proper work, I'll bloody kill you. Understand!' I began to give some pompous wordy, student explanation which he stopped with a brotherly punch in the mouth. 'Keep it shut! You've got nothing to say!'

Kevin was a great believer in the 'pre-emptive strike.' I saw him use this gambit a few times over the years. For a while he used his martial arts training for financial gain as a 'Door Operative' more usually known as a 'Bouncer.' In fact, he was in partnership with Pat Roach and some Irish Mafiosi running the 'Pink Elephant' club in the city centre of Birmingham. Things occasionally cut up a little rough and he had barred a set of brothers who worked the tarmac scam. ('We've got a bit of tarmac left on the truck – just enough to do your drive - £20 no questions asked.) These lads, the Sullivan brothers got themselves stupidly drunk and in search of excitement began to fight. Who they were fighting, and why was never clear. They were thrown out by Kevin and picked themselves up off the pavement uttering demonic oaths and threats. 'Look in the mirror Kevin Murphy and you'll be looking at the face of a dead man,' that sort of thing and more besides but not so poetic. One Saturday evening we were walking together to my parents' house where, parked outside was a grey Jaguar saloon, a 3.8S I believe, much loved by the criminal fraternity and associated spivs.

'Get behind me Danny. Those are the boys I threw out of the club. They're not here for a cup of tea. Stay out of the way!'

'I'm with you Kev. I'll watch your back.' I muttered some such rubbish but in truth was nervous. I will always remember my big brother's words of comfort.

'You're good on the mat Danny, but would be no use in a bloody fight. Stay out of the way and be told!' I did as I was ordered, shamefaced, but nevertheless dropped back and watched him, all smiles and affability approach the driver's window of the Jaguar with a friendly wave. He hit the first Sullivan brother through the closed side window which explosively shattered and continue to hit him saying with each blow, 'Out of order Jonell! Out of order! Never come near my mom's house. Never!'

'Ah for feck's sake Kevin we just came to ask if you'd let us back in the club. Fer feck's sake Kevin – you've broken my nose.' The other brother wisely stayed in the car.

'I'll be at the Pink Elephant tonight at eleven as usual. Ask me then and make sure you ask me nice. Now feck off.'

I watched the Jaguar roar down the road and in truth did not have a lot to say.

～

I knew where the university dojo was – past the sauna and straight down the corridor to the left. The sports hall was recently built and very well equipped. A swimming pool was planned to follow but, in the meantime, the latest acquisition was the sauna and ice-cold plunge pool. At this time a sauna was the stuff of fantasy – the sort of place that James Bond and his type might hang out. I believe it was the first in Birmingham. Now I had never given any thought at all to sitting in a ridiculously hot log cabin and then throwing myself into iced water. It was not the sort of thing that was done 'round our end' and to be honest I could not see any purpose to it. Until the day, now so long ago, that the Student's Union made an unusual decision. In the guise of equality between the sexes it was decided that both men and women could use the facility topless. This raised, amongst other things, the eyebrows of many a lusty student. I must point out that young women 'going topless' was quite in vogue at the time. Pubs advertised their 'topless barmaids.' The stage musical 'Hair' had a scene in which the cast (and the audience if so inclined) took off their clothes. Films with topless scenes, such as 'Blow-Up' were common-place. Some idiot fashion designer was making much publicity through his range of topless dresses. The idea of sitting in a red-hot room with naked young women seemed appealing. Sadly, it was empty when I looked in and so walked further along the corridor to see what was happening in the dojo.

One lone figure stood in the middle of the wall-to-wall green tatami. He was also topless with the physique of a gymnast; the perfect wide shouldered narrow waisted Herculean form. He was sandy haired, clean shaven with blue eyes and a handsome face. Aged about twenty-five I suspected he was not a student. He wore ironed *judo-gi* trousers and his jacket lay close topped with a coiled black belt. He moved easily and cartwheeled across the mat followed by a succession of handsprings and flick-flacks. He walked to the wall bars and performed a 'flag' incredibly powerful gymnastics move where the body is rigidly held horizontally from the bars by muscle power alone. An impressive display. This was Richard Barraclough and I was in awe.

↬

Another writer, an author quite famous and more successful than myself, has likened my writing to 'a ramble.' I was pleased with this critique as my intent is to wander through a story at no great pace taking in the view and the air, as it were. My son Joseph said he probably meant that I took a long time to get to the point.

'It's the same thing, surely?'

'Not quite,' he replied. (Well, if you want pace in a story, read Dan Brown – he writes quickfire rubbish!)

Anyway, one of my judo heroes is the great Belgian Johan Laats. Particularly so as he dumped the drug cheat Djamel Bouras flat on his back with *yoko-tomoe-nage* to win the 1997 European Championship. Bouras notably denied the great Toshihiko Koga the gold medal in the 1996 Atlanta Olympics but he was later found to have been using performance enhancing steroids. In my book he should have been stripped of his every title and all the silver medal winners upgraded.

Laats is more famous for popularising a technique that for a while was called 'the Laats' or 'the Laats move.' This was a sitting *kata-garuma* with the throw assisted by the attackers outstretched leg and the opponent thrown, more often rolled, onto his/her back. Johan Laats did this move incredibly well. The thousands of less skilled judoka, often children, did not and for a good few years competitions were marred by dozens of failed 'flop and drop' techniques. I was glad to see the back of them. Laats did not invent this move, far from it. Every amateur wrestler of quality knew this as a standard attack.

⌒

Richard looked at me standing in the doorway of the dojo, smiled and invited me in. I am a poor mimic, I cannot copy any accent well, even in print. Richard, a very well-educated man spoke in soft Huddersfield tones which introduced himself as completely confident in his own skin and at ease with his Yorkshire roots.

'Hello, don't just stand there, come in.' Richard came closer with his hand held out which I took and felt his firm grip. 'You're a *judoka* then?' He glanced at my feet – out of habit I had already removed my shoes. 'I'm Richard, the coach. The class is starting in a half-hour. Are you coming on the mat?'

'Sorry *Sensei*, I'm just being nosey. I haven't got my kit with me.'

'Don't worry about that. The University provides kits – all freshly laundered. What's your name?'

'Danny, *Sensei*.'

'It's up to you. Plenty of size five or six kits. And you can drop the *Sensei* bit. By and large the students use first names. What grade are you? Brown belt? First Dan? Second?'

'First Dan Richard. How did you know.' I was indeed puzzled as I had only walked a few paces on the tatami, relishing the novelty of a professional mat on a sprung floor.

'You seem at home in the dojo. I reckon I can tell a fellow's grade just by how they walk across the mat. Stay on – it would be good to have a decent *uke* – most of the class are beginners with a few yellow and green belts, one first kyu comes along occasionally.'

There are some people who, at first meeting, create a feeling of unease. Richard was the complete opposite. Calm, easy, relaxed are all good descriptions of the man. Oh yes, and gentlemanly. Richard Barraclough is a true gentleman in every decent old-fashioned sense of the word.

The session began and continued through its well charted course. Give or take the progression is the same in most clubs: warm up, tuition, standing techniques, practice; tuition, groundwork techniques, practice and to end either *randori* or a free mat. A word about *randori*: it is a word that means different things in different traditions of judo. I was coached to believe it to be 'free practice' with the emphasis on the practice. This is not always the case and, in many dojos, the only difference between *randori* and *shiai* (contest) is the absence of a referee. At the end of the session when Richard opened the mat for free practice, I was pleased to hear his dictum to 'take things easy.'

'Do you fancy a pull, Danny?' I most certainly did! To get on the mat with a player of Richard's quality was a treat. Besides I was doing okay. I was on a par with all the good midland players and had had a few decent wins. I'd rolled over Mick Jackson (BJA Midland Area Champion; Johnny Coles (U21 International) and a few more. I did not disgrace myself with the Solihull mob, mind you that big lump Tony Weaver was a pain in the arse and I found Chris Adams a nightmare. Nevertheless, I was keen, quite confident that I would put up a good show, even if he was a full International *judoka* and wrestler.

I had never been thrown with *kata-garuma* and I don't mean the easy Laats roll-over. I mean the *nage-no-kata* version where *tori* lifts *uke* high onto his/her shoulders before dumping the opponent to the ground. This is a silly throw, fit only for old men to demonstrate and to adorn the yellowing pages of useless, obsolete judo books. A silly throw for sure, unsuitable for competition use:

I lay struggling across Richard Barraclough's shoulders parallel to the floor and was pleased that he gently put me down feet first. I believe in the olden days of judo to hoist an opponent to this position was sufficient to score *ippon*.

'Bloody hell,' I said which seemed a reasonable comment given the circumstances. Richard smiled, an easy grin like a northern Robert Redford and our randori continued. I toughened up my grip and adopted a more defensive posture. He grabbed my left ankle in his cupped left hand, lifted and drove me hopping across the mat. A man cannot hop forever. My equilibrium was completely lost and I thumped onto my back. 'Having already said 'bloody hell' I changed tack to a casual, 'What was that throw called?'

'Don't know. I call it the 'Grab t'ankle.' A minute or so later I found myself once more laying horizontally across his shoulders courtesy of *kata-garuma*. This was becoming embarrassing. Co-incidences are always odd, that is their nature. I was trying to throw Richard of course, but it was a coincidence of purpose that I attacked with a strong left *uchi-mata* at exactly the moment when he was susceptible to this throw. He turned over and landed on his back – the perfect ippon. It was not an accident but it was my judo equivalent of a lottery win.

'Good throw!' said Richard. No bugger has thrown me like that; not Jacks, not Glass, not Kerr no-one. Great throw!'

'Just luck Richard.'

'Luck be damned! Great throw!' We bowed and shook hands. That was over fifty years ago and I am still pleased with his praise.

༄

In my last year at university, I bucked my ideas up considerably. I took to studying long and hard – a good job, as I had much catching up to do. The library was open twenty-four hours each day and I was not the only one who broke the rule about sleeping in a study carrel and smuggled in a sleeping bag to aid the process. Come the final exams held in the impressive Great Hall I realised the truth of the maxim, repeated by every sports coach and life style guru that, 'the only place that 'success' comes before 'work' is in the dictionary. Fortunately, I had worked my socks off - so much so that I made a complete hash of my final paper. There were three questions to answer in three hours. At the end of two hours and fifty minutes I had comprehensively answered two questions. You can see the problem. I recall checking my watch, (I had been engrossed in writing), realising my error and almost fainting with anxiety. I remember clearly the third question. 'Compare and contrast the contributions made to psychology by Sigmund Freud and Burrhus Skinner.' This could not be done in four minutes!

In desperation I wrote, 'If I had more time, I would elaborate these points' and wrote an extensive list. The exam finished and I sat bathed in sweat feeling sick and wishing there was some way matters could be rectified. I had blown it! The trouble was I had set my heart on becoming either an educational or a clinical psychologist and both required a master's degree qualification. Admission to either course required a first-class or at least an upper second-class initial degree. Perfect answers to my first two questions could only guarantee me sixty-six percent – not enough!

The next few days were anti-climactic; with exams finished forlorn students drifted about with no purpose. Even worse I had been summoned for a 'viva' the following week with the abjuration to attend 'gowned.' This was the process where failing students were given a last chance to mutter something in their favour to a faculty board of senior academics; surely I had not mucked up one of the answered questions as well? On the final university Saturday evening I went to a block party. Alcohol and mini-skirted girls failed to lift my mood. I had this terrible feeling of...? I can't describe it easily – sadness maybe? Three years had come to an end. Was that it? What was it all about? A line from a song lodged in my brain and would not leave *'But the good-times are all gone, and I'm bound for moving on – I'll look for you if I'm ever back this way.'* A miserable but pertinent song by a Canadian folk duo. I felt like crying but could not. A very good friend, Brian Morris, grabbed hold of me and suggested a stroll. We walked out of High Hall before dawn and drifted around the campus we knew so well. The air smelled of dew and spring optimism. He lit a cigarette and offered me one which I declined and walked to sit on the white limestone library steps.

'I don't suppose we'll see each other again Danny so there is something I want to tell you.'

'We'll keep in touch Brian, of course we will.' He looked at me in a strange way and spoke.

'I don't think so...' He drew on his cigarette. 'This something is a big deal – it really is.'

'Come on Brian. It can't be that bad.' I said making possibly the worst response anyone could make, aspirant psychologist or no. 'You haven't killed anybody? You're not dying...'

'Stop it!' His voice trembled. It was not a shout but nonetheless a firm command. 'I'm gay, Danny. I'm gay.' It seems ridiculous now but this was important then and I did not have a clue as how to best respond.

'Gay you say? Homosexual.' I added for unnecessary clarity. 'Are you sure?' Brian gave a bitter laugh.

'Well, I'm pretty sure. I mean homosexual activities are quite distinct. When I'm lying in bed with a man I've picked up from the Nightingale Club I'm not thinking 'Gosh, I've made a mistake, how on earth did that happen?' Danny that was the easy bit. The hard bit is that I have fallen in love.' He lingered over these words and hesitated for a few seconds. 'I'm in love with you. Now don't say anything. I know you haven't led me on or anything, but I'm in love with you or infatuated with you whatever the word is and I wanted to tell you. Now it's done – and yes, I am sure!' I had no idea what to say or do. After an uncomfortable pause Brian continued.

'You're not offended?

'I'm not offended Brian. I'm not anything much – surprised though. Very surprised. I've stayed in your room many times. We've shared the same bed!'

'Yes, that was very awkward. It's a good job I've got self-control. Danny it's time to say good-bye' I remained seated on the library steps. I remember scratching at a fossil embedded in the limestone. He stood up, and leaning over me kissed the top of my head. He walked away, head bowed and without turning. I recall the dawn chorus was in full voice but I was mute. I never saw him again.

⤺

The next day I walked into the meeting room of the psychology faculty, capped, gowned, trousers pressed and shoes shined. Four faculty members sat spaced either side of the venerable Professor Broadbent. In front of each, a crystal carafe and glass stood on the oak refectory table. A single chair was placed for me to sit facing my inquisitors. After curt introductions, in sombre tones, the Professor read from a paper in front of him.

'If I had more time, I would elaborate these points.'

He laid the paper flat and wearily studied me over the frames of his heavy tortoiseshell glasses. 'Mr. Murphy – now you have more time. Elaborate!'

It is a matter of record that when I received my results for the last question on my final paper, I achieved a distinction. Sometimes things work out!

⤺

I meandered for a couple of months after my finals, and generally took life easy. I bumped into Richard a few times; I visited his university club a few times. Once I encountered him in Paris:

In July I took touring holiday with my lovely, breezy girlfriend, Mary who I'd met in Birmingham's Central Library. In truth she was my first 'proper' girlfriend. This beautiful building was constructed in Victorian times. It consisted mainly of one great hall with books stacked from floor to ceiling. Access was via cast iron staircases which connected the tiers of balconies which circled the interior. The open lattice safety railings were designed at a time when female fashion was very different. I noticed her, standing, absorbed in reading, ten foot above my head. I surreptitiously glanced, and glanced upwards again

– it was impossible not to. I did not actually follow her when she left the building – more that we left at the same time. It might have been that, by chance, my departure was just a few seconds after her exit. She headed for the Kardomah café which was a common haunt, and as luck would have it, I was headed there also.

'Are you following me?' She asked as I stood behind her in the queue to pay for my espresso. I was horrified, mortified and petrified into muttering gibberish denials.

'Good Lord no!'

'Yes, you were, and you were looking up my skirt in the library.' I reddened and resorted to petulance.

'It's not much of a skirt – more like a wide belt.'

'True, but it's going to cost you a coffee and a cake anyway!'

A couple of weeks later we invaded Europe! We hardly knew each other but to go on holiday together, touring around France in my old mini-van seemed a good idea. As the holiday progressed our relationship skidded downhill, things had taken a decided turn for the worse. Holidays can become very stressful particularly when the delights of sharing a sleeping bag in the back of a mini-van have lessened. For a day or two she had hated me.

The final disagreement was simple enough and I have to say completely my fault. We were driving north from the sun and grapevines of St. Jean de Luz, and found ourselves near Tours. The Loire valley produces excellent wines and free wine tasting, 'degustation libre' is abundantly advertised. The idea is that the winery gives you a few sips of their hooch and a chunk of bread, in return for which you are pressured into buying a dozen bottles or so of quite pricey 'vin superieur.' There were about ten of us in the party that descended into the wine cave, a pit of ancient barrels and dusty bottles with water seeping from chiselled walls. Glasses were half-filled by the sommelier and an explanation given as to the type of wine and taste highlights to expect – all pretentious tosh and unnecessary in my book: I am Irish and know how to drink! I did little of that fancy examining by candle-light, slurping and spitting out. Quite the reverse, and I also polished off the leavings of those unappreciative fools who abandoned half-glasses of good booze. The wine, Muscadet

I recall, gave me an appetite. The bits of baguette provided for mouth clearing purposes were insufficient and I asked for some ham. Now I am the contradictory product of a lower working-class family and an excellent education – a sometimes awkward combination. I speak good French, and have found it particularly useful when in France, to speak only impeccable English. This way, when the inevitable insult is muttered, I pounce; the mutterer is unprepared for my protestations of offence. It's a game – 'les Francais' do the same when in England. The sommelier smiled at me and in French said.

'M'sieu is an uncouth English arsehole!'

'Gotcha.' I thought and then answered in his native tongue, albeit a little slurred. 'How dare you insult me, pigdog! I am Irish!' Strangely Mary, who was a student of foreign languages, did not find my behaviour humorous. Later, when we drove to Paris, she was frosty and quiet. I had a raging headache, a thirst of epic proportions and the urgent desire to urinate. She was driving and refused to stop the car.

'I will wet myself if you don't stop!'

'Well wet away, idiot!' She would not stop, even when out of complete desperation I used, messily, an orange juice carton as a receptacle. I filled it, but my bladder was still not empty and so, with only partial success, tipped the contents of the carton out of the window and repeated the process. She looked at me with contempt.

'He was right. You are an uncouth arsehole!'

'Frankly Ma'am, I don't give a damn!' It was a poor riposte, delivered with greater panache by Clark Gable in 'Gone with the Wind' – but it was the best I could do.

We arrived in Paris and somewhere near La Place de Concorde she stopped the car, took the keys, and wandered off. I shouted after her. 'I'm sorry – I love you.' Holding two fingers victoriously skyward, she shouted back without turning.

'I'm not – and who cares.' This could have been the worst ending of a terrible day except standing there, lost and forlorn I saw a poster plastered on a green painted pissoir. In large letters it advertised 'JUDO – an international competition between England and France at the Stade de Coubertain.' The match was that very evening.

'That's a stroke of luck.' I though as I headed to take the Paris Metro to the famous venue.

⌒

The British have produced some of the world's great judo players. You can make your own list easily; Starbrook, Adams, Jacks, Briggs, Bridge, Stephens, Randall, Gawthorpe, Fallon, Stewart, Howell, Powell and so on. I could add another dozen. The French also have a catalogue of great players. However, I believe that the French public have taken to judo as a spectator sport in greater numbers and passion that have their British counterparts.

I took my seat in the Stade de Coubertain and the atmosphere was charged with anticipation. The day had seen the French domestic championship but the main event was to be this international match between Great Britain and France. The rivalry between these two nations has always been intense – verging upon animosity. The French have never forgiven the British for inflicting upon them, many historic military defeats: Agincourt, Poitiers, Plessy, Waterloo, and the British have never forgiven the French for being smug, dressing neatly and going on and on about their cheese.

'Vive la France,' I shouted, adjusted the beret I had found in Orleans, and tried to fit in with the crowd of baying Frenchies. The guy sitting next to me must have spotted a failing in my accent.

'*Mais vous n'etes pas Francais?*'

'*Non, Je suis Irlandais.*' I thought this to be a damn smart move on my part. I bought a programme from a passing hawker. The British team consisted of the usual suspects but two names were of particular interest. Colin McIver (who I had seen recently thrown spectacularly by Tony Underwood) and my friend from university, Richard Barraclough. The format of the match was odd I thought. There were five weight categories and in each weight two contestants who fought each other – hence four fights per weight.

Richard took his place across the mat from his opponent and waited for the referee to call *hajime*. The crowd were wildly excited and had been since the loudspeaker had announced the Frenchman as Jean-Luc Rouge. I am not a xenophobe but, in those days, knew little about world judo apart from the absolute greats. Rouge had that very day won the French National Championship and so he was obviously good and in form. I doubted he would be a match for Richard but he had beaten McIver in the first bout easily with a quick *waza-ari* followed almost immediately with *ippon*. The Englishman and Frenchman bowed, and battled to take a favoured hold. Grip fighting continued for longer than usual; Barraclough normally took a strong right-handed grip – although he could 'go' off both sides. I was surprised to see him adopt a defensive posture and hold left. Rouge moved the quicker of the two and took a high hold forcing Richard's head down. There was no doubt that at this early stage the Frenchman was dominant. Quelle surprise! Rouge attacked with a lightning fast right-handed *harai-goshi* and took Barraclough high into the air. Only Richard's gymnastic skills avoided the score. The throw collapsed and both players fell to the mat with Richard in the dominant position for a *ne-waza* attack. Rouge locked his hands onto his own lapels and spread his legs defensively. I had seen Richard regularly break down this defensive posture. Indeed, he had rolled me over from this very position a host of times without noticeable effort. I waited in expectation for him to keep the Frenchman pinned and then work on his head to apply torque to turn Rouge over. I was most surprised when he broke off his attack and stood up. What was going on? An international wrestler not wanting to stay in *ne-waza*? Most strange!

The contest became oddly staccato – periods of static testing out, locking of horns you might say, punctuated by dynamic ferocious attacks. At one such moment Barraclough, from his knees, attacked Rouge with the earlier mentioned 'Grab t'ankle.' Rouge was powered across the mat and landed on his side. It is interesting to consider the move in the light of modern rules. The leg grab would have resulted in disqualification but the landing would be called a *waza-ari*. In these simpler times no penalty was given nor score, and the contest continued. Rouge again attacked with *harai-goshi*, lifting Richard and just failing to turn him onto his back.

Time went all too quickly and neither player had scored. The referee called for a decision and it was by this narrowest of margins that Richard Barraclough lost to the soon to become 'world great' Jean-Luc Rouge. Statistics are tedious but sometimes are worth mentioning, as is the fact that Rouge later wrote a best-selling judo book entitled simply '*Harai-Goshi*':

(Author's Note: Jean-Luc Rouge, World gold, silver and bronze medallist; European gold (x4), silver (x2), and bronze medallist; French open gold (x12), silver (x4), bronze (x4) and in total 74 International tournament wins – an unbelievable record which puts Richard's decision loss into praiseworthy context.)

~

I joined Richard after the contest by the simple expedient of vaulting over the security barrier and becoming a part of the throng of players, coaches and officials leaving the arena. Security was light; times were more relaxed. I avoided any checks by picking up a discarded coach's pass and slinging its lanyard around my neck. I must confess with some pride that I used it for many years at subsequent events to gain access to coaches' areas. Showing it and speaking in French was sufficient. I met any challenge with a Gallic shrug and said 'IJF' with authority. I spoke to Richard in the changing room. He was surprised but pleased to see me. 'Tough fight?' I asked.

'I tell you Danny, he was the best player I've ever been on with – and I've been on with the best. Aye, and that's including the Japs when I was at Tenri University. I thought he had me twice with that *harai*. He made McIver look ordinary and believe me Colin is no slouch. No, I can't complain about the decision. I was lucky to stay on my feet.' Richard explained that there was a reception for the British team but that the plan was to explore the delights of summer in Paris afterwards. 'Ah... here's Pip.' We were joined by a good-looking fellow of medium height and slim build with dark Mediterranean features and black hair. He had the look of the Canadian singer, Leonard Cohen. He greeted Richard with a smile, hug, handshake and the words.

'*Helo* Richard *Sut wyt ti?*' I could not place the words nor, to begin with, the accent.

'I'm a bit buggered after the scrap with Rouge. I was saying to Danny that he's the best I've been on with. Incredibly fast and strong.'

'It looked a hard knock.' To me he nodded and offered a hand. The man was Phillip Hearne, from the Valleys of South Wales He was a friend of Richard's from University and now a colleague. He had 'stowed away' with the GB team to watch the competition. We decided to meet up after the reception and take the evening from there. What can I say about the night that followed? In truth not a lot. There is a saying amongst rugby players, 'what happens on tour, stays on tour,' and I think the same dictum must apply to the activities of sportsmen and women of other disciplines. So 'what happened in Paris must stay in Paris.' Which is a pity as it transpired to be a great night. The worries about my girlfriend, Mary, were gone. We had a hotel booked and she was a strong independent 'free spirit' - she would be safe. She probably still hated me - so a night out on the town with the boys seemed just the ticket as they say

We picked a nearby bar in which to meet later and myself and Pip Hearne decided to eat there and have a few drinks whilst the British team were being feted. We dined well and cheaply on 'moules frite' and vin ordinaire - good old-fashioned French plonk, not greatly alcoholic, so there was no harm in ordering a second litre. Well into this bottle we talked of many things, unimportant gibberish mostly. Pip was a champion sprinter it turned out although not currently in training. He coughed in the smoke-filled room - smoking was compulsory in France at the time. 'I must get myself fit again, I really must. More wine?' A couple of hours passed before the door opened and in walked Richard, Tony MacConnell and others. They were a bit blurry and I wondered that I may have misjudged the strength of cheap wine. Pip looked blurry too – so maybe he had also. The bar was now full and rowdy, the stuff of a normal week-end night.

'I will sing to these Frenchies,' said Pip. 'I like them - and they deserve it!' Now, I enjoy opera as much as the next man. The arias from La Boheme can bring a tear to the driest eye and being Irish I am overly sentimental and can weep easily. Even comedic opera has its place. Pip climbed unsteadily upon the latticed iron chair and then onto the table. The happy hub-bub subsided, to be replaced with anxiety and alarm. The mood softened when Pip launched into the French anthem 'La Marseillaise' - a song of which the French never tire. I read a translation of it once and the words are blood-thirsty and mad. Phillip Hearne had a remarkably good voice in the operatic vein, a more than passable tenor. With the crowd now on his side and lustily singing, no-one took notice of the words he used, which I realised were pornographic and disgusting. Nonetheless he deserved his round of enthusiastic applause. His second song was a rendition of the famous operatic ditty, 'Funiculi, Funicula.' This time his translation was a raucous celebration of the world's most popular but usually solitary activity. Everyone knows this tune, but few the words beyond the first two. He encouraged the crowd to join in, which they did by whistling, humming, clapping while he, appropriately enough, sang solo. That he interpreted the tune with flamboyant hand gestures gave a clue to the more knowledgeable that all was not as it seemed

'Last Night! ... I contemplated masturbation; it did me good...I knew it would

To-night! ... I will repeat the operation; it's my desire ... I will not tire'

I won't go on nor explain. It's the 21st century and we have Google.

Tony MacConnell a bedrock of British judo, and lifelong friend of Richard's had already fallen out with France. The pair had scrounged a car from some unsuspecting do-gooder, in the hope it might be useful. Richard later confided to me that it was doubtful that Tony had a licence of any description and certainly had no experience of driving around Paris. But he did have confidence and a complete lack of fear. From the description given they fell foul of one of the huge circular intersections fed by six or more roads – probably Concorde or Etoile. It is not apparent to anyone other than the natives of Paris how one is supposed to navigate from one side to the other, there being no traffic lights, road markings or other such aids. In truth I do not believe that there is a system – you just have to do your best and sound the car horn repeatedly. There is a cultural difference here. In Britain blasting the horn is considered rude and tends to be avoided.

In France, and much of Europe it's just what drivers do. Horns were blared and Tony took offence. I have noticed over the years that most top judo players have a well-developed sense of what is appropriate and that this belief should be shared and, if necessary, enforced. 'Ah don't think much on this Richard. Rude buggers. If they carry on, I'll have to have a word.'

'I didn't know you spoke French Tony?'

'I don't. But I'll make myself understood, don't tha worry thee sen. They'll get the message. Be buggered if they won't!'

The hooting, pipping and blaring carried on and Tony MacConnell, true to his creed, decided to educate the French. He stopped the car and got out to be greeted with renewed clamour and infuriation from Parisian drivers unfamiliar with the expectations of good manners forged in Cumbria. He was a big imposing man with a confidence and composure impossible to ignore.

'I'm not moving until these chaps shut the buggery up.' He stood by the car, a small Renault, and surveyed the building chaos with a cold glare. No driver left the safety of his vehicle to remonstrate with this stalwart, this Heart of Oak. Gradually the bellowing noise abated; Tony MacConnell and Richard Barraclough were afforded safe unhindered passage forward.

I should not tell of how, later in the evening, as the wine took hold the desire to dance resulted in a mad conga which spread out of the bar and into the adjacent streets. This manic snaking took on tribal significance when the nonsense words which accompanied it were bawled out into the cool April air.

'Aye zigga zumba, zumba, zumba. Aye zigga, zumba, zumba hey...'

Young Frenchmen and impossibly beautiful French girls with long straight hair and long slim legs joined in and were happy so to do. That these girls were eager for the excitement of unimportant affection and other ecstasies will remain secret. The night progressed onto the steps of the great cathedral at Montmartre. I watched a full moon rise and break the hold of night. I was deeply in love with the girl by my side as we hugged for warmth and sipped stolen wine to wash down stolen kisses. 'Life is good.' I thought, and I was not even sad when she drifted off ethereally into the Paris night but wistfully regretted not knowing her name.

⌒

The flaking walls of the lantern lit Montmartre piano bar were a collage of a thousand posters, album sleeves, sheet music and scrappy notes left by visitors or wishful lovers. I read a few while Pip Hearne sat with an adoring mademoiselle on each arm explaining why the Welsh were God's own people and the English were boot-lickers. Richard Barraclough was leaning against a wall covered with messages, propping up a beautiful mademoiselle with the 'gamin' look and a well filled white jumper - I believed her to be Brigitte Bardot. One note read, 'Josh – the American boy with the Bob Dylan, tee-shirt, I love you - Natalie,' It was signed with a bright red lip-stick kiss.

Another exclaimed, 'Going to Marrakesh – Anyone want to come? - Jimmy.'

'Got room for two?' another hand had replied.

A very talented pianist was playing 'Unsquare Dance' by Dave Brubeck. A frequently emptied glass, half-full of Franc coins and assorted change, rested on the piano top. I went outside and lifted my head to see above me, shining white in floodlit splendour, the beautiful wedding-cake madness which is the cathedral crowning the Butte of Montmartre. I was happy and drunk, particularly drunk. Beaujolais nouveau has that effect upon me after a pint or two. I needed to walk to clear my head. An arm linked mine. *'Est-ce que tu vas bien? Ca va?'* My pretty companion of earlier had floated back.

'Je vais bien mais trop de vin. Je vais me promener.' She pulled me close and kissed me on the cheek. She spoke in English.

'Can I come? I also need to, 'ow you say, clear my head. My name is Marianne...' As I've said before, they were generous times.

⌒

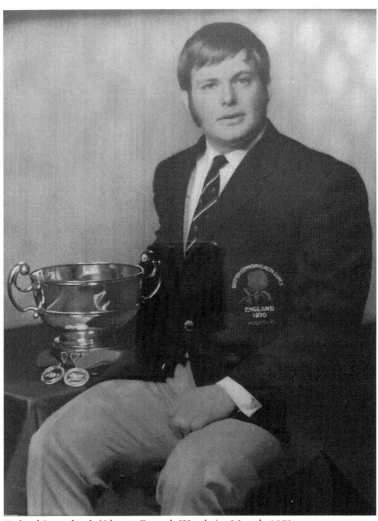

Richard Barraclough (Olympic Freestyle Wrestler) – Munich, 1972

Chapter Eleven
The Grand Joust Munchen 1972

THE NUMBER FOURTEEN bus that took me from Birmingham city centre to my parental home stopped directly outside the Morris Judo Club. It was seven o'clock, Thursday, and this just had to be my first port of call. I felt childishly excited when I alighted and walked up the driveway to the familiar building correctly known as Morris Commercial Cars Social Club. I hadn't seen the judo crowd for, at least six months what with cramming, final exams and my ill-fated trip to France. I had not come to train but more to break the ice as it were. I knew what to expect; maybe a few dull unenthusiastic greetings, calls of 'where's your kit or 'you've missed the kids' session.' Judoka are in the main not given to sentimentality. One of my fond memories of the Morris was when, a year or so earlier I had broken my collar bone towards the end of the session. It was obvious that I needed medical treatment. I sat on the mat with mates gathered round looking down in minor interest. I asked If anyone would run me to the hospital. A few shuffled, and then drifted away; the problem was obvious. We had worked hard; judo suits were soaked and steaming with warm sweat - lost moisture best replaced with a couple of pints of shandy in the social club bar. The choice facing my friends was to hang around with me for a few hours in A & E or go to the pub; so somebody called an ambulance. At least twenty chums had the good grace to stand on the club steps, foaming glasses raised high in salute, as the ambulance whisked me away. I watched them drift back inside all laughing. All in all, it seemed fair.

⌒

Climbing the six stone steps and entering the foyer of the club via the heavy Art-Deco doors with worn brass handles felt so familiar. The old doorman sat at his desk and gave a polite nod. I wondered, not for the first time, what his job was. He was certainly no deterrent to any undesirables who wished to enter. I think he was supposed to take an entrance fee, but never did. The unsophisticated smell of beer was welcoming as was the comforting 'clack' of snooker balls echoing from the billiards room. Break-fall thumpings emanated from the ball-room where the judo sessions were held. I opened the door and was hit by that most particular of perfumes – the smell of forty Judoka at hard practice. Bob Trevis looked up and called out 'You're late' and carried on. It was good to be home!

I scanned the mat and noted many of the regular Morris crew, Bob, Carole, Pamela, Pat and a set of new faces. Dave Walker, Tony Weaver, Roy Muller and Brian Regan were there – so the Solihull mob were paying a visit. The mighty frame of Bryan Drew from the 3Ks was intent on doing damage, so it looked like a good night was in prospect. But no Peter Donnelly. I wanted to see him: there had been no rift between us but our paths had diverged for a while.

I chatted, gave and received appropriate insults and the general opinion seemed abroad that I was a poor excuse of a person and needed to get back on the mat. I was spared from more of this rubbish when the end swing doors opened and Donnelly walked in – but not alone. He was in the company of a dark eyed, raven haired voluptuous beauty. After introductions were made, I could add 'Irish' to the adjectival list. She had that soft brogue that made one wish to be drunk in a ceilidh bar in Dublin. Her name was Eileen and Peter was unsurprisingly in love. 'There goes his judo career' I thought, but as things turned out, completely erroneously. We talked and she was as charming as she was beautiful. Peter and I exchanged affectionate hugs and vague plans to meet but it was apparent that his mind was elsewhere - mine also as it was now past nine and I wanted to see my mom and dad before they went to bed.

⌁

My parent's house, a dull, uniform terrace was literally no more than two-hundred yards from the Morris judo club and as soon as I made the right turn which put my childhood home in view, I knew something was wrong. Five or six cars were parked outside and there were usually none. As I walked closer, I saw that every light was on in the house. The next-door neighbour, Mrs Pemberton stood on her doorstep, a blanket wrapped around her shoulders. She called to me as I approached and I noticed that our front door was open. 'Tell Murphy me so sorry,' she spoke in the lyrical tones of one of the smaller West Indian islands.

My mother, Alice Gertrude, sat sobbing on the settee swathed in a shawl of grey Galway wool. Father John Power the aging family priest, sat close, holding her frail hand to give comfort while sister Shelagh cuddled her head. Eldest sister Joan was making tea in the kitchen and brothers Kevin and Brian were smoking cigarettes and talking quietly in the front room. In itself this was odd; Kevin had given up years ago and Brian smoked a pipe. For some reason it was the priest that spoke to me first and for the second time that evening I heard the tones of Ireland.

'Danny – how good it is to see you and what a fine man you've grown to be. What happened to the little boy who was a nuisance at mass? Ah Danny boy...' the priest shook his silvered head sadly... 'there has been a great consternation as to how to get hold of you in this time of tragedy - and here you are. The Lord moves in ways wondrous to behold.' Mom stared at me but could not speak. I tried to understand precisely the look in her eyes. After a while I realised it was fear. The man to whom she had been married for more than fifty years was gone and she had no idea how to face the world alone. He was flawed man often taken with 'the drink' but nevertheless he was 'Dad.'

Kevin was never the man to panic in a crisis. He entered the room and commanded attention. 'Excuse me Father but I need my brothers. Danny, Brian – he died in his greenhouse and he's in a bit of a mess. We need to put him in his best suit. Come on.' In sad procession we three brothers climbed the childhood 'wooden hill to Bedfordshire' to lay out Dad, quietly waiting in his bedroom.

I had arrived in Munich courtesy of Johnny Clark our local neighbourhood millionaire and friend of my brother Brian. They had been born and raised on the same street and were in the same class at school. They were and remained good friends. Johnny had noticed that he could buy hand-bags and the like directly from the sweat-shops of Manchester for a few shillings and sell them for double the price to the small shopkeepers of Birmingham. They in turn, could then sell them on at a profit. To begin with he drove up to Manchester each week in his Austin A35 and came back with every inch of space stuffed with saleable goods. Soon he swapped the small car for a Commer van, and a few months later, that for a Bedford truck. Selling his wares to shop-keepers proved time consuming so he rented a warehouse in Aston. It made better sense that the retailers came to him – which they did. Johnny Clark was a nice bloke and a dutiful son. Every week he visited his mother, who lived diagonally opposite our terraced house. On one such visit he knocked on our door.

'What do you think of her?' asked Johnny. We walked around his pride and joy – a brand new lime green 3.8 Jaguar S type. I said all the expected things and made envious mutterings.

'Keep your eye on it for me while I visit my mom.' I knew what he meant. There was a 'gang' of lads on the road who were getting into bits of mindless trouble – Jimmy and Paul Morrissey, Malcolm Smith and Derek Thompson. We were all of similar age, young teenagers. I went to primary school with Jimmy and Paul, and they were alright if a bit dozy. Malcolm and Derek were close neighbours and were fine. I had received a bit of ribbing when I had won a scholarship to a foundation grammar school but nothing worth being concerned about. The unimaginatively named 'Gowan Road Gang' caused me no trouble whatsoever. When they left school at the age of fifteen, they decided to be Teddy Boys. Now, I thought this showed flair on someone's part as Teddy Boys were the delinquents of the 1950s - most certainly not the mid-sixties. I was quite pleased with this turn of events. Four young men dressed in pink, yellow, blue and red 'drapes', drainpipe trousers and 'brothel creepers' added colourful interest to the neighbourhood. I found it quite jolly.

Johnny gave me five shillings for looking after the Jaguar. I gave Jimmy Morrisey two shillings to do the task for me and carried on with my homework. Years later when we had all grown up Paul Morrissey killed himself on a motor bike – which was unsurprising. His brother Jimmy divided his time between intervals of petty crime and vacations in gaol – also unsurprising. Derek hung up his drapes and became a jeweller and millionaire. Malcolm Smith kept his lemon-yellow Edwardian jacket for week-ends and made a fortune as the owner of a plastering company. In later years we would occasionally, accidentally meet when visiting aging mothers. They would discuss the relative merits of Derek's Rolls-Royce and Malcolm's Bentley. I left my Chrysler Alpine (Car of the year 1978) parked much further down the road.

⌒

Johnny Clark had diversified and was a major shareholder of a holiday travel company the founder and Managing Director of which became famous as chairman and financial supporter of a local football club. I was talking to Johnny and my brother Brian at Gay Hill golf club; Brian was pointing his pipe-stem at me while at the same time berating me for smoking. I was there to caddy and we were waiting to be called to the first tee. 'You should stub that bloody cigarette – it's stinking the place out. The captain will complain I'm bloody sure he will.'

'But it's fine for you to smoke that God awful pipe?' Brian and I always argued.

'You're depressed that's what it is. Ever since the Old Man died and you were ditched by that girlfriend of yours ...'

'I was not ditched as you so gently put it. We decided to go our separate ways.'

'Don't try and spoof me Danny – she ditched you. Shame though, a good-looking girl was Mary – great legs!' Brian and Johnny both laughed and Johnny unhelpfully agreed that Mary did indeed have great legs. And it was all true: she did have great legs, she did dump me because of my disgraceful behaviour in France; Dad's death had rattled me and I was brassed off. My elder brother Kevin, dismissed my romantic tragedy with these precise words.

'Never worry about a girl Danny. Women are like the number fourteen bus – there's one along every ten minutes and if you wait long enough the same one comes back.' I found this epithet to be less than helpful and in life generally to be only partially correct. (He was being less than truthful. In his own case, when hurt by the loss of a loved one, he had spent three years 'bumming' around France, Spain and North Africa.)

⌒

Brian and Johnny were right though. My life was completely aimless. I'd finished university in May; gone on a holiday to France with my then girlfriend, which did not end so well – and Dad had died. I had applied for a few jobs and was still waiting for replies – I had time on my hands.

'You need to do something,' said Brian. 'You can't just mope about. Get a grip! Go on holiday or join the army! That'll sort you out.' I ignored the army quip. Every man who had done National Service thought this the cure for every ill.

'I've already been on holiday - with Mary the girl who you kindly mention has given me the old heave-ho!' Johnny had a Eureka moment. He beamed, leaned forward, took the Gauloise from my fingers and stubbed it out.

'Go to Munich! Watch the Olympics! Perfect thing for a single fellow to do! We've got a coach leaving tomorrow. It's a five-day trip – a day and a half in the coach each way and two days at the Games in between. It's fully booked but you can have the 'Dead Man's' seat at the front.' I did not know what he meant and asked for clarification. 'Oh, we always keep the front seats vacant on a long-haul trip. Somewhere to store the stiff if anyone has a heart attack. I can't help with accommodation though. Every hotel room for miles around Munich is taken. But a good-looking single bloke like you should be able to chat up some lonely old granny for a bunk up – you never know!'

I gave it brief thought – an adventure! The idea really appealed so at six o'clock in the following morning I boarded the Bowen's Executive Coach bound for Munich. I took a small rucksack of essentials and not being in favour of Johnny's 'grab-a-granny' idea, packed my trusty sleeping bag. It was late August and the Daily Mirror had provided an Olympic schedule. It might just be possible! Providing everything went to plan I should be able to see Richard Barraclough wrestle and David Starbrook fight in the judo competition.

The journey went as expected and at three o'clock on the twenty-eighth of August, I alighted at Munich Bus station, and following my Baedeker's guidebook directions, headed for the Hofbräuhaus. The journey had been very long – about thirty hours including stops and the ferry crossing, but I had slept well enough over-night and felt in good shape.

I did not smoke, not normally anyway, but since the death of my father and my escapade in love, I had quite taken to the habit. I suppose I was depressed. I preferred the pungent French cigarettes popular amongst student 'intellectuals' at the time. Names such as Disque Bleu, Gauloise and Gitanes spring to mind. There were none to be had in the Munich tobacco kiosk and so I puffed with scant pleasure on an American 'Lucky Strike.' I marvelled at the large, traditionally clad 'bier-frau' who approached the refectory table, holding four steins of beer in each hand. I quickly calculated that each much weigh close to two kilos – an impressive feat indeed. She slammed one of the flip-topped crocks down in front of me and as she leaned forward, I was greeted with a wonderful smile and a considerable expanse of soft, white cleavage. Both cheered me up. I smoked and drank, surveying the scene while waiting for the pork dish which I had ordered. The *schweinshaxe* soon arrived on a wooden platter, disappointingly delivered by a tubby gent in lederhosen. The meal was a feast! A great roasted knuckle of pork with mounds of mashed potato and sauerkraut drenched with steaming gravy. It reminded me of the pie and mash that Dave Starbrook had provided a few years earlier. I was delighted with my meal even before I tasted it. To me, a working-class lad, the first requirement of dinner is that at the end of it, you should be full!

An 'Oompah' band took to the stage at the end of the cavernous but splendidly decorated beer hall. There was a swelling of enthusiastic applause, shouting and banging on tables from the audience which must have grown to over a thousand boisterous souls. I had already been in the Hofbräuhaus for an hour or so and the atmosphere rose from being joyful and unrestrained to loud frenetic abandonment. A hundred rows of red, white and blue triangular bunting were strung across the great room, interspersed with the rectangular black, red and yellow flags of West Germany. White and blue diamond pennants, the state flag of Bavaria, flew from every wall and huge drapes of the Olympic rings hung with Germanic precision from each baroque beam supporting the high ceiling. Strange posters of a multi coloured dachshund were plastered everywhere – this was 'Waldi' the mascot of the Olympiad, accompanied by the slogan, *'Die Heiteren Spiele'* which means 'The Cheerful Games' or something close. The band played a few songs to which young and old men and women sang, gesticulated, hooted, howled and cavorted. My command of the German language was, and remains poor, but there was no mistaking the orders called from the leader of the group, a fine blonde woman of Wagnerian proportions – 'Have a good time!' From somewhere she had procured two long trumpet-like glasses, you know, the 'yard of ale' things. The band struck up and the crowd went happily wild.

'In Munchen steht ein Hofbräuhaus – eine, zwei, g'suffa!'

This was obviously a favourite drinking song. At the command *'eine'* everyone stood up; at *'zwei'* glasses were raised and at *'g'suffa'* beer was quaffed. Luckless young men and girls were dragged to the front and given the fully charged long glasses with the inevitable result that they went back to their seats beer soaked and with laughing wet faces. At about midnight I left the famous beer hall full of beer, pork and happiness. Before my arrival in Munich the only thing I knew about the Hofbrauhaus was that in the 1920s Adolph Hitler had used it as a meeting place for his thugs. I drunkenly mused that I had had a much better time than the Nazis who were a seriously miserable bunch. Clutching my sleeping bag, I staggered into the warm air of a summer's night and resolved to find a secluded hedge under which to sleep. So far my adventure to 'The Cheerful Games' had gone well.

∽

In the manner of drunks, I found my inability to successfully light a cigarette ridiculously funny. I stumbled about for a while, occasionally laughing at nothing, until I found what appeared to be the ideal bush, and was soon fast asleep. I was woken at dawn by a large German boot kicking me affectionately in the ribs. In truth, the boot may not have been German but the policeman wearing it certainly was. The hedge I had found turned out to be an ornamental structure in the middle of a large traffic island. I had not recognised it as such, possibly because there were few vehicles buzzing around when I lay down well after midnight – that and the fact that I was blind drunk.

'Aufstehen! Steh auf!' It was not difficult to figure out that the officer wanted me to stand. I got out of the sleeping bag and stood in front of him clad in Levis and my Morris Judo Club tracksuit top. It was a pretentious affair really, royal blue edged with white and red. On the back was the legend 'Judo' in large white letters and in smaller size 'MCC' above and 'Great Britain' below. I was very thirsty, with a bad headache and desperately needed to urinate.

'Identifizierung!' I showed him my passport which also held the IJF official's pass, the one I had stolen from the Paris Open.

'Judo? Judo?' he questioned.

'Ja! Ja! Hofbrauhaus Bier – sechs Bier. Ich liebe Bier.' This seemed to break the ice and he laughed and gave me back the passport and pass. In poor English he said.

'Me too - I love drunk beer! I judo too! Go, go. Naughty, naughty!' He saluted efficiently and wandered off shaking his head. I thrust my way into the bushes and thankfully unzipped my fly.

I cleaned myself up in a nearby bar and had a coffee, water and a large sausage for breakfast. I had watched the Olympic opening ceremony on television in England, and was impressed by it – in particular the young blond, blue eyed perfect Aryan who ran up all those steps to light the Olympic flame. Given Munich's association with Hitler, either the organisers were being darkly ironic, stupidly insensitive or just plain dumb. I decided to head for the Olympic Park. The obvious way to travel was to use the '*U-Bahn*' or underground but it was a spectacularly beautiful day and still very early thanks to the alarm-boot of the Polizei. Breakfast and water had diminished my headache and a few kilometres walking in the sunshine seemed a good idea. As I headed north following the many direction signs to the 'Olympiapark' I could not but be enthused by the festive mood of the city. Flags, bunting, posters everywhere and incessant Oompah band music bursting out from the many cafes and bars. As I approached, the stadium complex did not disappoint. The towering structures were reminiscent of mediaeval fairground tents on an enormous scale, gleaming silver in the Bavarian sunshine. From somewhere close came the sounds of a Dixieland jazz-band and in the near distance I saw a gang of young people dancing wildly to the traditional strains of 'Alexander's Ragtime Band.' I meandered close and dropped my pack to stand in the circle of watchers.

↬

My personality is full of flaws and holes. I have one good trait, in my opinion anyway. I believe that I am a complete and utter dope, 'a wanker' as one might say. But I also believe that so is everyone else - which levels the playing field somewhat. Hence, for good or ill, I do not suffer from embarrassment. I am perfectly happy to make a fool of myself in the eyes of others as I don't believe that they, (the others), are in any position to judge. But I am not without self-awareness; many years later my wife said I had the dancing ability of a lame donkey. I was not offended but disputed that this was fair. She thought for a moment, agreed and amended her critique. 'You have the dancing ability of a pregnant, lame donkey.' I held her gently by the throat... She was wrong of course and in my mind's eye I could review the evidence to the contrary.

↬

In the sunshine of that glorious Munich day with the Olympic Stadium as a backdrop I spied gyrating boppers exhibiting differing levels of ability and grace as they pranced to the Dixieland music. I watched, appreciative of one young lady who lithely twisted and spun to the syncopated rhythms. Her hair was a fine flaxen blonde which flew loose as she twirled and when still, hung to her waist. Her eyes were bluer than robins' eggs and her features fine and flawless. She wore a short white summer dress made of cheesecloth and nothing else – times were kind. I was horrified when she grabbed me by the hand and pulled me into middle of the dancer's circle. I did my best. Slowly other dancers cleared until we were the only two. She danced around me and every now and then we touched and she spun coquettishly away. Too soon the music stopped and the watching crowed burst into enthusiastic applause. She kissed me deeply which drew further cheers and called her 'cool Englischer dancer.' To this day I am stunned by the memory of this event; I remember her so well, yes so well. Our romance lasted just long enough to share an ice-cream sitting together on the grass - but I recall it with deep affection. Her English was, like that of many Germans, perfect. She brushed aside the compliments I gave.

'I am a gymnast,' she said, 'and a ballet dancer. I've been training since I was two years old and I'm sick of it. When the Olympics are over, I think I will retire and take it easy and live off cake for a year.' She poked a finger into my stomach. 'I will become fat like you.' I involuntarily tensed my less than rock hard abdominals and she laughed. 'I like it! Don't worry – the only boys I meet are gymnasts also and they are all hard like cement and very vain. I want a soft man that I can cuddle.' This made me feel a little better but not much. We were interrupted by an older man who approached and stood glowering above us. He wore an East-German tracksuit. 'I must go.' she said and we briefly touched hands before she walked off. She smiled, 'Good-bye my cool Englischer dancer!' I have a photograph of her, kept safely over the years, standing on the gymnastics team podium wearing an Olympic medal. I saw her once more for the briefest time a few days later - but this turned out to be a forever sadness.

I realised that I no longer missed my former girlfriend Mary. One dance and one kiss, and my broken heart had mended!

$\backsim$

Although I will be glad to my dying day that I had made my excursion to the Olympic Park it turned out to be the wrong location as the wrestling and judo events were being held at the Ringerhalle in the Messegelande Exposition Park some kilometres distant. This was explained to me by a games' helper at the information desk but a shuttle-bus ran between the two venues so no harm done.

I sat with a group of rowdy Americans from Iowa State university - proclaimed such by the pennants they hoisted, tee-shirts and the many home drawn placards. The stadium was newly built and smelled of fresh concrete. I'd had no trouble getting into the venue – there were many spare places and I simply bought a ticket. The wrestling hall was about half full, perhaps fifteen hundred people but the crowd was gathering. I had looked around for the British contingent but could not see anyone I recognised so sat with the Americans who had taken seats closest to the action. The Americans turned out to be good company:

'I say you chaps. Do you mind awfully if I join you? One of my compatriots is performing later, doing a bit of the old 'catch-as-catch-can' - I want to get a good view, what?' I knew the Yanks would make fun of my accent so I thought I would give them plenty of ammunition.

'Hey. looky here. We've got an English Duke or something – wants to muscle in. Whadya say boys?'

'Oh my gosh! How exciting. You're colonials! I didn't recognise you without the cowboy hats! I'm sorry, you fellows, I didn't realise there were thin Americans.' A ball of screwed up sandwich wrapper bounced off my head, which I took as a sign of welcome.

'Move up guys. Let's make space for the Limey. Sit down young fella.' He held out his hand which I shook. 'Hi there, I'm Hank.'

'Of course you are.' I replied and he laughed. As I said the Yanks were good company - a mix of supporters, coaches and competitors for other or later events. As the time for Richard's fight drew close Hank asked me if 'Barraclow' was any good. It turned out he was the coach for the university wrestling team, which did not mean a lot to me. I came to wrestling late, as a side-plate to judo as it were. I was enthusiastic and had medalled in a couple of unimportant competitions, but I had little knowledge of the sport in depth.

'He's the best we've got. We've trained together at judo and wrestling, and I've never pinned him once or even come close. So, I'd say he's pretty good. How about your guy, this Jon Peterson? What's he like?'

'Man! You cannot be serious! Is Peterson good? Do bears shit in the woods? Does the Pope wear a big white hat?' He went on to explain that the American collegiate wrestling system was the best in the world and that the Peterson brothers, Ben and Jon were of the top rank. 'We expect them both to win gold. Jon has improved so much over the past two years. He was good in college but not that special. But the word is out that he partners Dan Grable – and you can't train with the best in the world without it rubbing off. Your friend 'Barraclow' had better have something special in the tank...'

⌒

Richard Barraclough stood facing his opponent in the spotlighted glare of the wrestling circle. My son who is a pretty good judo player, said to me when he was about sixteen, 'the loneliest time is being in the centre of the mat in a big competition, waiting for the ref to call *hajime.*' I could only imagine Richard's thoughts as he faced Peterson awaiting the referee's call. Richard stood very still and Peterson fidgeted, scuffing his light leather wrestling boots into the mat. The contest began and was greeted by the American supporters with whoops of encouragement and howls of delight.

'Go get him Jon! USA! USA! USA! The repetitive chanting was accompanied by synchronous stamping of feet and fists punched into the air. There is a brash self-confidence about Americans that can be quite overwhelming. They enjoy success are not humble when it happens. It is the American dream – start at the bottom, work hard and reach the top. Jon Peterson had worked very, very hard!

∽

I was tearful at Richard Barraclough's defeat and have no idea why. It's true, I am over emotional. The list of mawkish movies and sentimental songs that render me tight throated and snotty is long but I will exercise restraint.

I felt a desperate need to sympathise with Richard and screamed his name as he left the mat. He waved in acknowledgement, but that could just as easily have been to Brian Jacks whose unmistakeable voice could be heard above the din of a cheering crowd. I noticed the British judo team for the first time sitting on the opposite side of the arena. Dave Starbrook as so often looked impassive; he rose to his feet and respectfully applauded as Richard left the wrestling circle.

Excepting Richard's fights, it was the Judo that I mainly wanted to watch, but the return coach back to England was at dawn on Saturday morning so the only events I could see were the heavy-weights on Thursday and the light-heavies on Friday - Starbrook's event. Now that Richard was out of the competition, I was left pondering what to do. (In fact, Richard had not been eliminated – I just did not know how a wrestling competition was organised. At the time they used a 'negative points' system. He had accumulated four points against him by virtue of Peterson's pin but would still fight the next day. Eliminations would be made at the end of that day based on the players with most negative points. So sometime later, forty-eight years later, I asked Richard for his account of his subsequent fights.)

'I returned to the village disappointed with my performance and things got worse. I weighed myself and I had managed to put on two kilos during the day which had to come off before next morning's weigh-in. I knew at least a kilo would be fluid but could take no chances. I put on a sweat-suit and spent an hour running up and down the stairs in the accommodation block. In the event I made the weight and fought Bens of Belgium who I defeated with a lot of points. He was really a Greco-Roman specialist (no attacks below the waist) so

I had no trouble throwing him with *hiza-garuma*. He was incredibly strong and had a very powerful bridge. No matter how hard I tried I could not pin his shoulders to the mat. When I got back to the flats and weighed myself, I was once again two kilos over the limit so there was nothing for it to put the sweat-suit back on and spend an hour on the stairs. The next day I fought Peter Neumair from Germany. He was a tremendous player who lost out to Tediashvilli, the eventual gold medallist. I have no complaints – it was a hard fight and he was better than me.'

⤳

The gymnastics events were scheduled for the three days before the judo and I wanted to get tickets, in part to watch the events but also to see if I could spot the East-German girl I had briefly met – after all I was her 'Cool, Englisher dancer!' There were no tickets to be had so I drifted around the centre of Munich until I found a bar with a television. A monstrous great thing it was too - with a twenty-three-inch screen and in colour! I did not see my dancing partner but did see a young Russian gymnast called Olga Korbut.

The bar-owner, Christian, was about forty-years old, tall, slim, handsome and wracked with guilt. He had been a member of the 'Hitler Youth' and even worse had thoroughly enjoyed the experience. I had been in this bar most of the day, drinking, eating but mainly watching television. My terrible German prompted him to speak excellent English. To begin with we talked of this and that over the bar, but in the end, he could not resist talking about the war. I found in my later career as a psychologist that it is easy to find out what is troubling a person's mind. Simply listen to them and sooner or later they will tell you – generally sooner.

'You are here in Munchen to see the Olympics, Ja?'

'Yes, I have a friend in the wrestling - he just lost, and another in the judo but he doesn't fight until tomorrow. I wanted to watch the gymnastics today but there are no tickets...'

'You must stay here in my fine bar and watch 'the telly', Ja?' He seemed pleased to use that English colloquialism.

'If that's OK?'

'It is more than OK – it is excellent. We will become good friends, Ja?' We shook hands and made introductions. 'Yes, good friends, Christian and Danny. Where are you staying?' I tapped my rolled sleeping bag by way of response. 'I see. Camping! When I was a youngster, I loved camping, the midnight marches by the light of a burning torch, sitting by a big campfire, and singing rousing songs and then sleeping naked in a tent. Oh, it was great fun.' His face took on a nostalgic glow as he slowly shook his head in the memory of the good times past. '

'You were in the Scouts then?'

'Well, it was not exactly the Boy Scouts – but it was near enough. I was Bannfuhrer and carried the section's flag and had also an excellent knife. Oh, how I miss those days, the laughs, the midnight rallies with a thousand fires, the singing, the machine-gun practice...'

'What!' This puzzled me. I had been in the Scouts and identified with much of what Christian had said, but not the shooting of automatic weapons. I had earned badges for tying knots and being able to make a fire without matches – not for gunnery!

'Of course, machine guns, rifles and anti-tank bombs.' He said casually. 'You have to remember there was a war on, Ja?' My understanding arrived a few sentences later. When Hitler came to power all the youth organisations in Germany were banned and replaced with the '*Hitlerjugend*', the main purpose of which was to indoctrinate German children into the ways and beliefs of the Nazi Party. It was very successful.

'I know there was a war on Christian – we were on the other side of it! My father and brother were both in the armed forces.' He went pale and froze. The glass he was polishing slipped from his grasp and bounced on the bar counter without breaking. He picked it up and put it on the rack.

'Oh, *mein Gott!* I am so sorry! Please forgive me... I did not mean... No, I only meant to explain why we had gunnery practice. Forgive me please. I am an idiot, an *idiot Schwein!* He began to weep real tears of contrition which I found embarrassing.

'It's okay Christian. It was just an odd thing to say. A bit weird to my ears that's all.'

''Weird?' Danny. It is a good word. I am weird. Hitler, the Hitler Youth, the war has left me weird – I think we all are, my generation I mean. I am alive but I think the Nazis killed me. They are mostly gone now but inside of me they left a piece of Hitler.' A strikingly beautiful woman in a tight mini-dress with dark eyes, and dark hair cut short, joined Christian behind the bar. She put a hand on his shoulder and leaned towards him to whisper.

'*Komm schon. Leutewarten darauf, bedient zu werden.*' She squeezed his shoulder with neat hands and manicured nails. She wore a wedding ring and I assumed it was his wife. He replied sharply.

'Let them wait – I am talking to my English friend.' Rebuffed she reddened and turned away to serve other customers. 'I'm sorry. She is my wife, Daniella and she is right, I must get back to work. Please stay and we will talk later. I am so sorry – I need to explain.'

'Really there is no need. It's fine.' Normally I would have left, but the gymnastics were on the television and I had a good seat. A tiny, elfin like figure stood ready to mount the balance beam one of the women's gymnastics disciplines. The caption on the screen proclaimed 'Olga Korbut. USSR.' The commentary was in English and an American voice explained.

'She needs a nine point nine to win. I don't know if that's possible.' A co-commentator added, 'After the week she's had I think anything is possible!' Korbut vaulted onto the centre of the beam into the 'splits' – a technique, the sight and execution of which always upsets me. She proceeded to leap, pirouette, arabesque and hold beautiful balance positions throughout the two-minute routine. She performed with balletic perfection on the ten-centimetre-wide platform, without hesitation or waver. She finished this flawless demonstration with a back summersault which she landed to perfection - and the crowd went wild! Ten thousand spectators stamped and cheered in ecstasy. History had been made. Olga Korbut had won the gold medal and became the 'darling of Munich' and of television audiences world-wide

It was after midnight when I gathered my pack and made ready to leave the bar. 'You cannot go Danny! To sleep under a hedge or a bush, like a fox or stray dog is preposterous. You must not go. I, Christian, the owner of 'Das Schwert', this fine bar, forbid it. No, you cannot go – it is too much. There is an unoccupied room upstairs, you will stay there!

The day had passed and the television was a blank screen. In truth I had no wish to sleep under a hedge but doubted I could justify the expense of a hotel room – money was running low. The bar was closed and for the last hour, in the company of a shared bottle of Schnapps, Christian explained that he had a 'dead rat' inside him. This had been put there by the Nazi Party and had once been 'alive and kicking.' Now it was dead and rotting but it had not gone. He tried to explain.

'For example, I am terrified of the word 'Jew.' I wish the word did not exist but it does. You must remember that I was born in 1930 so all my childhood was spent under the Nazis. My father had this bar before me and we had a good life. But I was brought up to hate Jews and Munich was really a Nazi city. The Mayor was Nazi and Josef Goebbels had been Chief of Police. I was taught how bad the Jews were and how all Germany's problems were their fault. My family hated them, at school we hated them, and in the Hitler Youth we hated them most of all. It's funny though, I don't think I have ever met one. I remember, I went out with my troop one night – it was not cold but there was snow on the mountains, so I think it was October. We marched together singing brave songs and were told to smash all the shop windows with yellow stars painted on them. It was very exciting! Twenty boys being told they could smash windows! Can you even imagine such a thing? I threw one round cobble about the size of a duck-egg and the sheet of glass came tumbling down like a shimmering waterfall. I tell you now Danny that in my mind Hitler and God were the same thing. Near the end of the war, when things were going very badly for us, we were told how glorious it would be to die for the Fuhrer and the Fatherland. I believed this of course, and was not at all frightened. We were then told that it would be even more glorious to die and to blow up an Allied tank at the same time. We were all given a *Panzerfaust*, a small anti-tank rocket and taught how to use it. The best way was to lay down and let the tank pass overhead and blow it up from underneath. You'd be killed as well, but no matter.' His beautiful wife, Daniella approached and said a few words. He answered harshly in a bad-tempered manner. 'I must go – it's bedtime and I'm a little drunk. Daniella will show you your room.' He stood a little unsteadily. 'I know the truth of course, but I still feel sad when I think of Der Fuhrer – I miss him. One day soon I will take a bayonet and cut out the dead rat in my chest. It's the best thing to do, I think. *Gute Nacht.*' He left the bar weaving gently from side to side.

⤳

His beautiful wife came over and stood in front of me nervously smoking a cigarette. I do not know whether it is the universal curse of young men, but it certainly was the curse of me - the inability to look at an attractive woman without feeling desire and thinking of sex, regardless of how inappropriate the circumstances.

'*Sprechen Sie Deutsch?*' My German was indeed very bad and so all I could do was shake my head.

'*Nein.*' She paused and then spoke without confidence, hesitating frequently.

'Ze English.... no good.' I was surprised at this bluntness but being Irish, did not take it much to heart. Gentle tears began to run down her cheeks which she wiped away without removing her cigarette. 'Christian – *Gut mann. Er ist ein gutter mann* - but crazy.' She tapped her left breast and said again, 'crazy.' I figured out she meant that he was crazy in his heart. She held out her hand beckoning me to follow her.

'Komm *ins Bett* - You come to bed with me.'

'What!' I spoke loudly in excited alarm.

'Ja, come to bed with me. *Es ist gut, ja?* – 'Come to bed. Is good, ja?'

'Ja, is very bloody good. *Ist gut. Ja!*' I could not believe my luck! This sort of thing never happened. I know I should have felt guilty about Christian but I didn't. I didn't care at all. I was so aroused I could hardly breathe. I followed her out of the bar and as we climbed the stairs to the upper floor my eyes were transfixed by the beauty of her legs and the erotic glimpse of white panties as she stepped upwards. 'Thank you for mini-skirts, God.' I said this totally inappropriate silent prayer. My heart was pounding and I was thrilled, even scared by the prospect of the delights to come. She walked along the landing, quite gloomy in the subdued light of one bare lamp glowing yellow. She stopped outside a door and turned the brass doorknob.

'*Bett,*' she said. '*Alle ist gut.*' She stood to one side and smiled. I smiled back and held my hand out for her to take. I was already tense with expectation as I imagined pulling her gently towards me and feeling her fulsome breasts press into my chest as we kissed. I would place my hands around her small waist and pull her harder towards me and our embrace would become more and more passionate. I moved closer and noticed that, rather than desire, a look of puzzlement clouded her face. She took my hand hesitantly and shook it firmly. '*Gut nacht, mein Herr.*'

I realised with slight panic that my expectations of sexual delight were based on nothing more than our mutual linguistic deficiencies and my adolescent fantasies. I slept poorly that night and left early before the house was awake and made my way to the Ringerhalle and the familiar safety of a judo competition.

On the 31st August the wrestling circle had been replaced by judo tatamis and the under ninety-three kilogramme category was about to begin. It was the event that I most wanted to see and was lucky to get a ticket, the judo events were very popular. I looked around the *Ringerhalle* but there was no-one that I knew so I took a seat in the same section from where I had viewed the wrestling.

༄

David Starbrook (Olympic Silver Medallist) – Munich, 1972

Chapter Twelve
The Great Knight - David Starbrook

DAVID STARBROOK, THE great man, the main reason I was in Munich, stepped onto the contest area ready for his first fight. I had been in the arena for over an hour after my early departure from Das Schwert, and had examined the programme thoroughly. In my opinion the best judo occurs in the middle and light-heavyweight events. The lighter weights often move around the mat like frenetic whippets and perform outrageous techniques with which I cannot empathise. The heavyweights are often slow and ponderous, so I am not keen. I have to say that this is only a view and many will disagree with it. Any good judo player will be able to point out why I am wrong. 'Heavyweights, slow? What about Yamashita or Parisi? Lightweights dashing around? The best judo you will ever see! What about Nomura or Uchishiba?' They will be right of course and my argument will be shot down in flames - but I still prefer the judo of middle and light-heavyweight players.

Starbrook's event was full of world greats and there was no easy pathway to gold. As much as I wanted it otherwise there was no doubt in my mind that the favourite had to be the Japanese Fumio Sasahara. He was the current World Champion and had been so for three years. There was nothing in his first fight against the Australian Barry Johnson, to suggest that the Japanese was in anything but top form. After a few seconds fighting for grips Johnson was thrown cleanly with Sasahara's first attack – an immaculate *ashi-waza*. There is no disgrace in being beaten by the world champion but the whole fight was done in a few seconds.

My heart was racing as the referee called Starbrook and Hans-Jakob Schadler of Liechtenstein to the middle of the *tatami*. They both stood impassively waiting to start. The programme stated that Schadler had been ten times a national champion but other than that I had never heard of him. In the event the pattern was much the same as the Sasahara fight just gone. Starbrook closed onto his opponent and adopted a double lapel grip. His expressionless face had the look of an efficient automaton – the epitome of machine-like power. As soon as they tied up Starbrook threw the luckless Hans-Jakob with a perfect right-handed *ashi-garuma*. If anything, Starbrook was through his first-round match even more quickly than the Japanese world champion.

On the mat for the first fight of the second round was the relatively unknown Soviet athlete Shota Chochoshvili, a Georgian. He had not yet fought as he had earlier received a bye - his Korean opponent did not turn up. He was to fight Sasahara which I expected to be a good scrap and that the Japanese would win. I had seen quite a few of the eastern-bloc judoka and they all had a very similar style. They were incredibly powerful and very physical in attack. There was no history of judo in Georgia but there was a huge tradition in many forms of wrestling including sambo and chidaoba, both jacketed styles. The Georgians did not try to move the cloth – rather the man inside it. After the first minute it was obvious that my expectation of an easy with for the Japanese was not likely. Chochoshvili kept throwing his left arm over his adversary's shoulder, bending him forward and stopping any attack. Twice he managed to grasp Sasahara's belt and on both occasions nearly turned him with a powerful hip-throw. Five minutes had passed of the six-minute fight when Chochoshvili loosened his grip and swung the Japanese to his right. Sasahara resisted, and taking advantage of this reaction the Soviet executed the perfect winding *morote-seoi-nage,* which finished with the Japanese flat on his back and the Georgian prone on the mat. The defeated Japanese rose slowly to his feet, perhaps dazed but more likely shocked at his loss. With the win awarded Shota Chochoshvili bounced off the *tatami* to be gleefully hugged by his coach. This result also meant that if Starbrook beat Albertini, he would meet the Georgian in the quarter-final.

I had seen the Frenchman fight in Paris a few months earlier and he was very impressive. He was French light-heavyweight champion of course, but also the open-weight silver medallist – a formidable opponent. In idle time before the next fight, I checked the programme and counted that to win the gold medal the victor would have six fights. There was a repechage system in operation which meant that anyone knocked out by a pool winner would not be eliminated but have the chance to progress by winning against the other losers. I realised that this could lead to the unsatisfactory position where a player beaten early in the competition could still end up in the final against the player to whom he had previously lost – an obviously poor situation. Why should you have to beat the same player twice?

With the initial stages completed it seemed to me that the two best players were indeed Starbrook and Chochoshvili and if they met in the quarter final surely the winner of this bout would go on to become champion? But first Starbrook had to beat Albertini. The programme showed him to have an excellent domestic record – three times French champion in his weight, twice French open-weight champion, a win in the Polish Open and a European bronze medal winner. The Frenchman was no slouch!

From the start Albertini and Starbrook looked well matched. There was no discernible height difference - both stood just over six feet tall. They had the look of hard men, almost black hair and dark eyes both, but the Frenchman had a more rounded face than the rough-hewn Starbrook. The power generated by both men was immense. To the untutored eye little was happening but any knowledgeable judoka would recognise the force against force, muscle against muscle, testing and probing for weakness which produced this stalemate. After about two minutes Starbrook unbalanced the Frenchman with a right-footed *ko-uchi-gari*. In recovering Albertini left himself vulnerable to attack and Starbrook seized this opportunity with an almost perfect right-handed *taio-toshi*. Almost perfect – the referee ungenerously awarded a *waza-ari* - lesser player than the Englishman might have protested the referee's decision. The contest carried on in this trial of strength manner and with no further scores Starbrook's *waza-ari* proved decisive.

There was plenty of talent left in the competition of course, James Wooley of the USA and in the parallel Pool B, the crowd's favourite, Paul Barth of West Germany. Chiaki Ishii the ethnic Japanese Brazilian would be a formidable force (he was the current world bronze medallist). But having now watched several contests, the in-form players were definitely Starbrook and Chochoshvili, and they were up next. From what I had seen I was convinced that the winner of this quarter-final would become Olympic champion.

∽

The greatest Greco-Roman wrestler of all time is Aleksandr Karelin, known also as 'Aleksandr the Great', 'The Experiment', 'The Russian Bear' and so on. His statistics are unbelievable. Over three hundred and eighty career wins and two defeats; thirteen years without loss, ten years without conceding even one point. He won three Olympic gold medals, one silver and yet is not widely known outside wrestling circles.

Shota Chochoshvili was not quite as formidable, but in chidaoba, the Georgian wresting style he was an acknowledged great champion. When he fought in the Munich games, he was a judo unknown – but with a considerable jacketed wrestling pedigree.

∽

Starbrook and Chochoshvili had been fighting for over a minute and the contest was one of punishing attrition. The combatants were equally matched. Time and again the Georgian threw his arm over Starbrook's shoulder and reached down his back straining to take hold of the Englishman's belt. He attempted to dominate by keeping Starbrook's posture bent but the great man was made of sterner stuff and broke Chochoshvili's grip to remain upright. Repeatedly he attacked Starbrook with a ferocious left-handed *tsuri-komi-ashi* but the 'Iron Man' from London was rock like in defence. Three minutes passed and neither player had scored; it seemed that the immense early effort put in by the Georgian had taken its toll. Chochoshvili was less sharp in his attacks and was no longer trying to break Starbrook's posture. He was tiring – I was sure of it, and there was no-one fitter in the world to take advantage of such weakness than David Starbrook!

'Come on Dave!' I was on my feet screaming at the top of my voice in uncontrolled excitement.

In the last two minutes Starbrook threw in a flurry of attacks; *o-uchi-gari, uchi-mata, ko-uchi-gari*, and was unlucky not to score with this combination. When the contest was decided by decision in his favour it was to popular acclaim and the ecstatic delight of the widely cheering British team celebrating mat-side. Chochoshvili left the mat exhausted with dragging feet and arms hanging limply by his sides. David Starbrook had defeated his main rival but not eliminated him. Once again, I found myself reflecting upon a repechage system that could require a player to fight an opponent twice in the same event. It made no sense to me and in truth left me feeling slightly unsettled.

⤺

I felt a soft hand rest on my shoulder and turned in my seat to see my dancing partner of two days earlier. I felt a burst of absurd delight mingled with anxiety. I was elated to see her and my heart uncomfortably raced. I realised I did not know her name. I smiled like a happy fool but felt more like the village dolt. I had had no time to collect myself and present a cooler more sophisticated image. She smiled back but appeared worried. 'What a coincidence,' I stammered. 'It's good to see you, really good.'

'It is not a coincidence. I have been looking for you.' She continued to smile and look beautiful but I could tell there was something wrong. She seemed ill-at-ease and seemed pale. 'Please, I have little time. Will you walk with me?' She turned and walked slowly off as I left my seat to follow. I joined her and she took my hand which was unexpected - indeed somewhat awkward. 'My name is Hanna Richter and I am from the east, East Germany that is.' She seemed very serious and I did not know how to respond so I replied somewhat unimaginatively.

'My name is Danny Murphy and I am from the west – Ireland actually.' Her reply confused me.

'Oh, so you're not English – that's a pity,' she continued, further tangling my thoughts. 'But Ireland is much the same as England is it not? It is a good country?' I sprang to give better praise to my homeland.

'Ireland is the best country in the world...' She held her hand up to halt my eulogy.

'Do you like me Danny, even a little bit?' The conversation had taken me into areas for which I was completely unprepared and I didn't know what to say.

'I think you are very nice, very beautiful but we don't know each other. I mean we've only met for a few minutes. I don't know... I'm confused.' She stopped walking and faced me, tears flowing from her beautiful blue eyes. She took both my hands and held them very tightly.

'Will you marry me Danny and take me to Ireland. I promise to be a good wife. I promise...' A strident voice called out.

'Hanna! Hanna! Komm jetzt her! Komm her!'

She released my hands, her pale face consumed with panic. She ran' obviously terrified' along the sports hall balcony pursued by the same track-suited figure who had taken her away in the Olympic Park. I stood momentarily transfixed, unsure of what to do - but finally had the presence of mind to trip him as he hurtled past me in pursuit. It then seemed reasonable to throw myself on top of the scrambling figure. Now, my *ne-waza* has never been good but this guy was no judoka and I soon had him in a pretty good *kesa-gatame*. His only response was to rage and shout, which was uncomfortable in its way as his mouth was close to my left ear. I was controlling him easily with my left arm around his head and was considering whacking him in the face with my right fist to shut him up.

'Las mich gehen! Idiot – ich bin Polizei.

For the second time in a few days, I was bodily kicked by a large policeman's boot. To be fair, this time it was more of a stamp than a kick. I looked up and saw, to my surprise, that the stamper was the same police officer who had given me the early morning wake-up toe-poke.

'*Oben! Oben!*' he gestured with both hands for me to get up and I thought it best to obey. Immediately upon his release Hanna's pursuer began to scream at the cop, who, quite properly shouted back. A frantic Germanic argument ensued which I could not follow; the officer demanded identification, '*Die indentifikation!*' a phrase which I did understand. This was angrily produced by my recent adversary, who then hurried off gesticulating and cursing. The officer looked at me, his head shaking in remonstrance but mediated by a half-smile.

'Bad boy, two times. You bad boy again!' I tried to soften the situation by apologising.

'Sorry! Sorry! *Es tut mir sehr leid.*' The officer smiled and replied.

'It's okay. I like him no. Not good. Him bad – him Stasi.' I looked blankly without understanding.

'Stasi! James Bond,' He made a gun with his fingers and mimed firing... '*Ja,* Bang! Bang! Stasi *Geheimpolizei des Osten.* Secret police of East! You be good boy.' He wandered off and I stood perplexed. Around me gawping spectators gradually lost interest in this minor excitement and turned to the arena to watch a better display of judo. I never saw Hanna again, as I said a forever sadness. *(Author's Note: One hundred and seventeen communist bloc athletes defected to the west, one way or another, during the Munich Olympic games. In contrast, no athletes defected to Russia during the 1980 Moscow Olympics.)*

⤻

I was so shaken by this episode that I could barely concentrate. However hard I tried my mind quickly reverted to view the events that had just happened. Who was Hanna? What should I do? The Stasi – the East-German secret police? It was all too confusing. I was ashamed by my lack of action. I felt guilty, as if I should have done more.

I barely recall Starbrook's fight with Wooley except to note that when the American was thrown after a few minutes with a fast-spinning *ashi-garuma/maki-komi*, it was unsurprising. Starbrook had dominated throughout and his win seemed inevitable. He left the mat seemingly without emotion and yet this win had assured him of at least a bronze medal – the first ever Olympic judo medal for Great Britain! Gradually, I felt some semblance of calm return and I was able to focus. The next contest was the Pool B final between the West-German, Paul Barth and the Japanese Brazilian Chiaki Ishii. Barth was the crowd's favourite but the Japanese was a formidable opponent. He had expected to be the Japanese selection for the 1964 Tokyo Olympics but had lost out to Okano (who, did indeed win the gold medal). Ishii, in a fit of bad temper decided to give up judo and become a farmer in Brazil. It turned out that he was a terrible agriculturalist, and so did the sensible thing and took up judo again - along with Brazilian citizenship. He was an automatic selection for their 1972 Olympic squad. It was a grinding match with no quarter given on either side. After six minutes the referee awarded the fight to the German. In my opinion the roaring, partisan crowd gave Barth 'home advantage' and swayed the decision.

In the other repechage stream Shota Chochoshvili had made easy work of both Albertini and Wooley, which confirmed the semi-final bouts as Starbrook versus Ishii, and Barth versus Chochoshvili. It began to look as if my earlier fear might indeed happen: a final between the Soviet and British player seemed likely. The more I thought on this the more it seemed preposterous. To win gold Starbrook might have to beat the same player twice. Conversely to win gold Chochoshvili could lose once and win once, to my mind obviously unfair. The Soviet and the German were up first and the crowd went wild! The blond, mop-headed Paul Barth, wearing the red belt and displaying number fifty-two on his competitors back-patch, smiled as the crowd cheered. He had the ideal physique for a judoka, shorter than his opponent and in perfect physical condition. The Georgian, taller, black haired, grim and efficient wearing white and numbered one hundred and forty-one, bowed as the referee called *hajime*. From the start Shota exuded confidence. He danced on his toes and kept a fast pace. I noticed the time – the mat-side digital clock glowed 7.32pm. Barth was being completely defensive adopting a low *jigotai* posture with arms locked straight to keep the Soviet at bay. Chochoshvili bounced on the balls of his feet, reached over the bowed German and caught hold of the struggling Barth's belt. With his left hand he pulled the German close and attempted a mighty *koshi-waza*. Paul Barth could only resist and drop to the ground. (In modern judo this would have been penalised – but not then.) Shota attempted to roll Barth backwards and continue his attack into *ne-waza* but the referee called *matte* and the contest stopped. From the re-start Barth took a double handed grip and immediately attacked with a weak left *morote-seoi-nage/o-soto-gari* combination. Chochoshvili seized his moment of destiny and lifted Barth high with a leg assisted *ura-nage* – a favourite technique. Barth crashed heavily to the mat and rolled to lie prone where he stayed for a moment, perhaps stunned. The clock read 7.33 – the match had lasted one minute. The referee raised his hand to signify *ippon*. Barth got to his feet, smiling broadly and grabbed Shota's hand which he shook vigorously. They then hugged and the German left the mat still happy with his loss (and bronze medal), grinning and waving to the crowd. Chochoshvili seemed perplexed, puzzled by Barth's reaction; his own behaviour was considerably more muted. He was now in the final and still had work to do.

⤸

Starbrook stood facing Chiaki Ishii in the Olympic semi-final, a guaranteed a bronze medal was his - but this was not his goal. The formidable Ishii, world bronze medallist stood between him and a re-match with Chochoshvili for the Olympic title. In truth the Soviet had had a spectacular day. His wins against Albertini and Barth had taken barely a minute each, his fight against Wooley just two. Only world champion Sasahara had resisted him for longer but in each of these matches the result had been the same – a win for Shota, each time with a spectacular throw.

Starbrook looked expressionless but totally focussed upon the job in hand. From the start he pursued Ishii as a hunter eager for his prey. Both players stood upright, the stance for classic judo, but it was the

Englishman who took the fight to the Japanese Brazilian. A couple of minutes quickly passed with Starbrook light on his feet dominating the mat with the agility of a lighter player. Ishii attempted a foot-sweep which left his opponent unruffled. Starbrook returned the attack with a strong left *de-ashi-barai* which dropped Ishii to the floor. The Japanese saved the score by getting his right hand to the canvas and instantly stood up. The referee let the fight continue and both players quickly took double lapel holds. Starbrook changed to a high collar grip and with his mighty left hand now controlling Ishii he immediately attacked with left *o-uchi-gari*. Ishii resisted but the Englishman reversed direction and converted his attack into *uchi-mata*. The Japanese desperately tried to stay upright but to no avail as the powerful Starbrook continued rotating, and threw Ishii cleanly onto the *tatami*.

David Starbrook was through to the final of the under 93 kg category once again to face Shota Chochoshvili – the unknown Georgian whom he had defeated earlier.

၏

I realised I was very hungry; my mouth was also dry and so I left my balcony seat and headed for the canteen. In the war films of the nineteen-fifties and sixties which were a staple of English and American cinema, the Germans were often called *Krauts*. This is a foreshortening of the word *sauerkraut* which is indeed a popular Germanic dish of shredded, pickled and fermented cabbage. It's okay. But really the Germans, (if a comic derogatory nick-name was needed,) should have been called 'sausages' or something like that. They (sausages) abounded in Munich; every restaurant, butchers shop and delicatessen was full of them in a host of varieties - and damn good they were too! As for Germans in Munich I found that most were keen to be considered Bavarian. I loaded my plate from the self-service counter with knockwurst, sauerkraut, fried potatoes pickles and a few scoops of mustard and took a cold beer from the chiller cabinet. Why not? My coach for England was leaving early next morning and this would be my last proper meal. This was a pity because I would not see Brian Jacks in action – also a gold medal contender. I had tentatively considered missing the coach and hitchhiking home but I had no money and common-sense prevailed.

'Holy-smoke - if it isn't the English Milord! Hey guys – I've found the Britisher again!' I turned to see Hank, the wrestling coach from Iowa state with a bunch of the guys I'd sat with while watching Richard Barraclough wrestle.

'Hank, you clown,' a fair-haired young man bantered. 'He's not a Lord – he's a Count.' The American deliberately mispronounced this aristocratic title. Here we go again I thought. Still, it was good to see them, looking so happy, healthy and crew-cut with their Sta-Prest trousers and even white teeth. Each one a credit to Uncle Sam and mom's apple pie. Let battle commence...

'Ah the colonials! Jolly good to see you, what? I'll sit with you if you don't mind and show you how to use your knives and forks correctly.' A half dozen balls of serviette tissue peppered my head and shoulders. I was soon seated and stuffing great chucks of excellent sausage into my mouth.

'Hungry then?' asked Hank as I sat with my head close to my plate and chewed without speaking.'

'Starving Hank. I've been here all day and this is the first food I've had since yesterday.' I thought I needed to explain more. Hank was a comforting older guy and easy to speak to - he reminded me of my brother Kevin. 'I've had a mad few days Hank; you would not believe the things that have happened.'

'I'm all ears Danny – tell me.'

'Well, I spent yesterday in a bar with a nice chap who was a former Nazi. He'd been in the Hitler Youth - still missed old Adolph, and was planning to kill himself! And then I thought his wife wanted to sleep with me. She asked me if I wanted to go to bed but that turned out to be a misunderstanding and she just wanted to show me to my room. And today a pretty gymnast who I hardly knew asked me to marry her and was then chased by an East-German secret policeman... I tripped him up though and held him down while she got away. Mad eh! The good news is that Starbrook is in the final of the light-heavyweight judo. He's only just finished fighting so I would imagine the final won't be for an hour or so.'

'Have you been drinking Danny?'

'No Hank - I haven't had a drop – not today anyway.'

'Thant's a pity. Then I suppose I'll have to believe you. But I can help you out over the marriage thing. Dozens of Soviet bloc athletes have claimed political asylum since the games began. And the rumour has gone round that if you get married in Germany this automatically gives you German citizenship. I'm pretty sure this isn't true – but these kids are desperate and they'll do anything to stay in the West. It's nothing to do with your pretty boy good looks and your English charm – sorry to disappoint.'

'That's a pity. Anyway – I'm Irish.' Hank shook his head and frowned. 'Whose Starbrook fighting?'

'Shota Chochoshvili, a Soviet. I've never heard of him but he's been knocking hell out of the opposition all day – except Starbrook who beat him earlier on a decision. He's got to beat him again to get the gold. Mad don't you think?'

'Mad it may well be, but you have to play the cards that are dealt. It's a pity he's fighting one of the 'Commies' though. All our coaches are unhappy. Time and time again in the power events the Soviets and the Eastern communist competitors are proving to be unnaturally strong or have too much endurance. Something is going on Danny and it's not good!'

'I don't know what you mean Hank.'

'Well to put it into one word – drugs. Performance enhancing drugs. The Soviets are coming out of nowhere and winning events where players have no pedigree. They are using the games as an advertisement for how great the communist system is, and don't care what they pump into their kids providing they win! Have you heard of anabolic steroids Danny?'

'I think so – but don't know what they do.'

'Well in a nutshell they make you stronger, cut the fat and add muscle mass. I've been to a Team USA coaches meeting and from what was said I guess that a lot of the weight-lifters are on them, and all from the Soviet countries. We have our suspicions about the wrestlers and judo players as well...' The loudspeaker system blared.

'The final of the men's under ninety-three kilogramme category. In white, representing the Soviet Union wearing number one hundred and forty-one – Shota Chochoshvili. In red, representing Great Britain, wearing number forty-five – David Starbrook.' I looked at Hank.

'That can't be right. He's only just finished. He won't have had time to recover from his last scrap. I'm going to check.' I ran from the canteen with Hank shouting 'Good luck!' and returned to my seat in time to see the contestants for the final take the mat.

⤶

For a moment all was still and I still recall the tableaux laid out in front of me; a huge expanse of grey *tatami,* a ten-metre competition area marked out in red tape; the referee and corner judges resplendent in grey trousers and pastel green blazers with feet swathed in matching plastic over-shoes. Behind the mat were dignitaries - Olympic officials and guests many wearing IOC red blazers. To one side stood the Soviet team clad in pastel blue and wearing incongruous little white caps. A lone policeman, 'my policeman', stood guard in the adjacent aisle. The digital time display and score-board were set to zero. The Korean referee, a diminutive figure with prominent horn-rimmed glasses briskly called the contestants to their respective marks – Starbrook red and the Soviet white. The men were similar in stature, the Englishman slightly taller, the Georgian marginally less broad, but these fractional differences were hardly apparent. There was, however, a marked contrast in demeanour. Starbrook, composed and dignified whereas Chochoshvili restlessly fidgeted, shaking his wrists and twisting his feet into the mat.

'*Hajime!*'

The contest began; a ten-minute final to decide the greatest prize in judo, an Olympic gold medal.

⤶

It is now 2020 *Anno Domini,* and looking back through the lens of history we know that the Great Knight, David Starbrook did not achieve the 'fairy tale' ending to his Munich Olympic quest. The gold medal was not his, and to this date no Briton has grasped this prize.

And 'fairy tale' ending it would have been. The story of David Starbrook, an all-time great of British and world judo is a saga of a small boy from a fractured family 'raised' in an abusive children's home, rising above adversity and becoming the icon that he is today.

(Author's Note: I, Christo Murphy, hold an MA; MSc; and PhD in different aspects of psychotherapy and psychology. I am privy to some of the details of David's childhood but will leave it to the man himself to put to print – or not as the case may be. As a professional I am humbled when I witness stories such as his; how a person can have such strength of character to rise above life events which would have crippled most personalities, goes beyond easy explanation. But biographies like David's are rare – they are the stuff of exceptional people.)

Chapter Thirteen
The Evil That Men do

MATHIAS KOENIG WAS a good man who hated communism in general, the East-German police in particular and swimming. This last dislike was not always the case as there was a time when it seemed he was destined to become a champion 1500 metre free-styler. He was born in a sleepy little town called Wildau, a few kilometres south of Berlin. He was a kindly sympathetic soul, compassionate also and he made friends easily. He had no idea that he was a communist until he was made aware of this fact on his first day at school. He was six years old and felt troubled by this revelation.

'*Bitte Frau!*' He held his little hand poker straight, high into the class-room air, straining out of his seat in his struggle to gain attention. The teacher, athletic and grim faced read his name from a placard which hung around his neck. He and all the other children had been presented with such as they were marched from the playground into the austere room which was to be their educational home. '*Bitte Frau* – my papa said I am a German and a Catholic.'

'You are a child of the German Democratic Republic and a communist. You most certainly are not a Catholic, who are stupid people who think that their lives are controlled by an old magician who lives in the sky. No! Our lives are ordered by the Party to whom we owe everything. Your father must not fill your head with such rubbish.' She clicked her heels together and stood to attention. 'Now children the first thing you must learn is a song which reminds us of how wonderful our country is and how we must be thankful for the many things we receive from our glorious leaders. Let us all stand and listen to this song which I will play on the gramophone.' She took a large black disc out of its protective brown paper sleeve and furiously wound up the mechanical record player. Soon the crackling sounds of the East-German national anthem were stridently sounding out of the fluted horn. The teacher, *Frau* Gluck, stood to attention, her right hand clasped over her ample bosom. She indicated to her class of confused infants that they should stand in the same manner. The teacher's face shone with patriotic fervour which Mathias, as young as he was, found unsettling. When the music ended the teacher gave a militaristic salute which the infants were told to return.

At break-time he wandered aimlessly around the gravelled playground, kicking a stone here and there, until stopping in front of another small boy who was sitting on a bench. He had seen him before – they both lived in the same block of flats. The palms of the child's hands were pushed hard into his eyes while he softly cried. 'Why are you crying?' The boy did not answer so Mathias repeated the question. 'Why are you crying?' The boy uncovered his eyes, sniffed and wiped his face and nose on his jacket sleeve.

'I don't like *Frau* Gluck, she's horrible...'

'I don't like her either – but why are you crying?' The repeated question brought no verbal answer; the small child waved his hands in a dithering, despairing reply. Mathias could only think to introduce himself. 'My name's Mathias Koenig – what's your name?'

'My name is Konrad Bolz,' and then he added for good measure, 'and I am six years old.'

'I am six and a half. Would you like me to be your friend Konrad Bolz?'

'Yes please.' The boys were both unfamiliar with such protocols and so shook hands – it seemed the thing to do. Friends they became and friends they stayed.

But their friendship did not exist without argument. When they were nine, in the Autumn of 1958 they had a dispute about 'conkers.' It is a simple game: usually in late September, boys collect the nuts of the horse-chestnut tree. In case you're not sure they are the ones that come in a hard-spikey shell that falls open when the nut hits the ground. (I say boys because it mostly is a lad's game. Girls could play, of course, but tend not to.) A hole is made through the centre of the conker which is then threaded onto a length of string, knotted at one end to keep the nut from falling off. One player lets his conker hang still, and the other swings at it with his, attempting to break the dangling nut. Turns are taken, and this goes on until one conker shatters. And that's about it. However, there is a mythology about ways to strengthen conkers to gain an advantage – all of which are considered unlawful within the conker playing fraternity. Here are some: pickling in vinegar; slow baking; coating with nail varnish. I know from experience that none of these subterfuges work, and all are easy to spot.

Konrad Bolz was an artistic boy and when he found a wooden knob that had once graced a curtain pole, with much sandpapering and staining with shoe polish and oil, he made a very passable conker. He was also an honest boy and had no intention of cheating, but did think it would be fun to see the faces of his friends when his conker proved invincible.

All went well to begin with. But after his tenth conker had been destroyed Mathias Koenig smelled a rat. 'Konrad you are a cheating stoat!' (For some reason, in 1950s East Germany, to call someone a stoat ranked pretty high up on the insult tree.)

'How dare you call me a stoat! It is you that is the stoat!' and at that the fight started. It was not much of a scrap and was soon stopped by their teacher *Herr* Olaf Pischler (*Frau* Gluck being still the teacher of the youngest children.) Mathias was dragged away from the affray, *Herr* Pischler speeding him thus by pinching the cartilage of the boy's left ear. In the gloomy quiet of the teacher's office Mathias was surprised by an unexpected question.

'Do you like chocolate Mathias? Not the gritty state chocolate but the very best chocolate – made in England?' The boy did not know how to respond and remained silent. 'But of course, you do not know because you have never tasted English chocolate, have you?' Mathias shook his head. The teacher opened his desk drawer and took out the largest block of chocolate that the child had ever seen. The words 'Cadbury's Dairy Milk Chocolate' were printed in white across the purple wrapper. 'This is the best chocolate in the world Mathias. The English are very clever – there is a glass and a half of full cream milk in this bar. I have no idea how they do it but it tastes good. Please, try a piece.' The boy took the offered chunk and it really was wonderful; smooth and sweet and creamy – completely unlike the state chocolate which was bitter and rough. It was an addictive treat and of course the boy had no will-power to decline a second square. 'I saw that ruffian Bolz assault you – oh yes, I saw it all from this very window. Mind you it is not surprising when you consider that he comes from a subversive home. We have been keeping an eye on his father for some time now.' Mathias stopped eating, his jaw dropped in surprise at both what he was being told and that he was being given these secrets at all. 'You on the other hand we know to be a good boy, the sort of boy who would never shirk at doing his duty to the state...' *Herr* Pischler looked dreamily into the air. 'Did you know that there is an even more luxurious English chocolate that is reserved for their Queen and other aristocrats? Dukes and Lords – that sort; you know the English high-ups. It's called a 'Walnut Whip.' Would you like to try one?'

Thus, encouraged by chocolate, Mathias Koenig at the age of nine years became a spy for the East-German secret police. Later, Konrad asked him what had occurred in the teacher's office.

'Nothing much. He said the fight was all my fault and beat me a little – not much, so let's forget it.'

'I'm sorry about the conker. It is made of wood but I was not trying to cheat. It was only a joke – I thought you'd think it was funny.'

'Yes, Konrad. It was funny.' Said Mathias who nonetheless thought that the joke had backfired quite badly.

～

Mathias realised at once that he must never say anything about his new profession and never let it interfere with his friendship with Konrad. Spying on *Herr* Bolz was easy enough and consisted of answering questions asked in private, by his teacher. As he was never asked anything out of the ordinary it was easy to answer truthfully.

'Does *Herr* Bolz ever go on walks alone – to secret places maybe?'

'He goes out most nights *Herr* Pischler, but I have no idea where he goes.' And it was true: regularly his friend's father took a walk after dinner 'for the sake of his health.' But Mathias had no idea where he went and never asked. Why would he? *Herr* Pischler dutifully logged in his report, 'Bolz walks alone each night to a secret destination.' This information was passed on to his superior who in turn wrote:

'The suspect Bolz walks every night to a secret location for purposes of possible liaison with other subversives, the identities of which we are soon to ascertain...' Some while later Mathias was asked to follow *Herr* Bolz which he did. His friend's father walked a kilometre, sat on a bench in a country park and read a paper that had been left on the seat. He rolled a cigarette and had a peaceful smoke. Olaf Pischler explained these actions to Mathias. 'You are just a young boy and do not know the meaning of what occurred. The newspaper has obviously been left by a secret agent of the West. His instructions to *Herr* Bolz were undoubtedly written on a cigarette paper, which is why he smoked a roll-up – to destroy the evidence. Don't you see?' Mathias did not see. He assumed that the man had smoked the cigarette away from his home because *Frau* Bolz was a fearsome, bitter tongued woman who did not like her husband to smoke or indeed do anything which he might find enjoyable.

⤺

When he was not being a teacher and a Stasi agent Olaf Pischler was a swimming coach, an activity at which he excelled, in contrast to his other two callings. He observed that both Konrad and Mathias had a natural talent and enrolled them into the state swimming programme. As they progressed, training became more and more arduous but the lads enjoyed their improvement and successes. They thought nothing of the special diet they were required to eat nor the supplements, tablets and vitamin injections which were a constant feature of their regime.

'Normality' is just the life one gets used to; Mathias and Konrad lived the normal lives of East-German children. To start school at 7.00am was ordinary, and to have lessons until late afternoon caused no complaint. That the toilets in school were constructed without cubicles was accepted without comment. As everyone was equal in the socialist utopia of the German Democratic Republic, privacy was considered unnecessary. That Saturday was also a school day was accepted without thought – but both boys appreciated the fact that, as swimmers, for them it was spent mainly in the pool. In recreational time Mathias loved to read the weekly edition of 'Mosaik' a colourful comic which chronicled the exploits of the 'Didedags' - cartoon children who had preposterous adventures. Mathias and Konrad had heard of Coca-Cola the fabled American drink but had only tasted the East-German Vita-Cola which they were told was better. In their limited spare time, the boys collected bottles and cans which they sold at re-cycling centres thus providing themselves with much needed pocket-money. But mothers complained of food shortages and occasionally of ridiculous times of plenty:

'Last week there was only bread and nothing else to make a sandwich with. This week there are bananas and no bread – still no sandwiches.'

They were told at school, on the radio and television (although most families did not have a TV set) of the evils and dangers of the 'West'; of the decadence of its music and fashion. Mathias had never seen a pair of 'studded trousers' as Levi jeans were called, but as a thirteen-year-old knew he wanted some. He and Konrad frequently went to the cinema and watched 'cowboy and Indian' films in which the Indians were always the heroes and the cowboys dastardly villains. The main feature was always sandwiched between information newsreels which explained why their life was much better than that of the Americans and British. The Soviet achievements in space were frequently praised and they were told that the day would be soon when every East-German family would own its own car, The Trabant, which would be technically superior to anything made in the West. But western television (received illegally from nearby Berlin), radio and the quality of much sort after 'black market' goods, told a different story.

The arrest, when it came was quite orderly and predictable; a door kicked down at four in the morning; a bewildered frightened man dragged out of bed and then bundled, struggling in panic, into an anonymous black car with tinted windows. He was doomed of course – the Stasi did not make mistakes. Their actions were the actions of the state which, made them correct. Over the years his dossier grew and grew and was now an impressive document. The weight of evidence, (by now several kilos), proved him guilty. As the reports about him passed up the Stasi chain of command they became increasingly condemnatory. 'Possible' became probable became certitude as each official strove to demonstrate his or her worth in the hierarchy. A statement was altered or extended, each a nail in the coffin of guilt. Yes, *Herr* Olaf Pischler was a doomed man.

The first Konrad and Mathias knew of his fall from grace was when, without notice or explanation, a new swimming coach arrived to supervise their training. They were now both fifteen, strong and fit, (perhaps abnormally so) and members of the National Performance Squad. The next day on the school campus they encountered, presumably by chance, their old primary teacher. She looked much the same and the lads still found her unlikeable.

'Ah, boys! Such a shame about *Herr* Pischler. Who would have thought it? I hear he was addicted to the decadent pleasures of the West – in particular chocolate. Such a shame, such a shame.' Without waiting for reply she bustled on her way. She felt happy almost elated. She expected to be rewarded for her years of vigilance and meticulous reporting. A promotion within the school would surely be hers. And if it was not immediately forthcoming, well she had other files on other teachers...

Herr Bolz continued to take his evening walks to smoke his surreptitious cigarette. He sometimes left notes denouncing the unpatriotic activities of his wife, whom he hated, carefully hidden in the pages of a newspaper which was always waiting on a secretly designated park bench.

Mathias thought about his life, the demise of *Herr* Pischler and life in the West, as he and Konrad walked to do their early morning stint in the pool. 'How far do we swim in a training session?'

'Oh, I don't know. A warm up, repetitions, high intensity, warm down – I suppose about two kilometres. At the week-ends even more. Why?'

'Oh, nothing. I was just thinking...'

'About escaping to the West?' Mathias looked at his friend in surprise. He had hoped for understanding but was still surprised at the eager response.

'Me too!' continued Konrad. 'I'm sick of it – everything. I'm sick of the lot! The food, the rubbish clothes, the forced training, hearing about how good Russia is but most of all the Stasi. For God's sake, Pischler arrested – and I thought *he* was Stasi!'

'Me too! I thought he was, in fact I was almost sure of it. 'Mathias hesitated for a moment and then blurted out, 'Konrad, I've got a confession to make.' He had a sudden urge to clear his conscience.

'And I have! While we're on about the Stasi I'm pretty sure my dad is a spy. I'm certain of it. I've heard Mom say so when they argue, and that's most of the bloody time.'

'What! Your dad, *Herr* Bolz, a spy!'

'Yes, I think so. What's your secret?' Mathias quickly decided against revealing his own spying activities and changed the subject.

'Oh, nothing much... except that I'm going to the West, I've got it planned, and want you to come too.' Which was not completely true; he exaggerated the planning part. But he had given it some thought and in his idea was so simple that no preparation was needed.

'You remember when we went to the competition in Michenburg?'

'Yes of course I do. You won the medley and I won the two hundred metres. What of it?' asked Konrad.

'The River Havel runs northwards from there and continues into the western sector of Berlin. We could swim – it's about twenty kilometres, I've checked it all in my school atlas and the current is with us all the way. It's a good plan, it really is!'

Konrad considered this for a moment. 'Won't you miss your mom and dad?'

'Not really. Dad drinks and Mom cries. How about you?'

'About the same. They hate each other and argue all the time. But it's not much of a plan is it? In fact, it's not a plan at all. It's too far and there are border guards with guns. It's a crazy idea!'

'No Konrad. That's exactly what makes it a great plan. The barbed wire, and the guards start much closer to the West. Nobody is guarding the river bank at Michenburg *because* it's too far away. Nobody could do such a swim – except us. We are not good swimmers, we are great swimmers, amongst the best in East-Germany! We just go with the current until we cross the border and get out – on the left bank of course.'

'We'll be seen and get shot!'

'Not if we go at night and cover ourselves with black boot polish.'

'How will we know when we're at the border?'

'Searchlights, armed guards on the banks, barking dogs – that sort of thing. I think we'll know alright. What do you think?' Konrad thought for a moment and smiled.

'I'm not sure we've got any black polish. Do you think dark brown will work?'

～

They stood in a clearing on the wooded bank of the Havel clad only in black swimming trunks, goggles and rubber caps. Both were completely smeared with finger-lined streaks of black and brown boot polish. The boys thought it gave them an American Indian look. It was late evening in mid-September and in the faded light of autumn Mathias was confident they would be invisible in the water. Konrad pranced around performing some weird tribal dance. 'Me Big Chief Shit-in-the-Woods, you Chief Kiss-my-Arse.'

'Stop fooling around Konrad and tie your clothes to your bike.' They had cycled the twenty kilometres to the river. He knew why he had to do this; they had discussed the plan as they rode. Konrad shook his head but did as commanded.

'It's a shame. They're good bikes... Are you frightened?' he asked.

'Scared shitless!'

At which the boys threw their bikes into the deep water and further upstream dived in. They swam strongly to the middle of the river and then adopting an easy breast-stroke, made way letting the current do the work. The water was cool, not cold – the summer had been long and warm and the earth still retained a gentle heat which it gave to the kindly flow. They passed in silence rows of riverside cottages, curtains open and rooms lit, their occupants used to the privacy of water-side dwellers. No more than twenty metres distant Mathias watched a naked old man struggling to put on his striped pyjamas. He staggered slightly and grasped a chair to restore his balance. Mathias looked to his left and was comforted to see Konrad a mere two metres away swimming with a lazy, noiseless back-stoke and he rolled over to follow suit. They had agreed not to speak – both knew sounds carried great distances across water. The last houses of Michenburg disappeared and with them also the last residual light. Konrad waved to him and smiled; Mathias waved and smiled back. The world felt very different.

Above him a million stars blazed out of a black crystal night. He searched for the familiar constellations and quickly recognised Ursa Major – the Great Bear. Following the Pointers, he established the Pole Star from which he drew comfort. They were swimming almost due north, and Mathias fantasised the excitement of the western sector of Berlin. He continued his skyward search and found wonderment in yellow Betelgeuse, the shoulder jewel of Orion the Hunter. He had been taught not to believe in God, but tonight he felt the need to pray. 'Dear God, please look after me and Konrad. He is a good boy and I'm not too bad.' He knew his thoughts were clumsy but hoped God found them sufficient.

They continued, kilometre after kilometre to soundlessly float and swim ever northwards. At one point the river widened and became so shallow that Mathias could touch the gravelled bottom with his hands. Konrad came close and they sat in less than a half-metre of water but fifty metres from either bank. They held each other and pressed mouths to ears. 'I think we are nearly there,' breathed Mathias.

'Why so?'

'Look ahead. Can't you see? The sky is bright.'

'It's just the dawn – we've been in the water for hours.' Mathias shook his head forcefully.

'No, it isn't – it can't be. That's north and Berlin is north. There is no other town. It's the bright lights of the West. Nearly there!' Remember, we will pass under two bridges the second is a magnificent affair with two great turrets – like an ancient castle. One bank is the East and the other is the West and freedom!'

'Which side is which?' There was complete silence between the boys, only broken by the sound of water as it broke on the shallows. 'Mathias!' Konrad hissed. 'Which side?'

'I'm sorry Konrad. I can't remember. My mind has gone blank!' In the faintest glimmer of first light Mathias saw his friend's eyes widen in alarm and he regretted his joke. 'The left bank you stoat. We swim under Oberbaum Bridge, the one with the turrets and get out the first chance we get on the *left* bank! Come on – let's go!'

'I am not a stoat. That is, you -you are the stoat.' But his friend was swimming and Konrad quickly followed.

〜

The bridge was indeed an impressive if strange design modelled upon the mediaeval Schloss' of the Rhine valley. They could see it clearly a half-kilometre distant brightly illuminated by a host of flood-lights, as was the river bank for a few hundred metres on either side. Turret mounted searchlights scanned the river. The boys trod water and held each other by the shoulders. 'What shall we do?' Asked Konrad. 'We're bound to be spotted.'

'No, we will be fine. The guards will be concentrating on the bank or looking for boats. We're well camouflaged. How far can you swim under water?'

'About twenty-five metres I suppose.'

'That'll be fifty with the current. When we get to the lights swim below the surface and only come up for air when you have to. Pischler made us do it to expand our lungs, remember? As soon as we're under the arches swim to the left and get out.' There was little more to be said. 'See you on the other side, stoat.' The friends' grip briefly tightened and then, freeing each other, they swam towards the lights which illuminated the Havel river brighter than any day.

The searchlight beams penetrated the water to a depth of almost two metres and Mathias wondered what was leaving the trails of silver bubbles which sped erratically down from the surface. Perhaps small fish that rose to feed off insects and then swam quickly back to the safety of the deep? Anyway, whatever they were they seemed harmless. He came up for air and was surprised to see little fountains erupting close to him. To begin with he did not associate them with the discordant pops and cracks that sounded like small fireworks. He saw with satisfaction that he was less than a hundred metres from the central arch of the bridge. Without warning a nearby a siren began its mournful howl, increasing each second in volume and pitch. Alarmed, he gasped a lungful of air and once more submerged. The silver trails continued to proliferate, increasing in number. He felt a sudden sharp pain on his back and thought he had been stung. But what could sting him in a river? The realisation came quickly and he cursed himself as a fool – he was being shot at! He knew if he could reach the left bank beyond the bridge, he would be safe – the border guards could not shoot into West Berlin for fear of a diplomatic incident. His lungs were bursting! He must have air! Suddenly, it became dark. He could hardly believe it – a vagary of current had taken him underneath the left-hand arch of the Obenbaum Bridge protecting him from the searchlight's probing glare and the bullets of the guards. The flow was now spent and he gratefully rested against an outcrop of foundation stonework. No more than twenty metres distant a flight of age worn brick steps led out of the water. But would this be far enough past the bridge to ensure he was in the West? He could no longer think clearly and was beyond caring. As he swam to the steps, he noticed that the gunfire had ceased. With shaking arms, he grabbed an iron mooring ring and hauled himself onto the slippery stones and out of the river.

But where was Konrad? Too exhausted to stand he sat on the rough brickwork and surveyed the smoothly flowing waters of the Havel. Now, deprived of the water's heat, he felt very cold. He hugged himself but began to shiver violently. The commotion on the bridge had settled and the world seemed unnaturally quiet. The scene in front of him, the floodlit bridge and silver water had taken on the frozen surreal qualities of an over detailed flash photograph. He began to cry as the body drifted slowly past – before indeed he had properly identified the corpse as that of a bloated dog out for a peaceful early morning float.

'Hello stoat. Welcome to Freedom!' He turned to see Konrad standing on the topmost step, his arms wrapped tightly around himself in similar vain effort to keep warm.

$\backsim$

Hans Baumann was only forty-five years old, but the war had done for him and he felt worn and ancient. In 1945 he had been a part of the defence of Berlin as the Russians moved inexorably closer through the rubble of the already ruined city. Hitler, the leader of the 'thousand-year Reich' had seen it last a mere twelve when he blew his brains out in the comfort of his underground fortress. The Russians had killed most of Baumann's friends and family and, (he felt sad at her memory), Ulrike the pretty seventeen-year-old he was to marry.

But he liked being a policeman particularly when on night shift. After the drunks went home West Berlin was a quiet place and he enjoyed smoking his pipe as he patrolled the empty streets. Of course, strictly speaking he was not allowed the comfort of tobacco while on duty, but at four in the morning in an empty avenue, who was to know or tell? Today there had been a little excitement. About an hour earlier the East-German border guards had loosed off a good few shots – but that was not so unusual. They were forever blasting away at floating logs and other river detritus. He supposed that it broke the monotony and provided target practice. He was, however, unprepared for the sight of two teenage boys clad only in black swimming trunks walking towards him. Their bodies were streaked in what appeared to be some form of tribal war-paint. They seemed happy and were repeatedly chanting the word 'stoat.'

'Reefer addicts,' he thought. 'Good morning boys. Going for an early morning dip, are we?' The boys were laughing through chattering teeth.

'N-no sir. We've already been.' An answer which they found riotously funny and seemed to encourage them to dance around and further chant the word 'stoat.'

'Less of it boys. Where have you left your clothes? You'll freeze if you're not careful.'

'Sadly officer, our clothes are in Michenburg – but they would be of no use as they are wet, very wet indeed.' Again, the boys found their answer humorous and continued with their dance and chant.

'Stop! Stop it now!' Hans Baumann could be surprisingly forceful. Mathias and Konrad were used to obeying authority and snapped their bare feet to attention. 'Tell me boys, the truth now. Your clothes can't be in Michenburg? That's twenty kilometres away and in the East! What's going on?' Mathias spoke for them.

'Sir – it is true. Our clothes are in Michenburg, but at the bottom of the river. We threw them in along with our bikes. We have escaped from the GDR by swimming along the Havel.' Hans was perplexed but not quite disbelieving.

'But that's at least twenty kilometres – no man could swim that far!' Konrad found it impossible not to reply.

'But were not men, sir – we are stoats!' At which their chanting and wild 'stoat' dancing began again.

‿

Police Officer Mathias Koenig had started the day in good spirits. They were now somewhat dampened by the incident between the East-German 'coach' and the English lad who had taken him to the floor and was holding him with a damn good *kesa-gatame* when he had found it necessary to intervene. He puzzled how he would record the incident in his daily report. Probably it was best to simply note a minor disturbance between the two men and leave it at that. After all who was going to complain? Certainly not the GDR coach who was most certainly Stasi – they all were.

He had spoken by telephone to his foster father Hans, who was pleased to tell that they had received another card from Konrad who continued to do well in America. He had won a sports scholarship to Columbia State University and had high hopes of being granted citizenship and representing the USA as a swimmer – perhaps even at the next Olympics. His 'notes' were always the same; a beer mat with one printed side peeled, on which a cartoon had been drawn showing a ferret like animal or an American Indian chief. Hans sometimes found the bizarre pornographic situations shown to be embarrassing but nonetheless was pleased to receive them. Konrad had not lost his artistic talent.

Along with hundreds of other officers Mathias had been drafted to Munich to provide extra security for the Games. At every briefing they had been told that these were the 'happy' games and to police with a 'light touch.' Time and again they were reminded that the eyes of the world were on Munich, and the Federal Republic of Germany as a whole. There was a paranoia to avoid, at all costs, anything that would remind the world of Germany's militaristic recent past and 'You Know Who.' But Mathias thought that things had gone too far. The police and the 'Olys' (the games security force) were to be unarmed. In some ways security was so light and disorganised as to be non-existent. He had witnessed local police at the Olympic village literally turn and run away from a set of Canadians who, when asked for their passes, instead gave the Nazi salute and shouted 'Seig Heil.' The track suited boys thought this hilarious but Mathias saw the police retreat as shameful.

His thoughts returned once again to the incident involving the Stasi agent. He was quite pleased with his response when the man had shouted up at him whilst being pinned to the floor:

'Tell this idiot to let me go! I am police!'

'I know exactly what you are and you're not police. Not here anyway – you're Stasi, and from where I'm standing the Englishman's doing a good job.'

'Let me go! Tell him to release me or there will be trouble! I have diplomatic immunity!'

'And I can and will arrest you! It's a pity I don't have a bloody big gun. Nothing would please me more than to put a bullet in your head.' Nevertheless, he had made the Englishman let him go. There were no real grounds for arrest and so he instructed the man, now red faced with rage, to walk slowly away. Mathias had watched the incident from a few metres distant, his attention caught by the fleeing girl. He immediately guessed the scenario and hoped the she would escape to freedom and that her route would be easier than his twenty-kilometre swim almost a decade earlier.

⌒

One good thing about his posting to the *Ringerhalle* was that he was able to watch much of the judo competition. He loved judo much more than he had ever liked swimming. He became a swimmer simply because his teacher, Olaf Pischler, noticed that he had a talent for it. He was given no choice and became a cog in the state machine the sole purpose of which was to churn out athletes to demonstrate the superiority of the GDR.

But judo was different. He had enrolled in a club at Hans' suggestion. 'You're a big lump that's eating me out of house and home. You've got too much energy – you need to do something to burn it off. Are you sure you've given up swimming?'

'I'm never going in a pool ever again. I don't even like taking a bath!'

'That's true,' Konrad had added whilst holding his nose in affirmation. Hans took Mathias along to a local judo club and after the first night the boy was hooked. He came to love the paradoxes of the sport; it's violence and grace; super-human efforts thwarted and then a beautiful throw executed with no effort at all; combatants would inflict great pain on each other which only served to forge lasting friendships; judoka would demonstrate profound sympathy to friends - by showing none at all. Mathias stuck to the sport like glue and moved up the grades. His proudest moment was when he won his black-belt grading with six consecutive throws. He was the only *kyu* grade to advance that day and received a standing round of applause from the on-lookers. All heady stuff for an eighteen-year-old young man, but he had few competitive ambitions – he loved the sport for its own sake. His proficiency did mean however, that he flew through the combat and defence training at police college.

His work day was coming to a close but he thought he would watch the final which had just been announced. He stood in the aisle immediately behind the Olympic officials and had a perfect view – there were some advantages to wearing a police uniform. The Soviet team were below him in their light blue blazers and somewhat ridiculous white caps.

Shota Chochoshvili of the Soviet Union and the Englishman David Starbrook, representing Great Britain, stood at their respective white and red marks. Mathias had seen some earlier action from both players in the preliminary rounds but had no view as to the likely winner. His personal sympathies were with the Englishman. He had spent fifteen years behind the Iron Curtain and knew to his own cost the corruption of the Soviet system. (He had not even been aware, until his escape to the West, that the tablets and injections he had received as a swimmer were not vitamins and diet supplements but steroids and hormones designed to enhance his athletic performance.)

Mathias admired the countenance of the Englishman – he seemed made for this moment, standing calm and resolute. In contrast the Soviet fidgeted. Chochoshvili did not seem nervous exactly, more like an overwound clockwork toy or a hunting dog straining to run wildly. The small referee called *hajime* and both players walked directly to engage in *kumi-kata*. The Georgian attempted a high 'over the shoulder' hold but Starbrook would not yield physically or in spirit – his magnificent frame remained unbent. Twice Starbrook attacked to the left and twice Chochoshvili attempted his favourite counter, *ura-nage,* the devastating throw with which he had flattened Paul Barth. Starbrook seemed alert to this danger and Chochoshvili's attack failed. In return Starbrook threw in a strong left-handed *o-uchi-gari* which he immediately combined with a left *taio-toshi,* but the Georgian remained unruffled. After five or six minutes of battle, honours remained even, neither player was dominant – every attack had been parried or blocked. And then a game changing flurry occurred. Both men were hunched over and locked in combat; Starbrook attempted a weak left *o-uchi-gari* which Chocoshvili countered with a strong foot-sweep. There was a resounding crash of ankles. The Georgian showed his wrestling pedigree pulling the British player hard to the left with a technique derived more from *sumo* than judo. For a moment Starbrook teetered on his right foot and it looked as if the Soviet would roll him onto his back. Cat like the Englishman recovered and landed on his face. No score! In a flash the Soviet dropped onto his adversary, dominating and searching for a weakness in Starbrook's *ne-waza* defence. He forced his right arm through the Englishman's guard in search of a strangle or arm lock but without success. English voices roared encouragement. 'Come on Dave! Stand up Dave!' The referee called *matte* and David Starbrook sat upright – ominously massaging his left ankle.

Shota Chochoshvili returned to his mark and fastened his belt while his rival received medical treatment. The Georgian then respectfully knelt. The British team doctor massaged Starbrook's injured foot and liberally treated it with freezing spray. The referee called for the Englishman to stand, which he did, and then hobbled to his mark to the loud acclamation of the crowd. He tidied his suit and adjusted his belt but not to the satisfaction of the referee who then assisted. The match was restarted with Shota bouncing up and down, eager to begin and exploit a possible weakness. Mathias Koenig checked the scoreboard and the time clock and saw that with one minute left the contest was still even. Both players took double lapel grips and battled head against head. An easy left *o-uchi* from Starbrook was followed by the same from Chochoshvili. An English voice bawled out 'Come on Dave! Less than a minute left!' As if in response the Georgian threw in a left *maki-komi*, easily shrugged off by Starbrook. The clock ticked down; thirty-two, thirty-one seconds. Starbrook attacked with a strong *ashi-garuma* but Shota thrust his hips forward in defence and both players collapsed again to the canvas. The Englishman was up quickly, the Georgian took his time and wasted a few seconds slowly tucking his suit into his belt. The clock ticked off the remaining seconds and the hooter signifying the end of the contest blared simultaneously with David Starbrook's final attack.

The match was done. Soon the referee and the corner judges would decide which of these giants of judo was Olympic Champion. Chochoshvili was quickly to his mark; Starbrook took longer and then stood for a moment, hands on hips, before adjusting his suit. The small, green jacketed Korean referee cut a dapper figure as he stood precisely between the two great fighters. Starbrook, the Iron Man of judo looked tired – Chochoshvili looked remarkably fresh, surprisingly so after this epic ten-minute bout. The decision was called for and the two white flags raised proclaimed Shota Chochoshvili of Georgia the Olympic champion. David Starbrook stood tall, elegant in defeat. He stepped forward, the personification of the 'good sportsman', to shake hands with the Soviet victor but Chochoshvili was taken with the moment. He jumped for joy ignoring the outstretched hand and bounded off the mat into the ecstatic arms of his wildly cheering team-mates.

Mathias Koenig watched as David Starbrook calm, composed, almost noble walked of the mat to be consoled by the British team manager who gently ruffled the hair of the Silver Medallist in sympathy and consolation

'Ah well,' thought the young policeman. He checked his watch to confirm that his shift was ended and left the Ringerhalle feeling sad and disappointed at the Englishman's defeat. He now had three days to himself and would not be back on duty until Tuesday morning – unfortunately the early 'graveyard shift' which he hated.

～

The morning of 5th September was cold and Mathias lingered over his hot coffee, reluctant to leave the temporary Olympic police station. He did not like shift work but accepted it as part of the job. 'Two 'til ten' was the worst though. You arrived at work tired and stayed tired. He then found it difficult to sleep during the day. He had spent two hours catching up on paper-work but it was now four o'clock and was about to go out on dawn patrol. The duty telephone rang and it was answered by the desk sergeant Kurt Weiss, and old stager who wanted no excitement and was looking forward to retirement, his pension and an easy life fishing from his boat *Mathilde* – his one true love. He shouted to Mathias who was just about to leave. 'Hey Mathias.'

'Yes Boss.'

'There's something going on at the fence near Apartment One in the village. Check on it will you?'

'It's probably just some of the kids climbing over the fence again. Mind you they're back late.' Athletes entering and leaving the Olympic Village by scaling the security fence had become a common-place nuisance. The barrier was barely two metres high, lower in places and was not topped by barbed wire or any other security measure. The young Olympians found it easier to hop over the fence than to sign in or out. But four o'clock was late... Mathias patrolled the fence while walking towards the accommodation blocks. He liked the feel of the hefty metal torch in his hand – his only weapon in case of trouble. He looked up at the dour concrete buildings quite featureless, but punctuated here and there by a lighted window. He saw an indistinct form on a balcony but could make out no features – it appeared to be a man in a dark tracksuit but the shape quickly disappeared. The sounds of a minor commotion, doors banging, raised voices and hurried footsteps drifted in from the adjoining building. 'Just larking about,' he thought. And then he heard the gunshot. Briefly, he recalled his escape from the East when such sounds were unfamiliar. Now he was a trained police officer and recognised immediately the sound of a nine-millimetre automatic pistol. In alarm and haste he spoke into his radio.

'MK to control – over!' There was a nerve-wracking delay before his radio crackled in response.

'Control to MK – What is it Mathias?'

'Kurt, there's a situation here. Apartment Two – I've just heard a gunshot!'

'What! Are you sure? It's probably a fire-cracker.'

'Of course I'm bloody sure Kurt. I know the sound of gun when I hear it. Send back-up immediately. We need armed response here - now!' Sergeant Kurt Weiss thought for a moment. Mathias was not the sort of officer to panic – but armed response? For a start there were only four officers on duty and none were armed – no one was.

All guns were securely locked away and could not be issued without authorisation from Captain Baur who was at home asleep.

'You'd best check the situation out Matty. It could be one of the shooting competitors testing a gun or something...' Mathias heard a second crack.

'That's another shot! Check it out? I've got a torch – what do you expect me to do if there's a maniac with a gun – dazzle him?'

'Do your best Matty and be careful. I'll phone the captain. You'd better be right or we're both in hot water. I'll send Horst and Fritz over. Apartment Three you say?' Officer Mathias Koenig made his way to the stairwell and began to climb the concrete steps. He kept his torch switched off and allowed his eyes to become accustomed to the early-morning gloom eased only by the soft glow of the fire safety lights. He reasoned that torchlight would aid him, but also provide an excellent target for a hidden gunman. Towards the top of the second flight, he saw the form of a misshapen figure lying inverted on the steps with both arms inelegantly hanging down, a parody of upside-down surrender. White legs were visible in the low light. Perhaps he was wearing shorts? He waited for a minute, his chest constricted, his breathing shallow. The body did not move and there were no detectable sounds or signs of any assailant. He pressed a button – his powerful torch lit the scene and the beam of light seemed drawn to the bloodied, mutilated mess which had been the unfortunate's genitals. Mathias stepped closer and examined the identification pass that hung around the victim's neck.

'MK to control,' he whispered into his radio.

'Yes Matty – are you okay?' Mathias ignored the question.

'The situation is very bad Kurt. There is a body – an Israeli weightlifter – Yossef Romano.' He heard his sergeants voice raise in alarm.

'A body! Is he dead?'

'I hope so Kurt, I really hope so...'

Author's Note: On the morning of 5th September 1972 Palestinian terrorists perpetrated a most horrific attack on Israeli athletes during the Munich Olympic games. This attack is now known as the Munich Massacre. The plan was to take Israeli hostages and under the threat of their death extort political demands from the Israeli and West-German governments. The Federal Republic of Germany, after the atrocities of the Second World War, was desperate that the games were not seen as in anyway like the militaristic display provided by Adolph Hitler in the Berlin games of nineteen thirty-six. In consequence the security at Munich was completely lacking. When the attack came the West-German's had no effective response. Their only strategy was to offer the terrorists unlimited money to go away! However, we must not forget that the atrocity was of Palestinian making.

With the passage of time, the individuality of each of the eleven murdered has faded into a collective group of murdered victims. But for the generation that didn't grow up with first-hand memories of the shock and horror of the Munich massacre, it's worth reminding ourselves that:

Moshe Weinberg, Yossef Romano, Ze'ev Friedman, David Berger, Yakov Springer, Eliezer Halfin, Yossef Gutfreund, Kehat Shorr, Mark Slavin, Andre Spitzer, and Amitzur Shapira

were all accomplished athletes who followed their own individual paths to the top of their sports. We can only imagine how they might have impacted the sporting world had they not been cruelly cut down.

∽

Chapter Fourteen
Manchester Way

I RETURNED FROM my Olympic jaunt exhausted but in high spirits. I had left university by the grace of God and good fortune, with a first-class honours degree in psychology and for some reason decided that I would like to be a professional psychologist in one denomination or other. This would require a master's degree qualification and two years prior working in a related field. I had applied for a post as a 'Research/Action Fieldworker' to assess the needs of disaffected young people in Hulme, a redeveloped area of Manchester. On my return from Munich a brown manilla envelope awaited on the doormat of my Birmingham flat. I ripped it open without much care, tearing the letter inside. The job was mine and I was delighted! The perfect job I thought and with a hefty salary – well it seemed generous as I had never had any money except from vacation labouring jobs and a student grant. It also came with rent-free accommodation. My cup was filled to over-flowing! But I really was tired out – the trip home had been the proverbial nightmare journey.

༄

The Bowen's coach had arrived on time at Munich's bus station. There were fewer people on board for the return journey and so I took a seat at the back. The journey was uneventful as we travelled along the *autobahn* to Stuttgart where we stopped for an hour; four hours later we similarly stopped at Strasbourg. It was on the road to Metz that I first heard a very faint high-pitched squeal. With the passing miles it grew louder. A voice called out from the seat in front of me. 'Oi! Driver – you've got a wheel bearing going – I can hear it.' I found out later the man's name was Walter Heely and that he was a retired mechanic from Smethwick. The driver called back.

'Well, I can't hear nothing. There's nowt I can do about it anyway. You'll just have to put up with it.' As the miles rolled on the noise increased, by Metz it was a loud howl.

'Oi, driver!' shouted Walter. 'That bearing's had it. It'll be red hot already. Drive any further and the whole back axle will be buggered. You need to stop.' It was then that I saw the smoke and flames coming from the rear wheel, above which I was sitting. I decided to pretend calm but joined Walter in calling the driver.

'Driver! I don't want to worry you – but we are on fire!'

'I can see that!' he snapped back. 'I've got mirrors haven't I?' Nevertheless, he kept driving for another mile before pulling into Metz service area. He dealt with the matter quite well, jumping out of the coach with a fire-extinguisher and dousing the burning tyre with foam. It took six hours for the replacement coach to arrive and of course, when we reached Calais, we had missed the ferry and spent an uncomfortable night waiting for the dawn sailing. This was cancelled due to bad weather.

I have never been sea-sick – I don't know why, and claim no credit for this. It might simply be that I have never sailed on a rough sea. When we finally left Calais, the crossing was choppy enough for all passengers not immune like myself, to suffer. I was just very hungry and went to the cafeteria to spend my last pennies on a carton of *frites* – thin French chips. I headed to a nearby table to eat them, swaying and staggering, which I found fun. I sat down next to a quiet, middle-aged Frenchman. After a short while he motioned at my tray of chips; I thought he was on the scrounge but decided to be neighbourly – do my bit for the *Entente-Cordiale* so to speak. I spoke to him, '*Voulez-vous une frite, M'sieu?*' and politely offered him the tray. That he then filled it with vomit I thought was in bad taste and that he then thanked me was quite bizarre.

'*Merci, M'sieu,*' he said and then lurched to the nearest toilet without apology or payment for my ruined chips. I dozed on the coach from Dover to Birmingham and it was with some relief that I finally arrived home.

⌒

I put my job offer to one side, ate a whole packet of corn-flakes with milk and lots of sugar and went to bed. It was midday Monday 4th September and there I stayed, excluding bathroom breaks, for the next sixteen hours.

Like a lot of men, I appreciate tools and so forth - but only those of top-quality. For example, I believe there is something exceptional about a three-eighths 'Snap-on' wrench. I have a one, even though it really should be the preserve of the professional mechanic; it fits the hand beautifully and has a weight to it that exudes quality. At that time the only expensive gadget which I possessed was a Roberts world band radio receiver - but it was excellent. I could pick up signals from civil aircraft and the police; I could listen in to taxi-drivers from Delhi to Dublin. I used it a lot – particularly when I woke up early and had nothing to do. It was four o'clock in the morning, and out of recent interest decided to tune into the Olympic radio station in Munich.

To begin with, as I scrolled through the frequencies, I heard the usual diet of classical music and early morning talk shows – mostly in German but not all. On the shorter wave-lengths and side-band broadcasts, little was happening - until four-thirty when the police channels went wild! Discordant, frenzied communications took the place of lazy idle chatter. It was obvious that something serious was happening but my insufficient understanding of German prevented me from knowing what. I picked up one phrase repeatedly – 'Terroranschlag im Olympiapark!' I turned the fine-tuning knob and eventually found a conversation between two 'radio hams' fortunately speaking in English. I became fully aware of the horror that was happening in the Olympic village.

The rest is literally history. Like most of the world I watched the events unfold on television and was sickened by them. The Palestinians had taken twelve hostages but quickly killed three including Yossef Romano who was also castrated and left to bleed to death. They then threatened to publicly execute one athlete each hour until their demands were met. I was appalled at the seeming inability of the West-German state to respond to the situation; I admired the steadfastness of Golda Meir the Israeli Prime Minister in refusing to negotiate with the terrorists; I was outraged at the response of the President of the Olympic Committee, Avery Brundage, to insist that the Games continue while this terror attack was going on! I was shocked at the ineptitude of the police and the loss of life in the final airport 'shoot-out.'

But mostly I worried about my friends, new and old, still in Munich. I fretted neurotically that the heroic performance of Richard Barraclough and the tremendous achievement of David Starbrook should be in any way diminished by the horror that had occurred. I wondered how the 'rat' in Christian's stomach would respond and hoped that the troubled bar-owner did not feel that this was the time to cut it out.

❧

I am white Irish working class, raised in the filth of inner-city slums. My beginnings could hardly have been lower but would surely hold me in good stead for anything that life could throw at me in Manchester – or so I thought. When I arrived in Hulme, I realised I was wrong. The horror of the place literally made me feel sick. The first night spent alone in my flat, still damp with new plaster, was one of sleepless panic. I wanted to go home and be with my family and friends. My background was indeed lower working class but everyone worked. There is an ugly word, American I think – 'underclass' which identifies the demographic bottom of society. Life here is damn rough and is not characterised by employment or upward aspirations, but more a depressing cycle of poverty, benefits, aimlessness and the immediate pleasures of drugs, alcohol, trivial irresponsible sex, cigarettes, and cheap food often paid for by petty crime.

I was unprepared for this. I was unprepared for Hulme.

'Old' Hulme had been a decaying mid-Victorian district with inadequate housing but a spirited, diverse community. There were shops and shopkeepers, doctors, dentists, shoe-makers a host of small workshops and schools where the teachers lived nearby. When the area was flattened in the sixties everyone who could move out did, leaving only those who could not. Even worse the council used the 'Hulme Crescents' to solve their housing difficulties and soon the area was awash with problematic families. Services in the area soon began to fail – tradesmen would not deliver for fear of being mugged.

The housing itself consisted of half-mile long, six floor deck access crescents constructed in a style now called 'sixties Brutalism' – ugly, without adornment, angular plain concrete. The access decks were the night-time trading floors of the purveyors of white powders and multi-coloured pills. In the daylight hours packs of feral dogs took exercise. Ironically the 'Hulme flats' were given the names of great architects; William Kent and Charles Barry come to mind. Residents had nowhere to put rubbish as the chute system was woefully inadequate hence each crescent was surrounded by a halo of jetsam which steadily grew, as more and more of life's detritus was simply thrown from the balconies above. Council workmen were reluctant to clear the mess for fear of its contents.

On the evening of my first night, I steeled myself to explore the area. I was already worried that I had made a mistake in taking this job. My spirits sank lower as I crunched through a sea of broken glass. Ahead lay a rectangular flat roofed building guarded by a security fence topped with barbed wire. It looked like a gaol. As I walked closer, I heard a methodical thumping which though very familiar seemed out of place. I stood looking into the lighted windows with my fingers hooked into the heavy wire mesh of the fence. A solitary figure stood inside, assessing the figures hidden from me but responsible for the drumming. The instructor, clad in white *gi* secured by a black belt, was supervising a class of kids practicing break-falls. My mood lifted – at least there was one place in Hulme where I could feel at home.

The instructor was John Moroney – a youth worker and second Dan. I found this out, when we made our introductions. 'I've just moved into the area and I saw you had a judo class going on.' John Moroney registered surprise.

'Bloody hell, that's a first. Everyone and his dog are leaving. Hulme is no holiday resort.' I explained about my new job and that I did judo.

'Well good luck with that!' he smiled and carried on. 'The club here is okay but it's mainly for people from the estate – no grades as such. We concentrate on the kids in the hope that judo might keep a few of them out of trouble. It's a long shot mind. Hulme is a pretty toxic place.'

'You said 'we?''

'Oh yes – the club leader is a guy called Tony Bell – a good bloke. He's not here just now, he's out scrounging.' He showed me a bin which contained twenty or thirty empty bean cans. 'We make the kids eat beans on toast before the session starts. We tell them they need the extra protein before they train but it's really just to get some food inside them. We've packed in providing fruit, the kids won't eat it. The estate is a mess, trust me.'

'Is he a judoka, this Tony?'

'No, a wrestler and a damn good one – he trains at the YMCA with Richard Barraclough just back from the Olympics– you might have heard of him?' I was delighted and explained that not only did I know him from Birmingham but that I had seen him wrestle in Munich.

'There's a bit of a do for him and Joey Gilligan who was also in the wrestling team. Joey's only seventeen or so, it must have been great for him. It's at Cox's Bar on Saturday – come along it's an open house.'. I was surprised to hear that Richard was in Manchester. When I had seen him only a few months back he not mentioned that he was changing jobs. There again it was Paris and strong drink had been taken.

Predictably John Moroney and I talked about judo and wrestling - and the horror of the Munich Massacre – it was impossible not to. From such an unpromising start began one of the best periods of my life. I went back to my flat in higher spirits and did not feel unduly glum when local six-year-olds bombed me from the balconies above with paper bags containing canine unpleasantness - apparently a favourite pastime for the younger children of the estate. I comforted myself with thoughts of that wonderful night in Montmartre.

↩

The memories of the Parisian escapade once more resurrected as I entered a crowded Cox's Bar. Pip Hearne stood, pint in hand, talking to Richard and another big powerful lump, who had judoka or wrestler written all over him. It turned out, when introductions were later made, that it was both. He was the Manchester legend Steve Pullen (who, like Richard, was a world Sambo bronze medallist). Richard was dressed in navy-blue blazer and grey flannels. I noticed the Olympic rings on his tie and breast pocket embroidered with the British Olympic Team badge. A young lad sitting close was dressed the similarly but looked ill at ease; it was Joey Gilligan the seventeen-year-old Olympian. As I relaxed, I surveyed the packed bar and recognised the monolithic frame of Tony McConnell – who could not! I did not feel comfortable joining the group without invitation – the only person I knew well was Richard. I was rescued from floundering by John Moroney. He dragged me to an empty seat next to a mop of unruly curly hair, under which lurked Tony Bell the cheerful looking youth leader who ran the Hulme Youth Centre. I recalled that John has said he was a wrestler and it transpired a youth champion of great talent.

Ida seemed older to me then than she would now, but quite beautiful. Her figure was trim. Her feet were delicate and the neatly laced patent boots with a slightly high heel showed her to be trim of ankle. The knee-length tight black skirt clung close to her slim but rounded thighs and the wide black belt she wore emphasised her narrow waist. The grey broad striped blouse strained slightly at her bosom and was cut modestly square necked. She was not at all the caricature of the brash northern pub landlady. Her fine features and misty blue eyes were framed within the 'feather cut' coiffure popular at the time. Her hair was tastefully highlighted ash-blonde. She reached upwards to ring the closing bell putting slight strain on the pearl buttons of her blouse. She was a study in ageing elegance.

'I'd give her one,' said Tony feasting his eyes and slurping his pint of Boddingtons, how about you?' What can I say? Today there is an expectation, at least amongst the 'chattering classes' to be politically correct. For good or ill it was less the case then. I was spared the necessity of answering as she rang the bell to call for quiet. With mild foreboding I read the signs and concluded that a speech was imminent. A neat middle-aged blond-haired man with gold rimmed glasses called for order which was in part ignored. Another voice, Mancunian loud, stentorian and commanding raised above the still talking voices.

'Oi! Thee lot...Shut up! Let Bert speak.' In later years I found that Steve Pullen was never ignored. He was not then the legendary sports coach at the prestigious Cheetham's School of Music and he had not yet been decorated by Queen Elizabeth for his outstanding work with disadvantaged children. He was then 'Mr Manchester' and not to be argued with! The speech when it came was predictably of its type. The history of the Manchester YMCA was given in brief and the heroes of yesteryear recalled to life. People were thanked and the achievements of Richard Barraclough and Joseph Gilligan were lauded and applauded. Poor jokes were made and were given customary appreciation. The terrible terrorist attack which had blighted the games were acknowledged but quickly left – there seemed no place for it at a celebration.

'Who's the guy speaking?' I whispered to Tony Bell.

'He's Mark Jacobs, something to do with t'wrestling organisation. Might be president or chairman – something or other anyway. I think he puts some money into the kitty, the Jacobs family make biscuits.' Mark Jacobs oration was greeted with generous applause. Richard's reply was brief and appropriate thanking everyone, particularly his mom who made the best roast beef and Yorkshire pudding on 'on either side of the Pennines.' The Lancastrian crowd pantomime moaned at the Yorkshire reference, while Joey Gilligan sat quietly, almost sheepishly throughout. Ida once again rang the closing bell and said that food was ready in the back room for invited guests. About half of the assemblage made haste towards the rear door while Richard walked to me.

'Hello Danny. What are you doing here? Sorry I couldn't talk earlier. I thought it was you I saw walk in but I wasn't sure. Come and get some grub before the greedy bastards eat it all.'

'I'm not an invited guest Richard.' He pulled me off my chair and shoved me towards the rear door.

'You are now! He repeated his question. What are you doing here?'

'I'm living here,' and I told him about my new job in Hulme while we queued for food.

'Good luck to you that's all I can say. They've only just built the place and there are calls for it to be pulled down' I cut in a little too quickly.

'I didn't know you were moving Richard. Got a better job then?' He looked around and seemed a little uneasy.

'No, not really. Talk about it some other time. The food looks great!' It was apparent that for the time being at least, this subject was closed. (It later transpired that Richard had put his sporting career ahead of his academic one and returned to the north where he could better train.)

To the side, tables were burdened with northern delicacies in honour of the erstwhile combatants: a dozen steaming boiled hocks and many mounds of the cabbage which had partnered the hams in the pot; enamelled bowls filled to tumbling with jacket boiled potatoes, hot gleaming with rivulets of melting butter; steaming jugs of cabbage liquor and round loaves of freshly baked bread, some already hacked; hand reared pork pies and rings of black-pudding from Bury market; a half cheese from Cheshire and in the centre a huge Lancashire hotpot with pickled red cabbage waiting. Not for Ida the paltry pub fare of curled sandwiches that normally diminishes such occasions. With loaded plates we found a table and sat down and with no ceremony tore at the succulent meats. Tony Bell began munching through a half-ring of teeth staining black pudding. With a mouth full of ham, I mumbled to Richard.

'I saw you in Munich...'

'What! How come?'

'Yes, I watched you fight Jon Peterson. I was with a crowd of noisy Americans from Iowa. I shouted to you at the end of the fight. You looked up and waved – I thought you'd seen me.'

'No, I can't recall seeing or hearing anything. I certainly didn't see you. I was very brassed off about the fight. I don't think I did myself justice. I did see the judo lads and heard Jacks – impossible not to recognise *his* voice. Starbrook stood up and clapped me off the mat. I remember looking at the floor and wondering what 'it' was all about. I felt very emotional... I was so pleased when he won the Silver. He deserved the Gold. Anyway...'

'I was sitting with the Yanks and next to a coach from Iowa State. He tipped Jon for the Gold...' Richard disagreed.

'No. Tediasvilli was better. He deserved the gold and Petersen the silver – it were about right.'

'So, you lost to the second-best player in the world. That doesn't seem so bad does it?' Richard squeezed his lips together and answered with some anger.

'He pinned me! Only the second time I've ever been pinned! He was in a different league. Prior to the match I was very nervous – too nervous, I think. After all the effort I had put in to reach that point I was determined make a good show of things. I knew he would be good because the American college system effectively allows their athletes to train full time. All the Russians are 'in the army' which also means full-time training. I had done as much as I could; weight-training; running; keeping my weight under control. I spent as much time on the mat as I could fit in with work. At the Olympic village I trained every day with Ron Grinstead who was fighting under 90s and he was one hell of a hard knock – too hard for training sometimes. I knew Peterson would be good, but as you say he turned out to be great. He was impossible to tie up - I couldn't get through his defence. The 'under hooks' and 'arm drags,' I attempted were a complete waste of time. He bullied me out of any hold that could be effective. I think I lost focus for a moment and tried a leg grab, which was a complete mistake as he was on top of me in a flash and rolled me over and into the pin. I was embarrassed to lose in front of the Judo boys. Enough of this nonsense. How come you were in Munich, Danny? The last time

I saw you was in Paris sitting on the steps at Montmartre swigging wine from a bottle with a pretty little French girl slung around your neck.' We took a moment to eat a few more mouthfuls and wash it down with long draughts of excellent Boddington's bitter.

'Great food Richard.' He looked at me and slightly shook his head.

'Don't mention food. I was constantly having to lose weight at Munich. I trained like a madman every day and the next morning I had put on a kilo!' He changed the subject and asked again, 'How come you ended up at the Olympics?'

'You remember the night in Paris?' He said that he did just about - but there were gaps. 'I'd had a row with my girlfriend and in a fit of temper she stormed off - I did as well, in the opposite direction. I saw a poster advertising the judo match at the Stade de Coubertin. I went along to watch and as you know teamed up with you and Pip and ended up having a great night. I never got back to the hotel we'd booked.'

'Never?'

'Not until the afternoon of the next day. When I arrived at the hotel there was no need of the excuses I had made up because she'd gone, taken my car, and left me my passport, a letter and the bill.'

'What did it say, the letter?' This question came from Tony Bell who had finished the ring of black-pudding and was now wading through a bowl of hot-pot and red cabbage.

'I can remember every loving word. I doubt I'll ever forget, anyway I have the letter, I keep it with me as a reminder.' I took the folded paper out of my wallet and passed it to Tony Bell who read it out:

'Danny,

I am sure you have been told this many times before, but you are quite the most selfish and utterly arrogant man I have had the misfortune to meet! You have done me one great favour though - as you are all too aware, you are good-looking, intelligent and well educated and I'm sure many future admirers will be captivated by you. But never again will I assume these to be important qualities in a man! Scratch the surface and underneath you are about as sophisticated and desirable as a slime-filled decaying rat – but with less charm. I hope that when you read this note you are hurt, and that this hurt will be minor compared with the hurts you will frequently suffer later in your life.

I have little doubt that good fortune will remain on my side. Farewell, you horrible man! You are a credit to your gender.

Trust me - the pleasure was all yours!

Goodbye,

Mary.'

'She writes well.' Said Tony. Richard nodded and added,

'Quite poetic in a way.' I shrugged and said, by way of explanation,

'I had a fit of the miseries and went to Munich to cheer myself up, which, I have to say, worked.'

'Serves you right though, about the girl – Mary, I mean.' Richard mumbled through a mouthful of ham and in truth, I had to silently agree.

⤺

There is a song by the 'Village People' called YMCA. This is a humorous and exuberant ditty which incorporates specific dance moves. The singers, all male, are dressed in a variety of outfits for some reason; an Indian chief, a construction worker, a traffic cop and a motor-cyclist. When they do the dance their body shapes are supposed to represent the letters naming the song. It doesn't work for me I'm afraid, except for the letter 'Y.' I have been told that the song and dancers are representative of Gay culture at the time.

The Manchester YMCA had, as near as I am aware, no such connections but it was an excellent place for young men in which to strip off and indulge in rough, full contact, mano a mano sports. As I say no connection. But it really was a great place in which to train and attracted top sportsmen from a variety of disciplines; judo, wrestling, boxing, weight training, 'fives', running and not least rugby. There were two rugby teams and the first fifteen took the game seriously. A second team was started because there were many lads who enjoyed a game, perhaps had played at college or the lower-level club game, but did not want the fuss or commitment of first team rugby. The second team accommodated these dregs; enter 'The Goodies,' a name stolen from a popular comedic TV show. The name indicates the spirit of the team but hardly the status of the players: Richard Barraclough, Olympic wrestler and international judoka; Joey Gilligan, Olympic wrestler; Andy Bailey, wrestling champion; Tony Bell, wrestling champion; Tony MacConnell, champion judoka and wrestler; Steve Pullen judo and wrestling champion; Pip Hearne Welsh National Sprint champion and even me! The team punched way above its weight often beating creditable opposition through effort, fitness, intimidatory tactics and wherever possible getting the ball to Pip who could run past anyone – at least once in a game. I recall Richard being admonished by one referee after he had tackled several of the opposition with *kata-garuma*. The referee was, as seemed to be so often the case, Welsh. Captains were called and a word was spoken.

'Now boy. I confess that I don't know what you are doing – but I do know that I don't like it. I'm sure it must say in the rules that you can't run down the pitch carrying the man you've tackled. If it doesn't mention it – I'm mentioning it now. Cut it out! When you tackle drop him on the ground where God and nature intended, don't take him on a sight-seeing trip!'

⤺

There was one incident of sadness at the YMCA involving the late great football star, the brilliance that was George Best. He began to turn up at evening sessions and do a bit of this and that; wrestling, sparring, weights – nothing serious. I believed he liked the anonymity. Everyone knew who he was of course, but didn't care. I think he liked just being one of the lads. This private time did not last. The press got hold of his whereabouts and one gloomy evening the basement where we trained was descended upon by selfish photographers happy to intrude, to blight a person's life in pursuit of their own goals. Stupid suggestions were made:

'Hold one of the wrestlers down, George! Put the gloves on George! Throw one of the judo lads George!' He had too much dignity to entertain such foolishness. Instead, he got changed and left, sadly not to return.

My work in Hulme continued but in truth it was thoroughly depressing and distressing. I left the provided flat and was invited to move in with Richard who owned a house in Stretford – an act of charity which preserved my mental health, that and the regime of nightly training of one form or other – judo, wrestling, running, weights and week-end rugby. It is well known but not widely enough acted enough that physical exercise combats mental pathologies. It is easier for doctors to prescribe anti-depressants but in truth going to the gym works better. (Bin the drugs and get fit! This advice is not infallible nor always sufficient, but in general it is pretty good.) Training regimes tend to come with a built-in social life. For my set this invariably meant evenings in Cox's Bar and cheap Greek food at an excellent café. The early evening pints and stifado were sometimes augmented by a homeward supper of fish and chips – the appetites of young men in training can be wondrous to behold.

Have you noticed that people involved in judo, perhaps other martial arts, have an acute sense of fair play and a hatred of bullying? One incident comes to mind; driving home in Richard's Mini Clubman we stopped at a crossing to let an elderly gent with a walking stick cross the road. He was met in the middle by two 'scallies' one of whom kicked the man's stick away causing him to fall which filled the lads with mindless delight.

'I don't think much of that,' said Richard and he got out of the car to assist the chap and remonstrate with the lads.

'Hey, thee boys. I don't think much of that – it weren't right.' The dominant dope came rushing toward Richard all bluster, puffed out chest, foul language, spit and ignorance. In a split-second Richard inverted him with a crutch hold and held him powerless in mid-air. Nonetheless the lout kept up his barrage of abuse and pointless threats.

'Put me down – I'll effing kill you!'

'Now, I know you're not very clever – but think on it for a moment. I will put you down on your feet and you can say 'sorry' or I'll put you down on your head and then you *will* be sorry.'

This seemed crystal clear to me - a perfectly reasonable choice... I had a little bit of sympathy for the idiot because at wrestling a few days earlier I had found myself in the same position. I had the choice of taking the hit or extending my arms in the hope of spinning out. I chose badly and my elbow dislocated.

'Put it back in Richard.' I screamed.

'No chance! I don't know how to do it,' came the reply. Fortunately, Freddy Griffiths the Manchester City physiotherapist was present and he popped my elbow back. An unpleasant experience which left my elbow in plaster. As for the fate of the currently inverted youth you'll have to use your imagination as to the most likely outcome.

My injury did put paid to any chance of competing in the forthcoming British Team Trials. Just as well really – I would have been in the same weight as Richard, Roy Inman, Colin McIver, and a host of other top players. I was better off watching. My accounts tend to ramble and sometimes it is better to be brief: In cold December at Crystal Palace, Richard Barraclough had his perfect judo day. The entry in the half-heavyweight category was large and by virtue of the pool system in operation the winner would have twelve fights.

He had twelve and won twelve fights against the nation's best each with the maximum score of *ippon*.

'Great day Richard! Absolutely incredible! Unbelievable!'

'Aye – I did alright.' Richard Barraclough is forever modest.

⤴

It should never have happened in the first place; hence I blame the failure of my marriage to Helen upon Dean Martin or Richard Barraclough - I suppose it depends upon how far back in a chain of events it is reasonable to go when ascribing cause. Richard's involvement was the excellent *te-garuma* out of which I attempted a hand-stand spin. This conceit failed miserably and resulted in my left elbow being dislocated as mentioned. Dean Martin is to blame because of the overly romantic nature of his voice.

My work in Hulme was receiving some attention amongst Manchester City councillors to whom I reported; university sociologists who were also interested in the social catastrophe that was taking place, and the Manchester Evening News that reported an event in which I was involved. The word 'hero' was used completely inappropriately. I was alone in a local café, having a full Mancunian breakfast ('the heart attack special'), when my peaceful demolition of fried black-pudding was disturbed by the attempted robbery of the owner. Two local 'druggies' entered, threatened him with a knife and demanded that he opened the till. I recognised them – Bazza, a six-foot, six stone walking skeleton and Bernie his ghoul-like girlfriend. The threat was ludicrous; the users of intravenous opiates are never in good physical condition and these two were further along the road to oblivion than most. I am not brave, not a bit – but I did want to finish my meal and decided to remove the knife and throw them out. The first part was easy – I swatted Bazza's arm, applied a wrist-lock and relieved him of the knife. In the process of removing him from the cafe I ignored Bernie, who hit me from behind with a bottle of tomato sauce which shattered. They both then ran - well shambled off, and left me dripping with ketchup. It turned out that half the ketchup was blood. I required a set of stitches and was lucky that my carotid artery was missed. There were two direct consequences to this stupidity; I was asked to give a talk about my work, to a bunch of university sociology students - and to this day I will only partake of brown sauce.

෴

When I was about nine my father rented a television set specifically to watch the Cup Final played at Wembley between Aston Villa and Manchester United. Hence, for six months afterwards, we were able to watch television. I remember a science fiction programme called 'A for Andromeda' which starred a seventeen-year-old actress called Julie Christie. I did not know why of course, but the sight of this young woman made me feel pleasantly uncomfortable.

Helen West also made me feel pleasantly uncomfortable, but as a young man in my mid-twenties I knew exactly why - and yes, she did look surprisingly like Julie Christie, the beautiful 'Lara' in

'Dr Zhivago.' She was a PhD student researching 'the links between buildings and the effect they had upon the behaviour of people living in them.' Over lunch she explained that she was adopting a particular model of regressive, multi-variant analysis as more or less all the covariates were linked and it was very hard to find which variants were causal and which were mere correlations. I said I was pleased for her.

She asked if I minded her taking notes, which I did not, but did find this level of interest surprising. She took out a notepad and scribbled away in some strange hieroglyph or cypher.

'What's that writing?'

'Gregg's.' I looked blank, obviously puzzled. The only Gregg's I knew of sold pies. 'Gregg's shorthand,' she explained. 'It's better than Pitman's. It's 'light line' – much easier and faster.' I had no idea what she was talking about.

'Oh, it's shorthand?'

'No, it's Gregg's shorthand. I learned it to speed up note taking. It's easier and faster than Pitman's and I find easier to use in other languages.'

'Oh. You speak other languages then.' I was on safer ground here as I was quite proud of my French.

'Only French, German, Spanish and Latin – and I'm not sure that Latin counts really as there's nobody to speak to ... anyway let's press on.' She swopped the pencil to her left hand and continued to make notes.'

'You're ambidextrous then?' She laughed and nodded.

'My mom says it's why I can't tell my left from my right – they seem the same to me. I'm terrible with directions.'

'You're very talented – is there anything else I should know before I make a fool of myself?'

'I'm a whizz at mental arithmetic – only the 'four rules' – nothing fancy.' She paused and looked upwards. Her profile really was quite beautiful. 'Oh yes. I can do a trick with dates. If you give me a date, I can tell you what day it was or will be. I don't know how – but I can.'

'How about the twenty-sixth of September 2020?'

'That will be a..., it will be Saturday.' She laughed beautifully, and again I realised that my interest in her was straying from the professional and academic.

'Anything else?' I asked in pretend frustration.

'I don't think so. That's about it. How about you?' She laughed and playfully squeezed my hand across the table. 'No, one more thing. My great aunt was Agatha Christie - it doesn't mean anything of course but it's fun, don't you think? Now, how about you?'

'I can balance a kitchen stool on my chin and I used to be quite good at judo. That's it.' She looked at me steadily with serious, lime-water blue eyes, and reached to hold my hand.

'I've never met a chin, stool-balancing judo player before. Pleased to meet you!' The handshake changed to brief hand-holding with a frivolous kiss on the cheek thrown in for good measure.

But we got on well and liked each other. Over the next few months, we 'palled up' I think is the best term. I liked her company and she liked mine and although as a young man carnal thought were never far behind the scenes, that's where they stayed. And then I dislocated my elbow. Not much of a tragedy but I did take a week off work - apart from attending a Rotary Club lunch at a fine hotel in St Anne's Square. This hardly seemed to qualify as work anyhow.

⤿

Twenty of the great and the good of Mancunian industry sat around the huge polished oak conference table while I chatted about my job. I spiced up the misery that was happening in the Hulme Crescents and ate an excellent dinner - beef Wellington followed by spotted dick. Great stuff! The Rotarians were mightily impressed, gave me five hundred quid to aid my work and that was almost that. Albert Grimshaw, a Rotarian who had made a fortune in the Manchester rag-trade and was also a city Alderman, grabbed me by the good arm as I prepared to leave.

'Thee needs a holiday lad! How you can work with those drug fiends I'll never know' I smiled wanly and wondered if I had over done the doom and gloom.

'Oh, you know. You just plod on – one step at a time. I'm fine really – just a bit shell-shocked.'

'Enough of that! Don't soft soap me. Albert Grimshaw knows when he's being soft-soaped. Thee needs a holiday, now be told! Here take these.' The honourable Alderman took out an envelope from his inside pocket and thrust it into my hand. 'Two tickets for a week-end in Sorrento. I bet you've got a young lass, and I'm broad minded. I can't use them anyway. They were sent to me by a travel agent and there would be a conflict of interest, me being chair of the Ways and Means committee. No, you take them. Get your skates on mind - you fly out tomorrow and bloody early too!'

I hesitated with the phone call, not wanting to be too pushy but not indifferent either. I came to the point after the normal pleasantries. 'Helen, I've been given two tickets for a week-end break in Sorrento, flying tomorrow morning. Would you like to come? It's all paid for - flight, hotel the lot.'

'Sounds great. What's the catch?'

'There isn't one except getting to Manchester airport at three in the morning. Other than that, it's all sorted. A coach meets us in Naples and takes us on an excursion up Mount Vesuvius, and then to Pompeii in the afternoon. A surprise 'dinner al fresco', whatever that is, and then to the hotel for the night. A coach tour around Napoli on Sunday morning and then back to the airport. A real flying visit...'
She remained quiet for a moment.

'Do you snore?'

'What!?'

'I don't suppose this little jaunt comes with two rooms does it? I was wondering if I should bring ear-plugs.'

'That's the most romantic thing anyone has ever said to me. I am truly overcome. I assume that's a 'yes' then?' She laughed, and I asked 'Have you ever been on a plane, flown in one I mean?'

'Of course! Loads of times.' Therein quantifying a difference in our backgrounds. 'How about you?'

'No – never. What's it like, flying that is? Is it okay?' She decided to put me at ease.

'It's scary. Very, very scary! But don't worry, flying is the safest form of travel – mind you it's the crashes that you need to worry about – they are almost always totally fatal.'

⤶

The landing at Naples airport was terrifying. In high winds the plane buffeted and bounced around whilst I looked out on the famous volcano which ominously steamed. The plane could not land and had to go round again. For some reason Helen grabbed me by the hair and pulled me close.

'Isn't this exciting?' Her eyes sparkled and she kissed me affectionately on the cheek. 'Great fun.' The plane landed at the second attempt with every passenger quiet, a silence which served to emphasise the bangs and thuds of the roaring wind outside. Behind me a woman fervently whispered the Hail Mary. The three engine Trident bounced down the runway in a manner reminiscent of the bombing scene from 'The Dam Busters.' It taxied to a halt to the wild screams, whistles and thankful applause of relieved passengers.

The exhilarating ziggurat which is the track up Vesuvius was negotiated with dare-devil lack of caution by the coach-driver, and we happy day-trippers squeaked and gasped in expected fearful delight. I had the window seat and bravely did not look as Helen clambered over me to stare into the abyss, quite unconscious of her bodily curves pressing into my face. It was very pleasant all in all. The sun crackled with incandescent brilliance and the Mediterranean reciprocated, a million mirrors reflecting the garnered light... It was the clearest day I had ever experienced and I could see forever.

The coach pulled into a car-park about four-hundred metres below the summit of the ancient volcano. The driver, Mario, wished to regale us with horror stories, which he did in excellent but accented English:

'I shoulda be dead. I am thirty-five years old and was saved by my papa, a good shepherd who saw the sheep on the mountain-side fall over one by one. It was the gas! Poisonous gas from Vesuvio that swept down from this very crater. My father gathered me in his arms and ran.

Vesuvio had woken and later there was a great eruption. Thata was in nineteen-forty-four. I still missa my mama. She was taking a nap and papa did not want to wake her. Yes, my papa was a considerate man...' A few people nervously laughed, unsure of Mario's joke. 'The path to the top is rough. If you smell the stink of rotten eggs – it is nothing, only the Devil farting. If you have a coat, put it on. If you don't - stay in the coach. It will be windy!'

This was an inadequate description of the hurricane force, icy blast that met us as we stepped out. I did have a strong leather 'bomber' jacket but was wearing shorts. After a few minutes I was in agony, my legs in danger of being stripped bare, abraded by a jetstream of shotblasted pumice dust. I hobbled manfully on. Helen was wearing jeans, a thick blue coat, an Afghan hat complemented by a bright pink scarf. At the top of the caldera, we stopped and admired the impressive sight. She shook her head at my failed attempt to alternately shield a leg by hopping from one to the other. 'Men,' she said and again shook her head. She took manicure scissors from her bag, unfurled the pink scarf which she cut in half. 'Here you are.' I have never been accused of dressing well but even for me, I had stylistically outdone myself; brown jacket, blue rugby shorts and cerise leg-warmers, all-in-all quite snappy.

The afternoon at Pompeii was more normally touristic, and comfortably warm in the sunshine of a sea-level autumn afternoon. We marvelled at the preservation of the excavated town and shuddered at the fate of the petrified inhabitants who met their demise, slow-baked in clouds of volcanic ash. We sniggered at Roman pornography; mosaics of men of unlikely proportions and women in inevitable compliance as the couplings and triplings of two thousand years ago were once again revealed. Helen commented upon one lusty lad, depicted having his erect member weighed. 'Firstly, I can't see why this was in anyway erotic or even comedic and secondly such an appendage would have been a great inconvenience to him in life generally and sexually in particular. The size of it alone would have precluded intercourse with a human female - or man if that was his thing. Perhaps he preferred cows? You're not hung like that are you Danny?' I was aghast at the question and suggested ice-cream.

We bought junk gifts; a fake zippo lighter for Kevin and a glass snow-dome of Vesuvius for my mother. Helen bought similar tat. The coach took us to our hotel to change – a pity as my leg-warmers were now old friends.

〰

We discretely showered and changed in preparation for the 'surprise dinner al fresco.' Helen wore a short, white, woollen dress, calf length boots and a fur jacket and had done something to her hair. I'm not sure what it was, but it looked carefully disordered and very sexy. She was also wearing make-up – it was the first time I'd seen her powdered and painted. She was very beautiful and I could only stare.

'What's up cowboy?' She answered my unspoken words. I had put on my evening clothes – a fitted pearl buttoned shirt, jeans and a tapered Levi jacket.

'Oh, nothing – you look very nice, that's all.' She ignored this poor compliment.

'Are we going to dinner by horse? Where's your hat?' She grabbed me and we left the room smiling, walking arm in arm. She smelled of Chanel No.5.

〰

The coastline of the Mediterranean has meandered over the centuries and so the small amphitheatre built in the time of Domitian now jutted into the sea rather than being a kilometre inland. In place of gladiators and frightened animals destined for slaughter, the arena hosted a dozen tables and two enormous, stone wood-fired ovens, both already blazing. A hundred torchieres and braziers provided light and kept at bay the slight evening chill. A small Neapolitan band played simple tunes and every table sported a half-dozen straw bound bottles of Chianti and a tray of earthenware beakers. The black sky above was cloudless, and low across the bay sparkled the myriad of lights that were Naples. The brooding silhouette of Vesuvius was clearly visible against the last vestiges of the day's light.

Songs were sung and wine was taken. A scantily clad young lady lit lighter fuel which she squirted into the sand and did a fire dance amongst the flames. She later galloped around the arena and did feats of balance on a moving horse. A tenor sang '*O solo mio!*' The whole show was predictable holiday fare but none the worse for that. There is something magical about the night-time combination of, flickering flames, sentimental tunes, and peasant food washed down with simple rustic wine. The pizzas were taken from the ovens and displayed to the expectant diners by wheeling them between the tables on handcarts. Each was a two-metre-long delight of tomatoes, anchovies, and olives topped with the softest, stringiest mozzarella liberally doused with olive oil. If I'd have had any business sense whatsoever (which I don't) I should have immediately gone into the wood-fired pizza business!

'What do you think of the evening?' I spoke to Helen across the bare wooden table.

'Damn rootin' tootin' fine, Danny Boy. But I think we should mosey on down the beach and walk off some of this chow.' She was reluctant to let go of the cowboy asides which had given her so much fun during the evening. But it was a good idea.

The gritty volcanic sand crunched under our feet as we walked towards Sorrento, no more than a few kilometres distant. We were soon away from any lights and the stars above blazed brighter than I had ever seen.

'What are you looking at?'

'Stars.'

'Don't be smart with me, Clint. I know you're looking at stars, but anything in particular?'

'Quite a lot actually.' We sat down on a convenient rocky ledge. 'I'm interested in astronomy and recognise most of the constellations. But I've never seen them so clearly before. The 'Milky Way' for example. Everyone has heard the name but I've never been anywhere clear enough to see it.' But there it was in the black Italian sky; a swathe of a billion stars arching above us. Helen rested her head on my shoulder in support as she craned upwards.

'Very impressive. Anything else?' I indicated four prominent stars forming a square.

'That's the constellation of Pegasus – the winged horse. With a bit of imagination, you can make out the feet and the head. The lop-sided 'W' is Cassiopeia...'

'So, you're a chin, stool balancing, judo playing astronomer. Even more impressive. Let's go for a swim.' This surprised me and left me struggling for words.

'But...but we've not got costumes.'

'People were swimming for a long time before they invented bathing suits,' was her riposte.

'It's November. The water will be too cold.'

'No, it won't. The sea temperature in the Mediterranean doesn't change much throughout the year - and don't be a wimp. I thought cowboys were tough?' In truth my real objection was being naked in front of her. I most certainly was nowhere near the proportions depicted in Pompeii, nowhere near at all. And what if the cold got to me and made me look even less well endowed? Or worse still, what if the cold didn't get to me, and I became inappropriately aroused?

'I'm going in, and that's that!' I realised that I had been challenged. She stood facing the sea and stripped off her clothes. I was once again that young boy looking at Julie Christie - the perfect female form.

'Sod it!' I thought and took off my cowboy outfit.

She walked gracefully into the calmest sea and I followed obediently behind. My eyes were transfixed by the flawless trapezium of her back rising from the cool, motionless water. The full moon painted the bay of Naples silver. Venus, the evening and morning star of lovers hung, keeping bright sentinel watch. She turned to face me. Her perfect, symmetrical breasts, white in the moonlight, rested tangentially on the motionless surface. We drifted closer, and without thought of consequence I lifted her gently upwards and felt her warmth as slim legs entwined my waist. The stillness of the night rippled as the sentimental strains of Dean Martin singing 'Amore' drifted across the bay from a waterside bar.

We were married shortly after our return to England but, as every grown-up knows, a marriage needs a better foundation than one wonderful romantic night.

Roy Muller – World Veteran Silver Medallist

Chapter Fifteen
Royston Muller - The Jester

I SAT IN my office and looked at my new telephone. It was rectangular and space-age - a design out of Star Trek. The dial glowed spooky green in the dark and it did not ring but made an annoying little chirrup. I knew it was luminous because I had been sleeping in the office for the last week having being kicked out by my wife, Helen. She had taken terminal offence at my dalliance with another woman. In truth it was all for the best. We had married in haste, as they say, yes, it was all for the best - but I did feel incredibly sad and guilty:

⤳

We had been married for three years and things were ticking over – there were no dramas or crises. Dr Helen, as she now was, lectured in sociology at a rural university to the south of Manchester and was a rising star in academia. My contract in Hulme had thankfully ended and courtesy of the Social Science Research council and The William Piddock Foundation I had received funding to pursue a master's degree in psychotherapy. This qualification duly obtained I set up a private practice with an office in the city-centre of Birmingham. My client list was growing and all looked 'set fair' - and then I stepped on the land-mine which was Rosalind.

Helen was right of course. I knew I had transgressed a little bit – but I quickly came to understand that infidelity does not really belong on a rating scale. Somewhat like a woman being pregnant – she either is or isn't. She can't just be a touch pregnant and you can't have just a little bit of an affair. Without doubt I had been unfaithful.

True enough the woman concerned had encouraged me but it was up to me to say no. I remember the occasion well and know that my intent was to resist any sexual advances made. When the time came however, the refusal that I had rehearsed, became instead excited acquiescence. The passionate kissing began on a hotel stairway and the rest is a familiar history:

I was legitimately at a week-end psychology conference hosted by a distant university and housed in the function rooms of a well-known hotel chain. In the days before mobile phones continual communication was not expected. It was quite easy to answer Helen's question when I returned home.

'Why didn't you phone last night? I was worried.'

'Oh, you know how it is. There was only one phone and a crowd of people waiting to use it. I'm terrible with queues, you know that. I was going to phone you after the queue went down but it never seemed to and later, I'd had a few drinks...sorry.' She was very frosty and although my explanation could have been true, I knew I hadn't been believed.

∽

I had seen the young woman as soon as I arrived at the conference and could not take my eyes of her. She had long fair hair and a slim figure mostly hidden inside voluminous grey sweater and black trousers. Her face was pretty but not conventionally so. I was magnetically attracted for reasons I could neither understand then nor now, with almost fifty years passed to dwell on the matter. The first glimpse of her made me feel breathlessly excited. She glanced at me across the room of fifty people - or maybe she did not? I felt guiltily unsettled. My heart was racing and I felt pleasurably tense. I was panicky as if I had already committed a sin. The afternoon passed with the main speaker talking about something or other, I have no idea of what - my concentration was shot. Seminars followed, but again I attended only in body my thoughts elsewhere. At evening dinner coincidence placed us together. Coincidence? There's a thing. The idea of coincidence really stems from the philosophy that there are no forces at play in the world except those explained by physics and mathematics. Winning the lottery is nothing more than the chance matching of two number sets. All the praying, lucky charms, the calling up of dark forces have no influence on the matter because they rely upon the supernatural - which does not exist. A few things rattle me though, first amongst which is that many great minds, great thinkers, believe otherwise and I don't know why they should. Perhaps they are on to something? The great Carl Jung had mystical beliefs in such things as 'synchronicity' and the 'cosmic unconscious.' Anyway, we were sitting close; coincidence or strange forces had brought us together - and there was something very wrong with me.

We introduced ourselves. 'Hi, my name's Danny...' She offered her hand which I took holding gently the ends of her middle three fingers. She had changed for dinner, and was wearing a pressed white cotton blouse, so smooth and flawless, loose at the neck and with possibly one button too many undone. I could see that she was not wearing a bra when she leaned forward and I became pleasurably aroused at the briefest sight of her parchment smooth breast. Her youthful skin was flawless and quite pale. Her lips were without colouring but shone with the discreteness of satin. Her eyes were large and pale blue. Her nose was slightly asymmetric but this added to her magic. There was something wrong with me.

The touch of her hand was exhilarating. The hormone system of my body was out of control. I was transfixed, I most certainly could not stand up and was glad of the privacy of the table. 'Hello Danny. I'm Rosalind. Can I have my hand back please?' Her playful words excited and confirmed the sexual compact between us.

I believe in every cultural tradition there is the myth of a female demon who has sexual power over men – the succubus of the middle ages comes to mind. She often appears in dreams and takes a beautiful form - men cannot resist her charms. Her one goal is to entice men to have sinful intercourse. As a psychologist I've always thought this to be a damned good excuse for a range of male sexual transgressions. For example, a mediaeval man caught by his wife performing solitary midnight manipulations whilst thinking of his neighbour's pretty daughter had a ready excuse. 'Sorry love. A succubus bewitched me while I was sleeping. I didn't know what I was doing!'

Rosalind was my wide-awake succubus. I didn't know what I was doing. I had no resolve. I couldn't help myself.

↪

The building supervisor, Betty, was my saviour. She had noticed that I was entering the office block, unshaven and bedraggled, immediately after she opened up at seven. I then spent fifteen minutes in the toilet, washing, shaving, tooth-brushing and putting on my suit and shirt which I had brought with me on a hanger. It is possible to sleep in the back of a Ford Capri but it's not very comfortable. My head kept banging against the sloping rear window as I tried different positions in search of a comfortable spot. Also, that night I had been pestered by an intrusive policeman. At three in the morning, he tapped on the car's window. ''Allo, Sir. Might I enquire what you are a doing of?'

'I was trying to get to sleep, but now I'm talking to you. Why have you woken me up anyway?' He shone his torch officiously into my face.

'Is this your vehicle Sir? Can I see your licence?'

'It is my car yes, and you can't see my licence, no.'

'So, you are refusing to show me your licence, are we? May I ask why Sir? Have we something to hide Sir?' There is a certain type of policeman who confuses his own personal authority with that of the law which he is supposed to uphold. They show a certain dumb arrogance.

'I am refusing to show you my licence because firstly, I don't know where it is and secondly, I'm not required to carry it and thirdly you've no business asking for it. I'm legally parked in a legal car so if you don't mind officer, I'd like to get back to sleep.'

'Don't know where it is? My, my that's a bit silly of you Sir. Don't know where it is? Well, I never. I'm afraid Sir that you're going to have to find it PDQ as they say. I'm going to give you a 'producer' which means you have to take your documents to the police station of your choice within seven days.'

'For God's sake my licence is probably in a landfill somewhere, along with everything else that I used to possess, courtesy of my wife - I really am passed caring...'

'Having a touch of the old matrimonials are we?'

'You could say that, more than a touch.'

'In which case, I am an understanding fellow, and I will bid you good-night. Playing away from home, were we? Shagging a bit on the side?'

∽

'She's thrown you out then has she?' Betty did not beat about the bush. She was a good old-fashioned Brummie mother who had no time for small talk and was a plain speaker. 'Mind you I expect you deserved it - you've got the 'look' you have.'

'What look is that then Betty.' She sniggered and tapped the side of her nose.

'Don't come the 'old soldier' with me Mister. I was born in nineteen-fifteen, brought up a family through the depression, lost two babies and my husband in the war. I met a hundred soldiers that promised the earth for a night in bed. You've got the look alright; you're a handsome boy who can't keep his trousers buttoned! Sit yourself down Mister and I'll go and fetch you a cup of tea.'

'Can I have coffee please?'

'No, you can't! It's tea and be grateful.' We sat together in her basement lair drinking Typhoo made exactly as I didn't like it, strong, stewed, sugared and with sterilized milk. It was the best cup of tea I ever had. I told her my troubles and cried on her ample breast. 'There, there,' she said. 'You're not the first man nor the millionth to get himself into hot water over a woman. Most men are idiots in that way – but you'll get over it and so will she. The trick in life is not to be an idiot too often. Remember that Mister, everyone can be a fool once or twice but if you make a habit of it, well then you deserve what you get.'

She gave me a set of keys and a short list of rules and said I could sleep in my office until I sorted myself out. Rule one – Don't make a mess. Rule two – keep out of my way. Rule three – 'use you loaf.' She started washing and ironing my shirts also as she liked me to look smart.

'No, you will not pay me a penny. That would make you my boss and you certainly bloody-well ain't!' At first, I bought her flowers and chocolates but later I found she preferred 'a drop of Irish' to put into her tea.

⌁

The camp bed had been stowed and it was just gone nine o'clock when the green Trimphone began its annoying chirrup. I looked at it with distaste. Whoever designed it did a bad job. It was too light, uncomfortable to use and had that ridiculous tone. I promised myself that I would change it for a proper telephone that rang with a bell.

'Hello, Danny Murphy speaking. Can I help you?'

'Hiya mate. It's me Roy. How are ya? How're you doin'?' The unmistakeable cheery tones of Roy Muller answered my greeting.

'Hello Royston, nice to hear from you. I'm fine – but how did you get this number.' I was curious, not concerned, the number was hardly private, in fact quite the reverse.

'Oh, Underwood gave it me. He said you were now a psychiatrist working in Brum, so I thought I'd give you a call. He said your wife had kicked you out and that you were living in the back of your car.'

'Did he now? That was supposed to be confidential.'

'It is! He only told me and I won't tell anyone.'

'That's what he said.'

'Well now you're a free man again, why don't you come down to my club or visit Solihull? It'll take you mind off things.' This was quite a good suggestion. With one thing and another I had let training slide and was getting a bit podgy. I needed to lose about five kilos at least, probably ten. There was one difficulty.

'Not a bad idea Roy, but I don't have a kit.'

'God, she didn't throw your kits into the skip as well did she? That's taking things a bit far.'

'I suppose Underwood told you that didn't he?'

'Yes, but don't worry I won't mention it to a soul. What's it like being a psychiatrist – good fun?'

'I'm not a psychiatrist, I'm a psychotherapist...'

'What's the difference?'

'About twenty thousand quid a year. Now, sod off Muller I'm busy.' This was not exactly true I only had two clients that morning and an afternoon of reports and letter writing. I looked forward to the day I could afford a secretary.

'Hold your horses, hold your horses! My missus thinks I'm mad and should see a shrink so how about I come and see you?'

'Sounds like a smart girl, but I've already told you Muller. Sod off! I've got better things to do than to have you come round annoying me and taking the micky - and you've always been mad...'

'No, I'm serious! Things are getting me down – I've even been to the doctors but he just wanted to give me tablets. I'd prefer to sort things out with you.'

'It's not quite as simple as that Royston and I would have to charge you.' He seemed genuinely surprised.

'Charge me! Why?'

'Firstly, because people give more importance to something they've paid for and secondly this is my job. Would you charge me for re-wiring my house?'

'Yes, but not the full whack – 'mates rates' that's all.'

'If you're serious, that's what I'll charge you. I'll try to fix the wiring in your head for the same as you'd charge me for fixing, the wiring in my house.'

'That sounds a bit steep to me – I don't come cheap!'

'For the third time Muller - Sod off!'

⤙⤙

'Where's the bed?' It turned out that Muller was serious and he had turned up, on time, for the evening appointment which we had made. He looked around the office nodding his head and rubbed his finger along a bookshelf as if checking for dust. 'Where's the bed?' he repeated.

'I don't have one – don't believe everything you see on TV. - and it wouldn't be a bed anyway it would be a couch. Psychiatrists have a couch.'

'You're round the houses you are Danny. I'm wondering if I should talk to you at all. *Your* bed! If you're living here where do you sleep? Sitting up in the bloody chair?'

'Oh, I see what you mean. It's in the cupboard, it folds up. Let's get down to work Roy. Take a seat. We've got one hour – no more, no less.'

'Before we start how does it work, this psycho-bollocks?' He sat down and I sat facing him.

'Think of it as training. If you want to get fit you have to train. How long it takes to get fit depends upon what sort of shape you are to begin with and how much effort you put into it. And if you want to stay fit you have to keep working at it. Think of me as your coach. I can aid, assist and guide but you must do the work. Fair enough?'

'Makes sense. Where do we start, coach?'

'How about with what's troubling you, the reason why you're here. What's your problem?'

'I ain't got a problem. The missus has. She thinks my behaviour is too aggressive, not with her like, – but she's wrong!' The emotion in his voice conveyed real frustration and anxiety.

'Would it be fair to say then that there is a problem between how you see the things that you do and the way she sees them?' He didn't pause to consider and began a fast tirade.

'That's it, exactly – but she's wrong! I'll give you an example. Just last week I was fighting in the Black Country Open. Me and Trevis had a pact that we'd enter a competition every week if there was one going. This one was at Haden Hill, so no distance. I decided only to fight the open weight – I do well against the big bastards. There was quite a large entry and I had two easy wins in the early rounds. I don't know who the first bloke was but the second was big Ian from Solihull. I don't get on with him, so I was glad when I dumped him and didn't he go down - like a ton of bricks or what! Obviously when I left the mat, I did a bit of show-boating, 'call me King – bow down before me scum,' that sort of thing. Most people laughed or hurled abuse, the usual stuff. The ref, miserable bastard, called me back and said he'd disqualify me if I did 'that sort of thing' again. I told him to bugger off and that he couldn't disqualify me after I'd won. I left him and went back to sit down with the others.

The mistake I made, of course, was to bring her with me in the first place. It's always a bad idea to bring wives or girlfriends to a competition, but she begged me to let her come along as she wanted to see me fight. You know I'm right Danny. What do you think?' He paused briefly and I answered.

'I think I'd like you to carry on with the story. What happened next?'

'God! When I sat down, she was in a huff. 'You shouldn't do that sort of thing – it's embarrassing!' She hissed at me, quietly - but the lads knew something was up. I didn't pay her much attention then because Harry Hobbs was on the mat taking someone apart as usual. There were a few more fights, Mick Smith from the 3Ks was having a great day.' I thought it time to edge him back to the matter at hand.

'And what was your girlfriend doing while you were enjoying the judo?'

'She just sat there sulking - which was a bit of a nuisance. There was nothing I could do so I thought 'bollocks to it' and left her to sulk. Then I was called and went back on the mat. My next fight was against Bryan Drew from the 3Ks – an absolute nightmare. Now I quite like fighting the big guys, they're stronger but I'm usually a damn sight faster. Bryan is different. He's like Parisi, strong and fast and a bloody good judo player. I went to the mat edge and Sod's Law it was the same ref I'd annoyed earlier. The fight started and Bryan and I danced around for a bit. I tried a few *ashi-waza* but it was like trying to foot sweep a tree. He attacked with a left *maki-komi* but I managed to step off it. I attacked again and Bryan started to move! The ref called *matte* at the same moment that I felt Bryan shift. I'd worked too hard to stop so I carried on. Bryan went over, off the mat and I did a roll over the top of him. The ref lost the plot at that point. I stood above Bryan to apologise and help him up. He was as good as gold and didn't care. The ref then told me to get back to the mark as he was going to penalise me. I ignored him as I was talking to Bryan.

He then tried to pull me away and I thought 'stuff this for a game of soldiers' and threw him. Bloody good throw too – *harai-goshi*. The guys from Solihull and the 3Ks loved it and shouted out '*Ippon* - Mad Muller, the King!' the usual bullshit. To cut a long story short, I was disqualified and kicked out of the competition. Later they tried to ban me from the BJA but it turned out that the ref shouldn't have touched me

When I got back to the seat the lads were having a great time saying that I should get a special medal. But my girl had a face like thunder. What do you think Danny? You're the shrink. I was right, wasn't I? The ref deserved it and she shouldn't have played her face!'

'Royston, my friend. I think you owe me a curry and a pint. And I'm pretty sure you have authority issues.'

⮌

The psychology conference which began the end of my marriage was entitled 'Is there a place for Freud in modern psychotherapy?' At the evening meal I did my best to behave in an acceptably civilised manner. I spoke uninspiringly to other table members and tried to relate to Rosalind with no more than normal politeness. If anything, I remained slightly distant - I think she found this amusing. She asked me to pass the salt but when she took it our fingers touched and remained in contact for that unnecessary, briefest moment known to lovers. In this immeasurable sliver of time a world of communication passed between us. I believe I started to tremble. She leaned towards me and whispered, 'Are you frightened?' What could I answer, except the truth?

'Yes, I think I am.' She stared with unflinching eyes. Her answer destroyed any vestige of willpower that I possessed.

'Is that because you want to ...?' She silently mouthed her last two words as she stared without waver into my eyes. The obscenity of her question froze me in exhilaration; my chest constricted and I could not breathe.

⮌

Roy Muller took his seat for the second session. 'I enjoyed it last week – good fun. A load of bollocks mind but good fun.'

'A load of bollocks eh? Yet you're here again bang on time.'

'I'm always on time.' That was indeed true. 'But I think you're wrong. I don't think I have a problem with authority any more than the next bloke. I mean nobody likes being told what to do or being pushed around do they?'

'You have a point... I was more thinking of how you react, perhaps more extremely than most?'

'Nope. Wrong again! You're not very good at this psychology bollocks, are you? I've been thinking a lot about the session last week and I'm fine. I don't even know why I'm here.' I did not point out the obvious disparity between his statements. I decided to provoke a response:

'If I remember correctly you were arrested a few years back for assault or affray - something like that?'

'Utter bollocks! I was arrested for being drunk and disorderly which was completely wrong as I don't drink! And it was my birthday...'

'What? Criminal offences don't count on your birthday?' He guffawed in frustration.

'I didn't say that. Listen – this is what happened. I was in town with a few mates and they'd been drinking. I had tomato juice with Worcester sauce that's all. At throwing out time we decided to go to the Manzil for a curry. We were walking along Smallbrook Ringway having a sing-song and a larking about when a couple of 'plods' came out of the shadows and started giving us the old chat.'

'Larking about Roy? What was that exactly?'

'Nothing much. I think I was play fighting with one of the other judo lads and another was practising being a tightrope walker on the railings above the underpass. Just a bit of fun!' He paused briefly and smiled in happy recollection. 'One officer got a bit shirty and said we needed to calm down and go home otherwise he was going to arrest us for disorderly conduct. I said this was rubbish as I was not being disorderly - just practising a few judo moves with my mate. This seemed to annoy him. Just then a Panda car that was passing stopped and another two police got out and between them had us standing with our hands up against a wall.'

'Fair enough smart-arse,' said the cop who was giving all the verbals, 'it's your lucky day. I'm going to arrest you for being drunk and disorderly if that suits you better.' I said it did and added, 'Thank you officer.'

'Further-more if you walk nicely, like good little boys down to Digbeth nick, it will go down well with the magistrate in the morning and the walk will do you good.' Royston stopped abruptly and looked at me with piercing eyes.

'Did you know that I'm claustrophobic.' This sudden statement took me by surprise.

'No, I didn't. I've never noticed any sign of it.'

'Ah, well it comes and goes. But I am claustrophobic, definitely. It's why I don't do *ne-waza*.' He continued with his tale.

'Well, we got to the nick; the desk sergeant booked us in, took our ties, shoe-laces and belts. He asked for a load of personal details and wished me 'Happy Birthday' when he took down my date of birth. Then we were taken down to the cells and that is where I drew the line. I told him that I had a medical condition, a fear of being in enclosed spaces. The station sergeant looked like ' George Dixon of Dock Green,' the policeman off the telly. He said to me that he sympathised but as the superintendent's office was locked, he had nowhere else to put me and thought it best if I went into the cell. 'Otherwise,' he said, 'I'll call the heavy brigade and have you thrown in and add resisting arrest to the charge sheet.' The others went into their cells but I wasn't keen.' He changed tack. 'Do you like gangster films Danny?'

'I like some of them – the old ones best.'

'Me too! I'm a big fan of Jimmy Cagney and Humphrey Bogart, that sort of film. So, I shoved against the cell door frame and shouted for a laugh, 'Do your worst copper – you'll never get me to talk.' I think that's a quote from George Raft in 'Scarface.' This caused a right fuss. I braced my hands and feet against the door and refused to go inside. George heaved, his mate shoved then a third one came along but I was strong and fit and they couldn't get me in. One of the young constables said he'd break my arm with his truncheon if I didn't let go. By now the old sergeant was very red in the face – I thought he was having a heart attack! He mopped his head with a handkerchief and said, 'Let's all calm down - I'm too old for all this,'

I tell you Danny he was puffing and panting something awful. He put his arm around my shoulders and said, 'Roy, as it's your birthday how about if you go into the cell with the door unlocked. Would that be better? Call it a birthday present.' At that moment I knew I'd won! And that's what happened! English justice at its best. At five o'clock they kicked us out and told us to report to the magistrate's court for sentencing at ten. What do you think of that!'

'I don't know – I haven't a clue. You were lucky I think Royston. What happened at court?'

'That was a farce – but I must hand it to the magistrate, he had a brain in his head. We were all charged with being drunk and disorderly. I protested and said I didn't drink.'

'Fair enough young man, we will scratch the 'drunk' part from the record but you're still guilty of disorderly conduct. I propose to fine you all one pound and ten-shillings each. Do you have anything to say?' I put my hand up and asked for time to pay as I was broke. The magistrate played along.

'Well Mr Muller, as it was your birthday, I will remove the fine in your case, but justice must be served. Your friends will now be charged two pounds each payable within seven days. You can sort out the money with them. That is my final word. Next case!'

∽

I never answered Rosalind's brazen question - I could not. I found it shocking, disarming, and very exciting. I concentrated upon eating dinner which I recall was roast lamb but nervousness rendered it tasteless and panic constricted my throat. I could barely swallow. I attempted to converse with others and was trying to put forward a coherent argument in defence of Freud when I felt Rosalind's hand rest upon my inner thigh and then slide upwards. My critique ceased and five pairs of eyes stared at me from across the table puzzled at my sudden halt.

'A very interesting point of view Danny,' a distinguished, greying professor introjected to break the silence. 'Most interesting, please carry on...' Rosalind's hand closed tightly.

'Mmmph, oh!' I sighed in reply.

'Are you alright?' asked the professor. Under the table her hand loosened and tightened.

'Mmph, oh, ooh,' I repeated. The other table guests looked startled at my response. 'I'm sorry I feel unwell. I must go.' I grabbed the linen napkin and ensuring that it hung over my crotch hastily left the table bent double, and made my way to the toilet. I was painfully tumescent. I locked myself in the first cubicle and urgently relaxed myself. With some little relief found, I put the seat down and sat. 'What on earth is going on?' I asked myself. Her behaviour seemed clear enough. She was a beautiful woman, with all the power and confidence that comes from being sexually self-assured in a society when traditional restraints have loosened. I listened to my own pompous lecture with irritation. It was not her behaviour that was troubling – it was mine! Why was my body on fire with such primitive lust? I was hardly an adolescent but had urges so strong that, had they not been so exciting, would have been terrifying. When I worked in Manchester, I had been scornful of those lost to heroin. Was Rosalind my opiate? I remained seated for a further twenty minutes and made the decision that I would not return to the restaurant but go to my room, pack my overnight bag and go home.

She was waiting for me, leaning against the wall opposite the toilet door with one foot raised behind her. She was wearing old fashioned black school gym shoes which seemed more erotic than high stilettos. She was languorously smoking a menthol cigarette and gave a mischievous smile. I fell headfirst into her baby-blue eyes.

'I hope you're feeling better now?' A brief pause followed but her laughing, mocking eyes never left mine. 'Dinner is finished - shall we go up to my room for dessert?' I had rehearsed well the words of refusal - which I didn't say.

'Yeah - okay.' I took her beckoning hand and knew I was completely lost.

We went to bed and had 'dessert', and stayed for supper, a midnight snack, a dawn breakfast, a second breakfast, and elevenses. At lunchtime we pulled apart with a kiss and she sat up unclothed and unselfconscious. 'That was amazing,' she said. 'I expected it to be good – but it was perfect. You are a wonderful lover and so inventive! But all that exercise has given me an appetite and you, my lovely man, must need to refuel. Shall we go down and see if they're still serving?' She leaned over to kiss. I tried to pull her towards me once more and she playfully struggled. 'Don't you dare! Don't you bloody well dare!' she laughed and fell back into my arms.

⌒

When I returned home my mind was a contradiction of elation and guilt.

Helen was unhappy that I hadn't phoned and my excuses were hollow. She also commented that I smelled of perfume which in truth must have been the hotel's shampoo as I had spent an age in the shower after Rosalind left. Her departure was almost business like.

'I don't want your phone number so you don't have to worry that I might call when your wife is around.' She dictated her number. 'Now remember it – don't write it down. If you want to meet up again just call.'

The next week passed awkwardly with Helen being largely uncommunicative. This was manageable as I saw little enough of her. I was daily commuting from Cheshire to Birmingham which was not too bad in the Capri thanks to its three-litre engine and the M6 motorway. The little penitential things I did seemed contrived even to me, and were received with rebuff. 'Oh, how sweet you've brought me flowers.' Her voice was monotonous and unconvincing. She put the bouquet, still wrapped, into the sink and there it stayed for a day. I found the flowers the next evening - in the bin. On Friday morning she asked if we could exchange cars as she needed to bring home some boxes of paperwork – not an unusual request as her Triumph Spitfire was indeed short of space. On Friday evening while out for an evening run, I made a phone-call from the village call-box. On Saturday I put my golf clubs into the back of the Capri and said I would be back later than usual as I was meeting up with a set of old friends and we were hoping to play two rounds. There was no kiss good-bye nor affectionate wave.

I drove from Cheshire to Oxford, taking great care not to speed, and met Rosalind on the steps of the Bodleian Library. She lounged against the ancient wall wearing a baggy sweater, short skirt and working boots. I was once again elated and elevated – my heart sang. The following events were predictably carnal and unimportant.

On Sunday Helen and I got into the Capri – we had a standing Sunday dinner arrangement with friends and her frostiness seemed to be lessening. I had left my golf clubs in the rear seat but had made sure that they were in a different place and had also removed the head covers. On the way back from Oxford the previous evening I had stopped in a country lay-by and thrashed around with each of the clubs in a muddy ditch. As Helen got into the passenger seat, I casually looked at the clubs and remarked,

'I must give those clubs a good clean.' Her reply was monosyllabic – a passive/aggressive,

'Oh.'

⤻

I've mentioned that Helen was a woman of outstanding qualities, accomplishments and skills. In fact, we shared many similarities in personality but differed greatly in one; I am comfortable drifting through life in a state of relative disorder whereas she was organised and precise. We drove in silence for a mile or so.

'Pull over into the next lay-by,' she spoke coldly.

'What's up?' I pulled up, switched off the ignition, and turned to face her.

'I am going to ask you one question and want you to answer truthfully.' I started to worry but kept a calm demeanour.'

'Go ahead, shoot.'

'Where did you go yesterday?'

'I told you. I met some of the golfing crowd and we played a couple of rounds of golf. It was Roger's birthday...' I lied like a frightened school-boy. She opened the car door and got out.

'I used this car for work on Friday. When I got back it had twelve thousand, six hundred and seventy-three miles on the clock. I will walk home and I don't want to see you again unless you can explain how you managed to drive two hundred and seventy miles to play golf. Where did you play, Rhyl?' She angrily slammed the door and began walking back the way we had come. I turned around, and drove past her without waving. Guilt fuelled my rage so I collected a few shirts, suits and the like from our home and drove back to Birmingham. That night I slept in a cheap hotel but quickly realised that the money I was making was insufficient for this to be a long-term solution. On Monday I bought a sleeping bag and began camping in my car.

꙳

Roy Muller arrived punctually for his third session, carrying two large plastic carrier bags. 'Are you growing a beard?' He growled by way of greeting.

'No.'

'Well get a new razor.' He dropped the bags heavily onto my desk. 'These are for you – so no more excuses.'

'What's in the bags?'

'A course of therapy - proper therapy, not this talking bollocks. Two judo suits, flip-flops and a black belt. No excuses now, have you Danny? You can get back on the mat and I'll carry on beating you up from where I left off. They're top suits as well, not the Milom's rubbish that look like they've been washed in piss!' I was genuinely taken aback and even worse involuntarily welled up. Judo suits are not normally an emotional present but this represented friendship, warmth and understanding and for want of a better phrase 'judo love.'

'Two suits?'

'Of course – one to wear and one in the wash.'

'What size are they?'

'Size six – extra-large, you fat bastard. Anyway, down to business.' He pulled his chair close to my desk, 'and I really think you should get a couch.' He sat down and picked up a half-filled pint glass that I had inadvertently left. He sniffed it and began to take a tentative sip.

'I wouldn't if I were you,' I warned.

'What is it? Apple juice? Lager? – Whatever it is, it smells off.'

'There's no toilet here and at night it's too far to go to the one in the basement... '

'You dirty bastard! There's a window there for feck sake. You should use that like anyone else would.'

'I can't – it's too high.' Royston Muller sighed in exasperation, examined the window, made mental calculations and smirked.

'Well, I could reach – and you're taller than me.'

～

Since Helen and I had parted I had behaved like an adolescent coward scared to face the consequences of my own actions. I had not seen or communicated with her for a few weeks, but I had raced down to Oxford several times to see Rosalind, in search of comfort and physical gratification, both amply supplied. I knew I would have to face the music sooner or later and so summoned up the courage to phone. The conversation was brief.

'Helen, we need to talk...'

'Correction. *You* need to talk and I'm not prepared to have a conversation on the phone.'

'Okay, I'll come back on Friday...' she cut in.

'I'll be here until seven. Don't arrive any later as I won't be available.' That was that; curt, frosty perhaps masking a torrent of emotion. But I believed her, and just before seven, I pulled the Capri onto the driveway. In truth it felt good to be home. I liked the house - it was familiar and reassuring. Helen did not greet me but when I entered the lounge, she was sitting calmly on the vintage leather settee drinking a glass of white wine. I was flustered and something seemed wrong, the room perhaps? I felt ill at ease literally shaking at the prospect of the conversation to come.

'Hi Helen. If you don't mind just give me a minute. I'm sweaty and sticky and need to go upstairs and change. I won't be five minutes.' She sipped her wine and looked stonily impassive.

'Take as long as you need,' she spoke in a tone that was far from reassuring. I opened my wardrobe to find it completely empty, similarly so my chest of drawers. I looked around the bedroom. The Roberts side-band radio that rested by my side of the bed was missing. The bathroom was devoid of my grooming paraphernalia, bathrobe and toiletries. I rushed downstairs. Before looking at Helen I glanced at the fireplace where, to the side, should have rested an antique astronomical telescope; a beautiful six-inch Newtonian reflector all lustrous brass and oiled mahogany. My stereo system was missing from the sideboard and the record rack was largely empty.

'You've moved my stuff then – where is it?'

'Well, the first week I didn't hear from you I put all your clothes and small items into black plastic bags. The second week you didn't call I put the bags and the rest of your belongings into a skip, which by the way, was collected yesterday.' I looked towards the fireplace.

'My telescope?'

'In the skip.'

'The Quad stereo system?'

'In the skip.'

'My judo trophies?' She didn't answer but simply stared and sipped wine. 'You've thrown all my stuff away!' My voice raised into a shout. 'Have you any idea how valuable it was?' She answered quietly with tears slowly trickling down her face.

'You've thrown our marriage away. Have *you* any idea how valuable *that* was?' She looked at me, wide-eyed in sadness more than anger but with pointed sarcasm added, 'And you've still got your golf clubs.'

'What about my climbing gear in the loft?'

'It's your lucky day, cowboy – I didn't know it was there.'

⸎

A dojo is a safe harbour, a port in a storm. I looked around Great Barr judo club and recognised a few faces but most were strangers.

Muller was taking the class. I was wearing an unfamiliar, stiff suit but standing there at the edge of the mat, waiting to be invited on, I felt something which had recently gone from my life. Roy called me on to the *tatami*, I slipped off the *zoris* bowed and stepped forward; the mat was good under my feet. I felt protected; yes, that was it - relaxed, peaceful and safe. Every *dojo* is different but in a deep meaningful way they are the same. The Greek philosopher, Plato, wondered how such things could be: All trees are different but each is recognisably a tree. He came to the conclusion that there must be a perfect 'form' in the realm of the Gods from which every other tree derived its essence.

I think there must also be a perfect *dojo* – a place of learning, combat and sanctuary.

⌣

I greeted him as he came into my office. I knew his knock, and it announced seven o'clock to the very second. 'Hiya Royston, how's things?' He looked at me and frowned.

'You do know I suppose, that my name isn't Royston - it's just Roy?'

'Yes, I do.' I offered no further explanation.

'That's good – I just wondered.' He paused for a while and looked around the office. I had made it less sparse since his first visit a couple of months earlier; a few pictures on the walls, my grand-mothers art deco clock, plants and a coffee maker. 'You were rubbish on the mat last night.'

'Thank you, Royston – that's reassuring.' He seemed slightly ill at ease and hesitated before speaking.

'I've enjoyed out little chats but I think this will be the last one – for a while at least.'

'You think the re-wiring is complete?'

'I don't know about that but a few plugs have been fixed and a fuse replaced here and there. I feel good about myself.' Roy had arrived punctually for every therapy session and after two months of Rational Emotive Therapy had gained a few insights. He realised that his 'bravado' was simply a barrier built to protect vulnerable aspects of his core personality. This revelation caused him some concern. 'Does this mean I need to stop larking about?'

'Not at all: it means that now you have a choice. Do what you want – or not, as the case may be. But realise your behaviour is under your control and it is up to you to make good choices.'

'No shit Sigmund! Anyway, I've decided to go to Sweden. They want a judo coach over there and me and the girl have decided to split - it all seems for the best. How about you? How's your love life?'

'There's no fix to be had between me and Helen. She's mortally hurt and I have to say with good reason. So that's heading for the divorce courts – thankfully there are no kids.' Royston Muller shrugged his shoulders, a gesture of sympathy not of dismissal.

'I saw Donnelly last week and he was asking about you. What happened between you two? Thick as thieves, closer than brothers you were. He says he hasn't seen you for ages.'

'Nothing happened – just life got in the way. How is Peter?'

'He's great – taking his judo very seriously. He's at Solihull a couple of nights a week, Fishers on Thursday; Trevis is there now - he left the Morris. Pete trains with the squad at Crystal Palace most week-ends. To be honest he goes wherever there is a good knock. I think at the back of his mind he's hoping he might be considered for a place at the Montreal Olympics. We'll see.' It was apparent we were just two friends idly talking.

'Roy – lets go to the pub. I'll buy you a large tomato juice.'

'With Worcestershire Sauce?'

'Of course!'

⤚

Chapter Sixteen
A Poisoned Chalice

THINGS WERE NOT going well with Rosalind. There were many apparent psychological indications of this, but the first physical realisation came in the form of an irritating little itch. It was not normally present but became obvious, at first just minorly annoying but later sorely painful, during the act of sexual congress. I did not know quite what to make of it. The best thing about my relationship with her was the complete ecstasy of the sexual act. Now the ultimate moment was happening far too quickly and diminished by the unpleasant sensitivity that accompanied the procedure.

I did not say anything at first. I had gleaned a smattering of medical knowledge in my student days and from my work as a psychologist, so I knew damn well that my condition had not been acquired from a toilet seat. Alone one evening I washed and dried a straight sided beer glass and when convinced it was completely clean, I half filled it with urine – my own of course. This indicated two things. Firstly, that I needed to drink more water as the liquid was a darkish yellow rather than a healthy pale-straw colour. Secondly it was full of milky filamentous streaks which did not bode well. This worried me. I had not had intimate knowledge of anyone other than Rosalind for over a year, and so if my suspicions were correct there was only one source of the expected infection.

A visit to the 'Special Clinic' is less problematic than you might think. In my book it is far less nerve wracking than a trip to the dentist. It was all very matter of fact and anonymous. A urine sample provided and speedily analysed. The doctor, a handsome young fellow with a neatly trimmed beard sat down with me and cheerily explained the results. He introduced himself as Marcus.

'Well, there's some good news and some bad news...' Without waiting for me to respond to this corny line he pressed on. 'The good news is that you have a minor dose of the clap and the bad news is that we can easily cure it. Nothing to worry about, a course of Penicillin will put you right.' He sat there, fingers touching, content with himself, proud of a job well done.

'Shouldn't that be the other way round?'

'What?'

'The good news and bad news thing - you said it the wrong way round.' He waved his arm airily.

'Did I? Oh well you get my drift - nothing to worry about. We'll have to do a bit of contact tracing though, which can be a bit awkward. Have you been playing away from home, tasting greener grass on the other side of the fence, ploughing a different furrow - that sort of thing?'

'I have not, I most certainly have not.' He frowned.

'Sorry old chum. Then there is only one other explanation. You'll have to tell her - no way round it I'm afraid.' I felt anxious and unthinkingly replied.

'That's a bit of a bummer.' He laughed and managed to make his humour acceptable.

'Technically not. Had that been your mode of entrance, so to speak, you wouldn't be in this pickle.'

I drove straight from the clinic in Birmingham to my flat, a Victorian house converted into apartments, the days of sleeping in my office now long over. I was outraged, not so much about the venereal disease, but that I had caught it from Rosalind. We had been together now for about a year, but I was not sure how 'together' we were. I felt betrayed. I had ruined my marriage for her and the chaos that entailed had not settled. Helen was petitioning for divorce and I was not contesting – how could I? The house we had bought in Cheshire was now empty. Here at least there was some good news as there had been plenty of interest in it from prospective buyers. An offer had been made and accepted, documents signed, and a completion date finalised – I was a bit hazy on the finer details with other things on my mind.

A maxim I developed then, and still hold, is that it is never wise to discuss relationship issues when tired or drunk – both are a recipe for disaster especially the booze. Conversely, in the morning, sober and after a night's sleep, is a good time. Hence, I decided I would drive to Oxford first thing on the morrow, a Saturday, and attempt to have a mature conversation. I was bitterly conflicted. The anticipation of seeing Rosalind filled me with expectant excitement but that she obviously had another lover or lovers of which I was unaware, equally filled me with jealous dismay. I sat in my spacious but sparse apartment, poured a moderate glass of Jameson's and began to brood.

⤷

I had no right to expect fidelity of Rosalind at all. Considering my adulterous behaviour, I was being completely hypocritical. We were not married nor indeed had exchanged any other tokens of commitment. The manner of our meeting suggested that she was a 'free spirit' but nonetheless I expected her to be exclusively faithful to me and was hurt, jealous and angry that she manifestly was not. Mind you, truth be known I had had doubts for a while and so I sipped the whiskey carefully and pondered past events.

It's amazing how perceptive *homo Sapiens* can be, particularly if there is a hint of threat. The great biologist Richard Dawkins wrote a brilliant book – 'The Selfish Gene' which explains why nature has designed men to jealously guard their mate from others while at the same time being happy to 'play the field', 'sow wild oats' or any of the other euphemisms for male promiscuity.

I recalled one morning some months earlier and subsequent happenings:

I had arisen from Rosalind's bed and walked to the kitchen to make a morning drink. I heard her go to the door to collect the morning's post; she was back in bed when I returned with the coffee. I admired her sensuous curves as she lay face down and uncovered before me. Two things happened. Firstly, I noticed a single sheet of paper partially protruding from beneath her pillow. My eyesight was good, and I read the signature - 'Robin,' followed by a row of the alphabetical letter universally signifying affection. Secondly, she rolled slightly and covered the note. Rationally, there was no reason whatsoever to believe the doubts which were forming. Everything could just as easily have been a manifestation of my own insecurities but there followed an interesting succession of events.

A few weeks later we were at dinner with some of her friends, an Oxford set but I held my own easily in the pompous 'intellectual' conversations that were held around the candle-lit table of a Jericho restaurant. Some bright thing waxed lyrically about D.H. Lawrence. Rosalind mentioned that she had a friend who had a small yacht named after one of his characters – *Gudrun,* but then seemed flustered and eager to change the subject.

A month or so afterwards Rosalind departed for a week in Greece – a holiday she had already booked and paid for otherwise she would not dream of going without me – how could I think otherwise? She duly returned tanned and effervescent. The strangest thing then occurred, mere co-incidence of course. I was watching television alone, paying little attention until a well-known actress, now aging but her beauty still evident, told of the trials of being married to a much younger man. Her husband, it seemed had overcome his marital doubts by taking a few weeks alone, sailing around the Greek islands. She related how he had an emotional epiphany whilst standing, washed in the rays of a heart-breaking, beautiful sunset, in an ancient sea-facing temple dedicated to Aphrodite. The Goddess spoke to him, and he realised that his life's love was indeed she – his wife.

The boat was called *Gudrun* and his name was Robin.

⤺

The night's sleep had done me good. I had stopped drinking early and so was without a hangover – I was a bit fuzzy maybe, but nothing that water and paracetamol would not cure. I had arrived at some conclusions: I had no right to expect faithfulness or indeed anything of Rosalind. She was a free woman, and her body was surely hers to use as she saw fit? We had made no vow of commitment to each other. I was behaving as if she had broken a contract and none had been made. Perhaps this was the problem? I would drive to Oxford and explain the situation including the medical practicalities and suggest that we commit ourselves monogamously to each other. I was not yet divorced so any idea of marriage seemed somewhat inappropriate. Yes, I would calmly explain the situation and forgive her for giving me a dose. I would tell her that I loved her, and her alone. Yes, that should do the trick. Deep down I still wanted to strangle her and the poxy bastard who she was shagging behind my back, but I understood these thoughts were driven by childish emotions and as a rational adult I would keep such ideas in check.

It was very early when I left my flat without breakfast. There was a West Indian store nearby, and I called in to purchase a can of Nutrament and a snack before cutting across Birmingham to the M40. Even with this detour I would arrive at her place before seven, but what the hell – I would take something for breakfast, and we could then discuss our bright future like the adults that we were.

I liked the handwritten sign on Alista Constantine's shop. 'Robba man – Keep Out! I have a gun and will choot you!' I had once suggested to him that it was not the best warning to have posted and could get him into trouble with the police. He said that everything was cool and that he had a 'rangement' with the police officer. Ali Constantine talked with a slow, honeyed, drawl that conjured images of a blue ocean, surf lapping onto white sands and palm trees waving in a gentle warm breeze. He said he was related to royalty and his grandfather was a Baron. 'A Baron for playing cricket, man. Can you imagine that?' It was impossible to be with him without feeling cheerful, relaxed and having an inexplicable desire to drink white rum and coke whilst wearing a garish shirt. Ten years earlier his store had been robbed while he slept soundly upstairs, since which time he never went to bed but dozed all night in a dilapidated recliner chair, lights on and store open. In his lap nestled a Smith and Wesson snub nosed .38 calibre pistol – the famed 'Midnight Special.' His manner of nocturnal rest may have contributed to his nickname. The doorbell of the shop tinkled as I entered.

'Good morning 'Laidback,' are you awake?'

'Ah Danny! My man – Hi yam horlways awake. And what can I get you this fine day. Are you up early or been party-ing?'

'Up early. I'm off to Oxford and want a can of chocolate Nutrament and something nice for breakfast to take with me.'

'Oxford eh? I don't think you're off to the university. I bet there's a pretty young thing who's going to get a dawn surprise?' I smiled and shrugged.' I thought so Danny. Take two cans, boy – you might need the henergy! And take a couple of mangoes – they're ripe and juicy, know what I'm saying? Nothing like something ripe and juicy for breakfast!' We both laughed at the ubiquitous male smuttiness, but I took the fruits. It seemed like a good idea.

The journey was uneventful. I listened to the radio and the date proclaimed, June 6th rang a bell and made me feel uncomfortable. I knew of course that this was the date of the D-Day landings some thirty years before – but this was not it. Something important was happening or had happened but I could not recall what it was. I arrived at Rosalind's at about six-thirty still puzzling and uneasy. It was unnecessary to ring her doorbell as the girl in the downstairs flat was up early. She saw me arrive and let me in after I waved and tapped on her window. 'Thanks Wendy. I'll just nip upstairs and surprise Rosalind if that's okay? She is in, isn't she?' Wendy stood still in a white fluffy bathrobe, her hair wrapped in a towel, and stared blankly for a moment before replying.

'I think she's in. I'll go and check if you like – yes that's probably best.'

'No need Wendy. I know the way.' At which I skipped nimbly passed her and quietly climbed the single flight of stairs clutching the two ripe mangoes supplied by Laidback Ali. I have no idea why I decided to try the door of Rosalind's bedsit rather than knocking – but I did. It opened noiselessly and I entered closing it gently behind me.

I don't think that I looked a menacing figure as I stood over the bed. I mean is it even possible to look vicious while holding a large ripe mango in each hand? I don't think so. That being said, he did scream in terror or panic. We knew each a little. He was one of her crowd and we had been in company a few times. His name was Elric. The racket woke the sleeping Rosalind who, seeing that I was the cause for the alarm, smiled happily and jumped out of bed naked with arms open wide. I noticed that she was clean shaven, a recent departure and an unwelcome distraction.

'Hello Danny! What a nice surprise! What are you doing here?' She seemed genuinely pleased and flung her arms around me and nakedly hugged. A greeting not returned, in some part due to the fruit clogging my hands. I'm pretty good with words normally, a quality which I attribute to being Irish and the Gaelic story telling tradition. I had nothing to say, no cutting response, nothing at all. I was devoid of speech and lacked even rage. My relationship with Rosalind ended with possibly the worst, most ineffectual parting lines ever.

'Good-bye Rosalind. Enjoy the mangoes.' At which I tossed them, without force, in the general direction of Elric's flaccid genitals. June 6th D-Day– a date to remember.

⤺

As I drove back to Birmingham, strangely unemotional, Brian Redhead, a Radio Four presenter was reminiscing with old soldiers about their wartime experiences. They had poured out from landing craft onto the Normandy beachhead into heavy German machine gun fire, on their quest to liberate Europe. And then it came to me – my earlier disquiet at this date became startlingly clear. Today was the day the house, our house, the matrimonial home of myself and Helen, became the legal property of its new owners. At mid-day the sale was complete. I had arranged to meet Barry and Anna, the buyers, at eleven-thirty to hand over my keys and to confirm that everything not included in the sale had been removed. How on earth could this have slipped my mind? 'Damn!' – I shouted aloud and banged the steering wheel in frustration. I had no option but to drive north and keep the appointment.

⤺

I parked the Capri on the road outside my house as it was obvious that the driveway would soon be required by the new owners – removal vans and so forth. My key turned easily in the lock; I recalled the day that I had fitted it to meet insurance requirements. The near empty house was nonetheless full of ghostly reminders of the few years Helen and I had lived there; the décor, fitted carpets, a breakfast bar. Each room was bare except the main bedroom, the new bed and fitments being included in the house purchase. It was eleven-thirty when I remembered to check the loft. I opened the trap door and extended the ladder. As I climbed into the roof space my hands encountered a small pile of glossy magazines. I threw the rucksacks of climbing gear onto the landing and carried the literature into the bedroom.

It is strange to recall that the most frequently indulged form of human sexual activity is the solitary act, which is also the least discussed. The Kinsey Reports, early studies of human sexual behaviour, were controversial and tremendous accomplishments both scientifically and socially. But they were of their time. (*Male Sexual Behaviour 1948; Female Sexual Behaviour 1953*) The reported incidence of masturbation was very low in both cases for the simple reason that the participants in both studies lied. It's not difficult to see why. If I was asked, even in the strictest confidence, how often I indulged myself, I would lie too

⌒

It was just past eleven-forty when I laid the magazines lovingly on the bed. Some had the status of old friends and one or two were particular favourites. Take *Men Only, June 1972*. I found 'Lady Jane' of artistic merit. I have no idea why stockings, suspender belts and other frippery are erotic – but they are. *Miss June 1973* and her playmate pouted lasciviously as they fed each other strawberries. One of the silly girls had obviously made a mess with the squirty cream and they were happily, and sensibly licking it off their respective chests. Waste not, want not! My favourite was *Penthouse, October 1974,* in which Dolores and Sonia, both conservationists, were having a bath together thus saving water. Soapily washing each other was simply the most practical thing to do, bath space being limited.

I was interrupted from my appreciation of the fine photography and artistic merit of these pictures by the doorbell ringing and the sound of muffled voices outside. I zipped up my jeans and looked out of the window. By my watch Barry, Anna and the estate agent were early. I grabbed the bags of ropes, harnesses, karabiners and the like and rushed downstairs.

Memory is funny isn't it? Both the things we remember and the things we forget. There was a celebrated case in the nineteen-thirties of a bishop who had been arrested while indulging in immoral behaviour with a woman who provided 'discipline for naughty school-boys.' This of itself is nothing much – a big deal in those days but not now. The odd thing was that when he woke up in a police cell the next morning, he did not know why he was there. Eminent psychiatrists examined him and testified that he was not faking this memory loss. In a later statement his Grace confessed that it had been of long concern that he regularly woke up with a sore backside and had no idea from where the welts came. He had assumed they were either of divine or diabolical origin and had prayed hard to be given guidance as to which.

↩

Barry and Anna, a pleasant couple had fallen in love later in life and this was to be their first home. They were thoughtful, caring and compassionate and had met as members of the local church choir. They had brought with them a bottle of cheap fizz and four plastic cups in order that we may 'join in a celebratory toast.' Anna also asked that we might hold hands in a circle and allow Barry to say a short prayer by way of blessing the house. I agreed of course but warm Cava and an impromptu prayer meeting were neither greatly welcomed, and so with some haste I handed over my house keys and made a quick exit.

I was getting into the Capri when the screaming began - a high screech of anguish. I was momentarily puzzled but then recalled the display I had left in the bedroom. Anna came rushing out of the house clutching an armful of what by any standard was only soft pornography and threw the magazines at the car as I drove off. I heard her rage above the engine noise.

'You bastard! You dirty bastard! It was the first time I had seen anyone actually stamp their feet and gesture with a shaking fist. It had rained a little, just a light drizzle but sufficient to stick the centrefold of one of the glossy mags to the sloping rear window of the Capri. I recognised her. It was *Miss December 1972* from Playboy's Christmas edition. She was not one of my favourites; posing naked in the snow, except for a red Santa Claus hat and furry boots, seemed a little silly. I don't know why I'd kept her for so long.

❧

I didn't like my life much after my divorce from Helen and the disastrous affair with Rosalind so decided to have some time off.

When love's tragedies struck my brother Kevin, he ran away. First to sea in the guise of being a merchant sailor and the second time love's boat hit the rocks he became a bum, a hobo drifting around Europe. This was an accepted thing to do; the late 1950s were, after all the time of the 'beat generation.' Jack Kerouac did well when 'On the Road' (his account of 'dropping out' and travelling around America) hit the bookshops. It was obvious to me that in my current state of mind I could no longer continue as a psychotherapist – there were and are too many crackpots masquerading as counsellors. I decided as an alternative to uncomfortably traveling, sleeping in ditches and the like, as did Kevin, I would instead become a rock star. I mean, how difficult could it be?

❧

Dave Law looked at me with a slightly bemused expression. Dave, a practical man, did not like 'bemused' – it did not suit him. His world was ordered and straight forward. Also, he always called me Murph rather than Danny and I liked him for it - but would not, were it anyone else.

'Let's get this straight. You want to play in a band but don't play an instrument?'

'Yet,' I added. 'I don't play an instrument *yet*. That's why I'm here. You've played in bands. Which is the easiest to learn. I'm in a hurry. I want glamour, money and sexually compliant young women.'

'Well good luck with that! You're not making any sense Murph. I can't tell you what instrument to play. What do you like to listen to? Guitar, keyboards, percussion, brass? And what sort of music do you like? Rock. pop, blues, reggae, soul - what sort?' Dave is a calm individual, but I could see he was getting a bit edgy.

'Well actually I like jazz.'

'Stop right there Murph! Jazzers are the top of the tree. You can't just decide to play jazz. It will take you twenty years. Far too complicated – regardless of what instrument.'

'Okay, if jazz is too complex what is the least tricky?' Dave sighed and gave in.

'Blues I suppose. Twelve-bar is a piece of piss and only three chords. Anyone can play bad blues. But to play well...' I cut in.

'Okay, blues it is. Now what instrument. What is the easiest?'

'Murph, your question doesn't make sense. It's like asking what the easiest judo throw is?'

(Dave was a good judoka. Not a great player but a solid journeyman, the lifeblood that keeps the sport of judo going. On his day he would give anyone in the country a good scrap. He was a team player through and through. Shove him in a representative team and he would chew through iron bars rather than lose. He adopted a strange grip, his hands on either side of the *gi* low down at about waist level. He would pull his opponents in and upwards and perform an unusual left *harai-goshi*.)

'I've got work to do Murph. Come around to my place tonight. I've got a spare bass guitar, let's see how you get on with that for starters. Dave was a trained garage mechanic but for the last ten years had worked as a doorman around the clubs of Birmingham. He was a few years older than me and a lot wiser. 'The trick to being a good doorman is not how well you can fight but how well you can convince others not to.' Sensible stuff! He left his inner-city school in Aston at the age of fourteen and did bits and bobs. Yes, I know it should have been fifteen but, in those days, who was really counting? He became an apprenticed mechanic but, in the evenings, practised guitar and was soon playing around the pubs in a band called 'Spectre' that started to do well. The Birmingham rock scene was booming and produced talented bands that achieved international fame. Most have heard of The Moody Blues, The Spencer Davis Group, The Move and so on. So why not Spectre? Well, after doing national tours with the likes of the Rolling Stones the band's manager disappeared with his pockets full of cash leaving no forwarding address but instead a basket of unpaid bills.

It turned out that playing twelve bar blues was, at its most basic, very easy as Dave had explained. 'In simple tunes there are only three chords, so as bass player you can get away with just playing the root note, at the right time. That's it, easy.' And it was! In time I progressed but never learned to play anything complicated. Strangely this elevated my status in the band community. I remember Trevor Burton, a great guitarist and the bass player of the sixties band The Move, complimenting my playing:

'I like what you do Danny. You don't do much - but what you do is smack on the beat. That's all a bass player should do in a rock band. Anything more is just showing off, and no-one wants to hear it.'

Putting the band together was quite straight forward. I knew a lead guitarist from my work as a therapist. He was a paranoid schizophrenic and a phenomenal guitarist. His psychosis was drug induced. In the sixties he had uncritically ingested every psychoactive substance which came his way. This left him a physical and psychological wreck of a human being who could still play phenomenal guitar but was a nightmare of a person in every other respect. He's dead now and I will call him 'Rick.' He had been referred to me by the Employment Rehabilitation Centre in the hope that I would proclaim him sane and fit for work, hence saving the taxpayers some benefit money. It was quickly apparent that he was neither. A few months earlier, after watching some television police drama, he squashed his obese body into a hall-way cupboard for two days on 'stakeout' convinced that two students with whom he shared the house were mafia assassins. He arrested them with a red plastic water-pistol and phoned the police to inform them of his success. The students were rightly terrified of his manic appearance, erratic behaviour and smell. Rick was in turn, righteously indignant when it was he that the police took away, first covering the back seat of the police car with two black bin-liners.

Rick knew a drummer whose name was 'Shell-Shock.' He played his drum-kit with hate, and cotton wool stuffed in his ears. 'Tinnitus,' he explained. 'Too loud – I play too loud. Always have.' This explanation had come too late to serve as a warning. Now, the only relief he got from the continual aural hissing was to continue to play loudly. This seemed to drown out his internal noise. Shellshock was an easy drummer to play with and kept perfect time. It was impossible to miss the snare drum rimshot with which he conducted the band, delivered with such force that at most gigs he destroyed at least one stick.

The lead singer arrived by a process of accretion. We were practicing in a commercial studio when the padded soundproofed door opened, and skinny bearded long-haired rocker strolled in. His leather jacket proclaimed him to be a 'Cycle Tramp.' He spoke in a gruff Brummie voice, fashioned before the levelling influence of television.

'Yow nid a singer.' He looked at the drummer. 'Hello Shell-shock, I thought it was you. Still wrecking drum kits are ya?' This was Kirk, reformed wild man and born-again Christian who had had brief fame with an early sixties rock band. He idolised Jim Morrison, the famous singer of The Doors, so much so that when on stage singing a Doors number, he *was* Jim Morrison. In tribute to his famous hero Kirk would regularly strip off and perform naked or at least with his penis on display. At first, I found this disconcerting but in the end was content to notice that he was very well endowed and had a neat backside. The band did well quickly, thanks in the main to Kirk. Rick was both an asset and a liability. His guitar playing pleased the audiences, but his complete lack of personal grace and tact often offended the managers of venues, and cost us future bookings:

'How're you getting on lads,' asked a friendly northern club owner.

'Your sound system is shit,' answered Rick.

'Well, it were good enough for Shakin' Stevens last week...'

'He's shit as well. He wouldn't have noticed.' Rick delivered insults without thought or venom. He was saved from any further rigours of the Mental Health Act by an early death brought on by kidney failure. He was found by the paramedics who arrived to take him for bi-weekly dialysis, stone dead but still clutching a two-pound family pork pie. He was, as mentioned, an exceptional guitarist. It was his one good point

The band did well and made almost enough money for me to live frugally but necessitated that I did a few other jobs on the side. For example, an art student I met at a gig said that his college wanted a life model and that I should apply. This seemed like easy money and indeed proved to be. The lecturer was pleased that I should 'sit.' He explained that he'd had enough of skinny little runts and it would be nice for his students to sketch someone with a 'bit of beef' for a change. There is nothing erotic about sitting naked in a room full of teenagers. It is tedious and quite challenging. It's not that easy to remain motionless for twenty-minute stretches – but the money was appreciated. I also did a bit of gardening cutting grass and trimming hedges, bushes and so on.

༄

I explained all this to Roy Muller who I was amazed to see at a gig the band was playing in London. It was 'half-time.' The first set had gone well, and the band sat recovering. A powerful hand gripped my shoulder from behind and I turned to see the, not quite smiling, face of Royston.

'Bloody hell – what are you doing here? I thought you were in Sweden.' We shook hands and hugged but I felt he was a little reserved.

'I'm back for a couple of weeks and the London Open is at the week-end - I thought I'd go along and watch the lads. But what's all this?'

'All what?'

'Guitar playing with...' He looked at the rest of the band with suspicion perhaps even distaste and left his thoughts unsaid. In truth we were a strange mob; obese Rick in grubby tracksuit bottoms and a too tight Che Guevara tee-shirt; Shellshock wearing combat gear with a spider's web tattooed on his shaven head; Kirk in full bikers rig with waist length hair and me neatly dressed in a black business suit with white shirt and slim black tie. The others approved of my appearance. 'It makes you look like a misfit,' said Kirk. Roy and I moved table to speak privately. I answered his unfinished enquiry.

'It's what I do. A new job if you like.'

'What happened to the psychology bollocks then?'

'Nothing happened to it. I'm having some time off. I needed a rest.' This seemed to be the wrong thing to say.

'Rest! Rest from what! You didn't do anything except sit about chatting all day. I never took you for an idle bastard Danny. A bit weird yes – but not idle!'

'Thank you, Royston. That's good to know.' This seemed to appease him.

'It's your life Danny – waste it as you please, I suppose, but all the time at university what was all that about?' He sought for a saving grace to my new occupation. 'Pulling in good money are you? Or is it the sex? I hear you get a lot of girls - groupies that sort of thing.'

'Sorry to disappoint you Royston – no groupies, and the money is bad too. But I get along okay doing a bit extra on the side.'

'Such as?' Now I admit that my answers were a bit ambiguous, but I was getting fed up with his 'third degree' and the second set was due to start.

'In truth Roy, I'll do anything for a bit of LSD*. Well, I sell my body for a start – strip naked for people – it's a bit humiliating but pays the rent.' Royston was aghast.

'What! You're a gigolo! I don't believe it. You'd never make any cash! I've seen you in the showers; mine's bigger than yours and I've never been paid for it! You provide a service for old women who can't get any better – is that it?'

'Not at all. Teenagers mainly – of both sexes. Mainly girls, but a fair few boys.'

'I don't believe it - you're a lying bastard.'

'Nope, every word is completely true. Other than that, I cut a bit of grass which is more profitable than you would think and trim the occasional bush. Anyway, Roy we're back on stage.' I lit a liquorice-paper roll-up.

'When did you start smoking that shit? He asked accusingly.

'This? It's nothing Roy – it's not even tobacco, just herbs.'

(Author's Note: LSD – either the initials of a well-known hallucinogenic drug or a name given to money before decimal currency.)

Chapter Seventeen
The Quest for the Holy Grail

THE HOLY GRAIL, the ultimate prize in judo, is undoubtedly an Olympic medal - a gold medal preferably of course, but at these heights any medal is a supreme accolade. Peter Donnelly was completely committed to his noble task.

The Holy Grail is the stuff of Arthurian legend. Richard Wagner wrote a long and powerful opera on this theme, much beloved by a German dictator who will remain nameless. The cinema has profited greatly from these myths including countless bits of nonsense about 'Knights of the Round Table' – the best being 'Monty Python and the Holy Grail.' None of this stuff has any basis in history and interpretations differ. The Wagner opera is full of doom, gloom and bad things happening, dangerously shrieked at the audience by high pitched women and low growling men. The Monty Python film is ridiculously funny; I know which I prefer.

What is less well known is that the whole shooting match is a psychological metaphor for a young man's growth into independence – at least according to Carl Gustav Jung it is. He knew a thing or two and might have a point. A central idea of Jungian psychology is that you cannot pursue happiness:

"One cannot pursue happiness; if he does, he obscures it"

Somebody should have told me this, for as Peter sought his Holy Grail, I had gone off on a different tack.

౿

Peter Donnelly woke up and instinctively knew it was five-thirty. As softly as he was able, he got up without disturbing his quietly slumbering wife. Their beautiful baby daughter was still asleep in her bed-side cot and would hopefully remain so for the next hour. Before work, in a couple of hours, he had things to do. He consulted his training diary, an unnecessary foible as he knew full well his schedule for the day. He was in fine physical condition perhaps nearer ninety kilos than his normal weight of eighty-six. The extra training and protein rich diet were paying dividends. He had a healthy appetite but did not as a matter of course overeat. His breakfast was normally a couple of eggs for protein, cereal, fruit and nuts washed down with tea without sugar. But before this was the little matter of a six-mile run. He did not exactly hate running but as a big man did not enjoy it too much either. He aimed to keep an even six-minute mile pace but would not be disappointed if it took forty minutes. He would be back before six-thirty which gave him an hour to do a weight training session in the garden shed before showering, eating his meal and bidding an affectionate farewell to his loved, loving family. Then there would be the tedium of a gruelling five-hour factory shift before his lunch-break which would be dominated by more training.

The likelihood of him being selected for the Montreal Olympic team was by no means high – but it was a fair aspiration. Weight gain was a problem though; the great David Starbrook had made the under 93kg category his own. Peter knew there was no realistic possibility of stripping down to fight middleweight – and even if he did there was the little matter of Brian Jacks, the World and Olympic bronze medallist. His best shot was to train on the muscle and hope for the heavy-weight spot; the current holder, Keith Remfry could easily move up a notch; he was an excellent open-weight fighter.

He drank a morning cup of tea and left another on the bedside table next to Eileen. He kissed his fingers and touched baby Jade's head before creeping out of the bedroom. He quietly closed the front door of his home and headed off to do battle with Sutton Park. The November morning was chilled and crisp – there had been a light frost. Street lighting was plentiful and the yellow sodium glow lit his route with an eerie, monochrome hue. Not so the measured six-mile route around the park which was unlit - but the paths were in good order and clear.

'Peter, Peter! Wait!' He was pleased to hear the soft tones of Eugene Codrington his training partner. Pleased, but tinged with a hint foreboding. That Eugene had joined him meant the run would now be even harder work. The current European and World Wado-Ryu karate champion was ferociously dedicated and pushed training to limits which Peter found difficult. He was a natural athlete; lithe, graceful, agile, perfectly proportioned with general strength to match his own, even though Eugene had lighter musculature. In the gym, Peter would do bench-press repetitions with a seventy-kilo bar whereas Eugene moved a more modest sixty-five. But that both had phenomenal core strength was down to the insistence and dogged determination of Eugene; iron hard abdominals being the result of thousands of weight loaded sit-ups on an inclined bench. But running was different; Eugene was a 'natural', covering mile after effortless mile with an easy long, loping stride that Peter could not emulate. 'Good morning, Peter. How are you this fine day?' Eugene Codrington had impeccable manners.

'Well mate, very well. What torture have you got planned for me?'

'This morning my friend, you will run six miles in under thirty-five minutes. It is time Peter...'

'Come off it, Eugene. Thirty-six is the target!'

'No, thirty-six *was* the target. You're trying for the Olympics, aren't you? An Olympic shot-putter could do it in thirty-six minutes. No, it's thirty-five – and today's the day. It's all in the mind Peter, All in the mind!' Peter Donnelly's thought association led him briefly to think of his psychologist friend Danny Murphy. 'I wonder how he is?' But this speculation discontinued as he chased after his partner who was already running along the pathway alongside the park lake.

They raced the last hundred metres shoulder against shoulder until Peter tapped the gate post which marked the finish of their efforts. Eugene checked his stop-watch as Peter, bent over with hands on knees, vomited a meagre steam of lukewarm, bilious tea. 'Very good, my friend. Thirty-four-forty. Very good!' Peter lay on his back, avoiding the mess and looked through the trees, black silhouetted against the lightening sky.

Friendly farewells were exchanged and he jogged the half-mile to his home, cooling down relaxing and coughing. He was accustomed to this – the symptoms of his childhood 'weak chest' had never entirely disappeared. He took his door-key from his tracksuit pocket and let himself in. The post had been and he picked up a solitary letter from the door-mat. The kitchen sounds of plates and cutlery being set out for breakfast came from behind a closed door – Eileen was obviously up. He opened the door and flopped on a wooden chair.

'Hello sweetheart. How was the run? Sure, you look like a fella that's put in a hard shift.' Her soft, lilting Irish tones washed over him like a healing balm. 'Sit yourself down and have a cup of tea.' He did as bid and noticed for the thousandth time that she was beautiful – more so than any woman wearing a bathrobe and slippers had any right to be. Her face had that indefinable glow of an Irish rose emphasised and framed by cascading waves of raven hair.

'I see you've got a letter. What is it?'

'No idea... Where's Jade?'

'Oh, she's still sleeping – she's fine. Enjoy the quiet while it lasts.' She poured his tea while speaking the words that are understandable to all parents of a young child. 'Open the letter – we might have won the pools.' He thumbed open the envelope and immediately noticed the headed notepaper of the British Judo Association. He read it and was nervous to announce its message. 'Well go on then, what does it say?' He felt apprehensive and apologetic.

'Sorry darling, I don't know what to say.' He passed her the letter:

Dear Peter,

I have the pleasure to inform you that you have been selected to be a part of the British squad travelling to Japan for pre-Olympic training...

He feared the worst. What young mother would relish the prospect of being left alone in such a manner. 'Oh, Peter!' She joyously smothered him in affectionate kisses. 'That's great news! I must write a letter to Japan and tell them to watch out. Peter Donnelly in the Land of the Rising Sun – sure the eejits are not ready for such a calamity!' He felt humbled by her unqualified support. She never voiced complaint nor criticism; indeed, she had brought her own skills to his training programme:

'I need to be lighter on my feet. I need to be a bit nimbler in competition,' he confided to her after a mat session where he had felt leaden. She provided her uniquely Irish solution.

'Dancing will do the trick! Irish dancing. You'll never see lads with quicker feet than the boys that can dance. Skipping also...'

'I can't do either and I don't think...'

'That's true – you don't.' She placed a forefinger over his lips. 'But worry not, my beautiful boy – I can do both and will teach you well!'

Soon Peter was incorporating the skipping games which Eileen had learned in the playgrounds of Dundrum and the dancing steps from the streets of Dublin into the rigorous regime of a judo athlete. He realised just how much he owed to her support. He found himself making an internal vow. 'Whatever I achieve I owe it all to you Eileen. A fact I will never forget.' Unasked, she brought a clean towel which had been warming by the small kitchen fire and draped it over his head. 'Don't drip sweat on the floor – 'tis me who has to wipe it.' She kissed him and left to tend to their daughter who was lustily announcing to the world that she was awake.

&

Five British judoka with little else to do, ran through the midnight streets of Tokyo; still crowded, still bright, illuminated by a thousand neon light banners which draped towering skyscrapers. Brian Jacks and Peter Donnelly ran side by side talking – the pace was leisurely. To Brian, a sometime resident of this great city, the scene was familiar – not so Peter. 'Are you okay Peter? You seem to be limping a bit.' It was true, Peter was finding the run difficult. Each time his right foot landed on the tarmac he experienced a shooting pain which, though not agonising, made running uncomfortable.

'I'm okay Brian but the 'pull' I got training with Remf hasn't quite gone. I'll be alright.' This answer was only partly true. He had indeed damaged his leg while training at Crystal Palace with the mighty

Keith Remfry but he had kept the full nature of the injury hidden from his team-mates and Ray Ross the British Team manager. He cast his mind back to the event of a month or so before:

If he was to make the team for Montreal his only realistic option was in the heavyweight ranks. David Starbrook was without doubt the right and proper selection for the light-heavyweight slot. Peter knew he needed to put on ten kilos of muscle and train hard with the 'big boys.' During a randori session Keith Remfry attacked with a powerful *ashi-garuma* and as soon as Peter blocked the move, 'Remf' dropped onto his back attempting a fast-spinning *yoko-tomoe-nage*. Somehow, Peter's ankle locked between the mat and Keith's powerful, muscular frame. Something had to give and in this case the something was Peter Donnelly's right leg. Ray Ross, the team manager, took him to hospital where his lower leg was x-rayed and pronounced sound. The doctor examined the plates:

'No breaks I'm pretty sure of that. Probably tendon and ligament damage. We'll strap you up and you should be fine in a few weeks. Keep your weight off the leg as much as possible. I'll give you a supply of pain-killers. That's about as much as can be done.'

Later, Ross dropped him at Euston station for his return to Birmingham. 'Are you sure you're alright Peter. The Japan trip's in a month or so – I'd hate you to miss it.'

'I'm fine Ray. Just a bit of a 'pull' – I'll be fine, and don't worry!' His journey north was uneventful. He sat with his leg resting on the opposite seat placed on a newspaper that Peter carefully positioned. The pain was not excessive so he tipped the painkillers out of the carriage window. Eileen met him at Sutton Coldfield station and viewed his crepe bandaged leg with some alarm.

'What have you done this time my beautiful eejit? Another injury to add to the list – are you going after some record or other?' She kissed him affectionately and carried his kit-bag as they walked to the car.

'I've had it x-rayed and it's nothing – just ligaments.' Nevertheless, he gasped with pain as he got into their little Ford, his right leg momentarily supporting his full weight.

'It doesn't sound as if it's okay, that's for sure!' That night he found it impossible to sleep and he regretted his too hasty disposal of the co-codomol. Fortunately, he did not have work the next day. The personnel management at Fishers and Ludlow were very supportive of his Olympic quest and gave him time off after squad training week-ends. On Tuesday he struggled into work, now convinced that whatever his injury was, it was not as diagnosed in London. For a start there was no swelling around his ankle, and the pain, if he could locate it anywhere, seemed more in his knee. At morning tea-break, frustrated and to test out the limits of his injury, he jumped from a loading bay and landed four feet below, where he promptly collapsed in agony onto the oil-stained concrete.

≈

'I am very surprised,' said the radiologist at the Accident and Emergency hospital, 'that my London colleague only saw fit to x-ray the lower half of your leg. Poor practice I must say! As you can see, I have x-rayed your full leg, which shows clearly that you have a longitudinal fracture at the knee-end of your right femur. Not bad as these things go, but an irritating little brute. We're going to plaster you up from toe to top as it were. You won't be able to drive home so you'll have to make arrangements for someone to collect your car.'

'I didn't drive here.' The radiologist brightened.

'Oh good. You got a lift then? Very good – saves us the fuss of booking an ambulance.'

'No,' said Peter. 'I came by bus.' The doctor shook his head.

'Mr Donnelly, walking around and catching buses on a broken leg is not to be recommended. It is quite foolish.' He absorbed himself in reading his patient's notes. 'It says here you are a top judo chappie, an international player no less?' Peter nodded.

'Oh well, that explains it no doubt. Sorry, old son, you're *Hors de Combat* as the French say. Out of action for a few months. You'll be six weeks in plaster.'

'Sorry Doctor, but that can't happen. I'm off to Japan in a month so the plaster must be off by then.'

'Mr Donnelly that's quite impossible. Impossible!'
'Doctor, with respect the cast will be off by then – even if I have to
cut it off myself with garden secateurs!

〜

Peter Donnelly and Brian Jacks shared a room at the world famous
Kodokan – the spiritual home of their sport. Brian was an 'old hand'
as far as Japan was concerned having visited many times and had lived
there fifteen years earlier when he was the teenage prodigy of British
judo. It transpired that they had similar expansive personalities and
liked each other - which is why they ended up in gaol and briefly
met a world-famous pop star. They shared a cell for different reasons;
the judoka for releasing a chicken and the legendary Liverpudlian for
possessing the leaves of a banned plant.

〜

Morning training at the Kodokan was going well. The *Kangeiko*
(mid-winter) sessions were demanding but not as hard as Peter had
anticipated. The atmosphere was calm and very ordered. *Randori* was
tough but not brutal - the etiquette being to 'go with the throw' rather
than maximum resistance. He was coping well even though under
instructions to work only with the heavyweights. The main problem
was that his favourite throw, the left-handed *o-goshi*, was not firing
at all well. Even though he threw with his weight supported on both
legs, it was his right leg which normally provided most force, and at
each attempt it buckled slightly under the strain. He was desperately
conscious that he did not wish to worsen his injury.

Training completed for the day, they showered and changed; Brian
suggested that they went to a favoured bar 'The Tokyo Dome' on the
nearby Hakusan Dori, the main street outside the Kodokan. Peter
had developed a taste for Udon noodles and raw tuna even though a
large portion still left him hungry. Tony MacConnell said he would
'come along to keep you buggers out of trouble!' The food and beer at
The Dome were good, reasonably priced and the atmosphere friendly

but there was one thing that annoyed the three judoka – the 'Chicken Machine.' The Japanese have strange tastes in entertainment ranging from the precisely ordered, refined traditions of the tea ceremony to the madness of Karaoke, the much-favoured relaxation of drunken businessmen. There are animal cafes where you can eat your Teriyaki in the company of owls, penguins, pigs, snakes or whatever. The Japanese are quite fond of pastimes that involve some form of torture and this passion has spawned many trashy programmes of daytime television. Peter and Brian left Tony eating, and went nearer to watch in disgust the cavorting antics of the customers gathered around the Chicken Machine. Men and women with twisted faces laughed at the desperate performance of the animal trapped within it.

They stood together as a customer dropped a Yen into the coin-slot. The chicken was trapped in the apparatus somewhat like a pinball machine. On receipt of the coin, the fowl was freed into a Perspex enclosure. This was only about six inches high, so the bird had to flatten itself, wings spread wide, in order to scrabble around and peck at a series of coloured buttons which lit up in sequence. Each generated a musical note which electronically mimicked the sound of a chicken squawking. The clucking strains of 'Baa-baa, black sheep' sounded out as the flattened chicken pecked, and then flapped back into its box to receive its reward of a few grains of corn. Excepting two, the spectators thought this to be great fun. Peter and Brian watched dismayed.

'The way they train the animals to peck in the right order is called 'Operant Conditioning.' I've got a mate who's a psychologist.' Brian was hardly listening to Peter's explanation.

'Whatever it's called I don't like it. You should set that bird free.'

'Me! - Why me?'

'Because you're the biggest and I'm the higher grade.'

Perspex is a remarkably strong plastic, but Peter did manage to remove the cover, setting a security alarm off in the process. The frightened bird flapped madly around the bar creating uproar amongst the diners and drinkers. Two armed police appeared immediately and four more in a matter of seconds. 'You didn't think that through very well did you Peter?' Brian Jacks, laughing, was seemingly oblivious to the Nambu revolvers pointing at his head.

'What do we do now?' asked Peter.

'Go quietly down to the station I suppose. Whatever you do don't resist arrest – this mob don't seem to have a sense of humour!'

‿

Alfie Tomkins, the Junior Secretary at the British Embassy received the call that two British International judo players were in gaol, said 'Bugger it!' and prepared to have his afternoon ruined. He was further vexed when minutes later the phone rang again and he received the news that a famous British rock and roll wallah was also in custody for the possession of a banned substance. He grabbed his coat and hat and phoned the embassy car-pool for transportation to Naritsa Gaol.

The holding area outside the cells quickly filled with police officers and all manner of civilian staff, in particular young secretaries in short plaid skirts and white blouses. They were all chattering excitedly and pointing at the famous musician. At the front of the bunch were a group of senior officers holding low-throated important conversations.

Peter and Brian gawped at the famous Liverpudlian face now looking back at them through the bars of the adjacent cell. Brian spoke. 'I recognise you, aren't you...?'

'Yes, I admit it – I am Mick Jagger. At least that's the name I gave at the airport.' They laughed at this morsel of wry humour. More and more people arrived and the holding area outside the cells rapidly filled. They prisoners introduced themselves and shook hands through the iron bars. 'I've heard of you Brian. You're one of the top players in the world, aren't you?'

'We both are.' Said Brian and Peter was proud to think it was true.

'I wish I spoke Japanese,' said the musician. 'I wonder what they're saying?'

'He speaks Japanese,' said Peter indicating Brian Jacks, who told him to keep quiet.

'Shut up Pete, it's better that they don't know – then I can listen in to what's going on.' Undeterred the rock-star persisted.

'Well, what are they saying Brian? Tell me!'

'Most just want your autograph. Some want you to sing for them and some of the girls want to be locked up in the solitary confinement cell with you. The Japanese can be a bit dirty minded if you understand.'

'Well, if they can provide a decent left-handed guitar, I don't mind singing – it'll pass the time and be fun.' The Japanese are an efficient race and in very short order a left-handed guitar was found and passed through the horizontal bars.

'Is the guitar any good?' Asked Brian as the musician turned the tuning heads and struck up a few chords.

'Yeah, it's cool – a Takamine. Any requests? Let's have a sing-song!' Peter quickly answered.

'How about that one where you all live in a margarine tin?'

'I don't know that one. Perhaps it was one of John's. He wrote a lot of muck when he was on Acid.'

'You know the one.' said Peter and began to sing:

'We all live in a tub of margarine, tub of margarine, tub of margarine
We all live in a tub of margarine---'

'You were a big fan of my old band then Peter, by the sound of it?'

'Not so much – I preferred the Stones.'

'Funnily enough – me too!'

Soon the jailhouse at Naritsa was rocking to an impromptu concert; hit song after hit song was greeted with rowdy applause. Swooning girls were dancing excitedly and screaming, activities which seem to be required at such events. Alfie Tomkins stood at the back of the heaving crowd, as the famous musician quietened the mob with a slow variant of the most recorded song in the world.

'When I wrote this song, I had no idea what the words would be. I'd had the tune in my head for weeks – but just for a laugh here's the original version.' He began the mournful lament.

'Eggs and ham
Are much better than baked beans and spam
But I like toast, and strawberry jam
Especially when – it's made by Mam...'

Why..., that is so I don't know - I couldn't say...

Order was finally restored and the room cleared by a senior police inspector who only listened to Mozart. This allowed Alfie to speak to the three Englishmen which he did but first gave the pop star gentle applause. 'Very good. Very good indeed – I predict a bright future. But down to business.' He looked at the charge sheets he had been given. 'O'Donnell and Jacks,' he looked at the two judoka. 'That must be you two?'

'It's Donnelly - not O'Donnell.' Alfie made an alteration on the paper. 'You're charged with criminal damage, affray and grievous bodily harm. Doesn't look good boys – what happened?' They recounted the tale with the rock star listening.

'That's bloody ridiculous!' said Alfie. 'I'm sure we can sort this one out – the Japanese don't like to be embarrassed. International judo players in gaol for setting free a chicken is far too silly for Her Majesty's Government. Say you're sorry, bow and scrape and pay for the damage.' The pop-star intervened.

'I'm a vegetarian and I think the boys deserve a medal - I'll pay for the damage.'

'That really is most kind, Mr Jagger.' Alfie looked up from the charge sheet, looked at the musician and laughed. 'I have to say that's jolly funny. Bravo! But your case is a little more serious, I fear. A half-pound of marijuana? That's a great deal for personal use and the Japanese have very strict drug laws. But you're very rich and famous – I'm sure your lawyers will have you out in a few days. In the meantime, keep the old chin up!'

☙

The British squad returned to England without further mishap and were once more settled at Crystal Palace. Peter Donnelly and team manager, Ray Ross were in conversation. 'Mac says you did okay over in Japan but seemed a bit out of sorts and had trouble with the heavyweights. What do you say Peter?'

'Well Ray, it takes a bit of time getting used to fighting the big guys, and I'm still light. I'll be okay in a month or two when I've put on more meat. I'd like to train up to about ninety-seven kilos and I'm nowhere near that now.'

'I tell you what Peter. There's a three-corner match in Bruxelles in ten days; GB, France and Belgium. It's short notice but I'll put you in as heavyweight and see how you get on in competition. What do you think? Are you up to it?' Of course, Peter said that he was.

He lost his first fight; when attacked with a right *o-soto-gari* he could offer little resistance and he went over easily. In his second fight he attacked out of habit with a strong left *o-goshi*, felt agonising pain and knew something disastrous had happened.

An x-ray back in England confirm his worst fear: the crack in his femur had re-opened and worsened. The doctor made his pronouncement. 'You're young and fit so there should be no problem with it healing. Six weeks in plaster I'm afraid and nothing strenuous for a couple of months after that – none of that judo malarkey. You can start gentle exercise in June.' Peter understood that his hopes of a place in the Montreal squad, never strong, were now shattered.

'What do I do now?' Ray Ross, the British Team manager held the dispirited Peter Donnelly in an affectionate but painful stranglehold. He playfully squeezed with the lazy power of an older athlete.

'More of the same until Moscow Peter – just more of the same.'

～

Time passed quickly for Peter, now a sponsored full-time athlete. Four years later he found himself back in Tokyo, but this time, fully fit. Peter Donnelly looked out of the small kitchen window which neatly framed the distant, beautiful symmetry which is *Fuji Yama*. He marvelled at the majestic mountain silhouetted on the skyline, against the cloudless pale-blue of a south-western winter's sky. He could understand well why this scene had been an icon of Japanese art for a thousand years or more. He placed his hands on the bare wooden window-sill, leaned forward, and began to cough.

The great judoka Kisaburo Watanabe had long been a friend to British judo. His competitive prowess was legendary; Asian Games champion and All Japan bronze medallist – a prodigious feat in an

Open-weight competition for a player of less than eighty kilogrammes. He threw spectacularly with *uchi-mata, taio-toshi,* and *o-soto-gari* all from a double lapel grip. In 1962 he came to England at the invitation of Trevor Leggett to coach at the Budokwai and Renshuden. He was tremendously influential to the development of British judo although the move away from Japan cost him the chance to compete in the 1964 Olympics. He maintained close contact with his judo friends in London on his return home, and frequently played host to visiting players to Japan. The British judo team, as ever strapped for cash, were happy to accept his offer of accommodation in his spacious, traditional home in the old quarter of Tokyo.

Great Britain lies in the middle of the Eurasian tectonic plate, well away from any cracks in the Earth's surface. On the other hand, Japan lies on the fault lines caused by the joining of the Eurasian plate, the Philippine plate and the Pacific plate. Japan has lots of earthquakes and volcanoes – Mount Fuji itself is merely dormant. So traditional buildings are cleverly constructed out of wood and interior walls are lattice work covered with paper. The buildings are flexible and less likely to fall when the ground shakes. But of course, old, dry wood is very flammable and so these buildings tend not to have open fires or even fires at all. Cooking is traditionally done over a small charcoal brazier. For the Japanese this does not present much of a problem: Springtime in Tokyo is mild and the Summers are hot. Autumn is quite benign but the Winters can be cold. The British judo team arrived for its pre-Moscow Olympic training in January and took up residence in the upper floor Kisaburo Watanabe's picturesque, draughty and unheated ancient home. Pretty soon, and with good reason, the house became known as 'The Fridge!'

Peter Donnelly continued to cough. 'I can't put up with this Mac. The cold's getting to my chest and the last thing I need is a bout of bronchitis.'

'I never took you for a southern softie Peter.' Tony MacConnell was used to the wild weather of Cumbria, and the hundreds of hours he had spent as a young man fell-running on bleak, windswept northern moorland had hardened him to the cold. Nevertheless, he wore a down padded mountaineer's jacket with his blond hair covered by a black woollen hat. Peter gave him a withering look, and once more began to cough. 'But it is a bit chilly like,' continued Tony Mac, 'I'll give thee that...I'll get you a room at the Kodokan or the YMCA.' He called for the team to gather for breakfast which *Sensei* Watanabe had provided on the lower floor. Duvets and the hard Japanese pillows were returned to store behind a paper screen – there were no beds; uncomfortable nights being spent on the floor of rice-straw *tatami* mats.

Sensei Kisaburo Watanabe kneeled at the head of the low table in the traditional *seiza* posture known to all judoka: known, but not necessarily a comfortable position from which to eat at table, unless familiar with it from infancy. The English judoka sat more easily cross-legged as they ate breakfast. The thin *miso* soup, steamed rice, vegetables, pickles and salad was less than satisfying to the team, all used to heavier fare and craved more substantial food. Watanabe spoke to them without interruption in his good but heavily accented English.

'In England you all big fish – yes you are best. In England one or two big fish in each pond.' He looked around the table. 'The pond of Radburn has few big fish; the pond of Neenan has few big fish; the pond of Donnelly and Adams the same. You understand? In Japan many ponds each with many big fish. Today you go to Keishicho Dojo – big pond with very many big fish. Remember, you are all champions – but only champions of *judoka* you beat. You not champion of guys you did not fight. Remember this.'

Tony MacConnell put it differently. 'The Keishicho Dojo is the toughest on the planet, full of hard knocks that were champions or could have become champions if they wanted. There are players that beat Okano that no-one out of Japan has even heard of. So be prepared for a battle. There will be no teaching or standing practice or lazy ground-work. It'll be two hours of back-to-back contest judo, and you'll get no rest. They'll be queueing up to knock the crap out of you – so be warned. Anyway, so you've got something to look forward to, there's a reception for us tonight at the British Embassy which should be fun!'

The dojo was quite unimpressive from the outside, a rectangular concrete structure reminiscent of an office block. The training hall was different. The mat area was as big as any Peter had seen including at the Kodokan. The wood panelled walls were decorated with pictures and martial arts paraphernalia, in particular the bamboo practice swords used in Kendo. The far wall was dominated by a large circular mirror and a traditional hammered bronze gong suspended from an elegant oriental wooden frame.

'What's the mirror for Mac?'

'Well not for combing your hair that's for sure. It's a shrine to signify perfection or purity – summat like that.' The start of the session was very formal. The British squad had taken to the mat with no introduction and waited in silent rows along with about seventy other judoka. A line of senior players, all older, all wearing the high grade red and white panelled belt, entered at the top of the dojo in silence. A standing bow was reciprocated and then the formal kneeling bow exchanged.

'What happens now Mac?'

'Well, I will respectfully leave the mat and join the other old farts and you and the rest of the bunch will fight for your lives. Good luck!' The mighty gong sounded and Peter Donnelly found himself at the centre of a melee of Japanese fighters all keen to do battle. The winner was an older judoka of perhaps forty years, shorter than himself but running to fat. They were of similar weights but Peter judged that his opponent was probably a middleweight in his prime. Peter was in excellent condition: his stamina and core strength were both as good as they could be. His upper-body strength was equal to that of any judo athlete in the world - Tony MacConnell and Dave Starbrook had seen to that. He was nimble and agile of foot...

He was thrown with a fast, low 'through the legs' left *ippon-seoi-nage* and was furious with himself and the Japanese who had dumped him. Something snapped. He stood up completely oblivious to his surroundings. He was icily calm, critically focused upon his only task, to return the compliment with an *ippon* of his own and if possible one that hurt his opponent as well. The fight continued and he could hear the words of his old coach, his first *Sensei* Kevin Murphy; 'Judo is like a tree ... the trunk is *o-goshi* – never forget that young Peter.' His opponent swayed right, momentarily losing balance. Peter attacked with a left *o-goshi*; the first throw he had been taught; the throw he had repeated a hundred thousand times. His back was straight, his legs bent at the knees, his feet made the angle of the letter 'v', a detail that *Sensei* Kevin boringly laboured. The Japanese lifted high into the air; Peter maintained control throughout the technique ensuring that he landed his full weight on top of his opponent when they hit the mat. The gong sounded as they rose from the floor. His Japanese opponent gasped.

'What name? What you name?'

'Donnelly. Peter Donnelly.' The Japanese smiled broadly as he bowed.

'You bastard. You Donnelly bastard!' He held out his hand to shake. 'I Maruki. I Maruki bastard!' In the few seconds before new pairings were formed Peter spoke to Neil Adams.

'Who was that I just scrapped with?'

'Maruki – world champion a few years ago; a hard knock if there ever was one. You've got another by the look of it.' Peter looked up from tying his belt to see the unsmiling features of Fumio Sasahara facing him and ready to fight. It was going to be a long few hours.

⬃

Alfred Alexei Tomkins, was the second 'Alfie' in his family, the first being his father. But he alone was named with this touch of Russian flamboyance. He was quite enjoying himself. The reception was going well; the judo boys cut a dash clad in the blazers, ties and flannels of the British Judo Team. The atmosphere was jolly, not at all the dry, formal affair that often made these gatherings so dull. He was dressed immaculately of course, in black suit and perfectly starched high collared shirt, as befitting his new role as First Secretary to the British Ambassador to Japan. He was sporting a deep maroon bow tie, not quite the thing, but damn the conventions. He prided himself upon being somewhat of a rebel. He was engrossed in conversation with three fellows – damn big chaps!

'Yes, I did a bit of judo at school. Quite the rage it was – still is I understand from my little brother. It almost got cancelled, you know – there was one hell of a fuss a year or two back. I'm not boring you, am I? That would never do.'

'No, not at all.' Tony MacConnell, Peter Donnelly and Paul Radburn encouraged him to continue.

'I went to school just outside London.'

'Eton? Peter questioned helpfully.

'Good Lord no! Nothing so coarse. No, the other place, up on the hill. Judo was on our games curriculum and bloody popular it was too – still is, as I said, but the 'Old Beak' nearly binned it! A couple of judo fellows, top players, were invited to come along and give the 'oiks' a chat about the sport – dedication, training, commitment – that sort of thing. Now I must talk about an old school tradition...' He broke off, noticing his three guests' empty glasses. 'Oh, I'm sorry. More fizz!' Peter answered.

'Not really my cup of tea, Champagne.' They laughed at the intended pun. 'To tell you the truth I prefer beer.'

'Well, there you're in luck. We had another bash a few nights ago sponsored by Guinness. I'm pretty sure there's a crate or two left. May as well polish it off. What?' He called to a waiter, whispered in his ear, and carried on with his story. 'There is a tradition in school that dates from the war, when a 'Cheesy Ragger' hid in one of the cellars and this saved his life – he was being chased by a gang of soldiers with murderous intent ...' The story floundered as three faces stared at Alfie in puzzlement.

'Why? Was he a German spy?' asked Paul Radburn.

'Not a bit of it. English of course – a Royalist. Oh! Sorry chaps, wrong war. I'm on about the English Civil War a few hundred years back. No, the chap was the Master of the 'Rags', the Royal and Ancient Guild of Cheesemakers - otherwise known as a 'Cheesy Ragger.' They were Royalists and Cromwell's mob were after him. Anyway, as I said, he got away by hiding in the school's wine cellar. Ever since, a 'Great Cheese' is given to the school by the 'Cheesy Raggers.' It arrives on a farm cart on All Hallows, accompanied by a mediaeval band of minstrels and troubadours. It really is quite the occasion. All the boys put on their Sunday best, tailcoats and boaters and sing the 'Ode to the Truckle' to welcome the cheese. It really is such fun! The cheese is then escorted by a guard of pikemen to the Great Hall where it is ceremoniously rested on a bale of straw and there it stays until the third Sunday when it is shared. Before that, every Friday supper, we 'Cheer the Cheese' and bang the ends of our knives and forks on the table. This has been going on for over three hundred years – you can imagine the state of the woodwork!' Tony MacConnell maintained a blank expression.

'Sounds great. Thee must a bin pissin' yoursen wi' excitement!' Alfie was unabashed and sipped champagne. A waiter arrived carrying a silver tray laden with eight bottles of Guinness and placed it next to the small group.

'Now, now,' said Alfie, 'one mustn't tease. I'm sure you northern chappies have your own traditions, probably involving tripe, meat pies and black pudding.' They all laughed. 'Anyway, to continue - a plug is taken out of the centre of the cheese and each Sunday until it's eaten, a small amount of vintage port is poured into the hole and then the plug replaced. This helps the cheese ripen and gives a very rich flavour. The measure for the port is called 'The Dick.' Do you wish to know why?' Peter Donnelly finished his second pint of Guinness and stated forcefully that he did.

'I want to know why you put a Dick into the cheese.' More laughter and Peter quaffed his third stout feeling happy.

'The last wild boar in England was shot by the first King George in the grounds of the old school. He liked shooting things, did Georgy, but didn't like pork, so he gave the carcass to the Headmaster. King George was German and spoke bloody awful English.'

"Eat all – *Dich!* Waste not. Use *Dich!*' At which the hunting party galloped back to court leaving a hundred-pound pig and unusual instructions. The old Headmaster was a resourceful chap and had the animal's member dried, hollowed and mounted in a silver cup. To this day it is used to add port to the cheese.' Tony MacConnell grimaced and shook his head.

'I don't believe word of it. Not a bloody word – you're 'avin' us on! And what's all this baloney got to do with judo!'

'Every word is true! As for the judo, the two top lads I mentioned gave a talk at the old Alma Mater, I can't remember the names. One was Irish - O'Donnell I think and the other perhaps Mueller. Ring any bells?' He looked pointedly at Peter who stared resolutely into his fourth glass of Guinness, shook his head vigorously, and swore he knew of no such people. He had met Alfie four years earlier, on his first trip to Japan, and was sure that the elegant First Secretary had not forgotten their meeting in Naritsa gaol. Tony MacConnell and Paul Radburn glowered at Peter in silence. 'It was the third Sunday in Advent or 'Cheese Day' as we call it,' continued Alfie. 'The opening of the cheese really is a big event and dinner is more like a party. The Masters are well oiled with port and brandy by this time and even the older boys are allowed a tipple. The cheese is cut in half with the very sword that took the head of Jonathan Cromwell, Oliver's cousin. At which the Beak shouts, 'Behold the Cheese.' This is greeted by great cheering and the stamping of feet. A musket is fired, only a blank these days, and this starts 'The Stampede' where the boys, armed with spoons, rush to get the first taste. This time the 'Opening of the Cheese' was the occasion for indrawn breaths and gasps of alarm; its centre was missing! That cupful of gooey delight, the best part was gone. Someone had removed the plug, gone in with a spoon and taken the lot! There was a most tremendous fuss.'

'Oh aye. That would wreck anyone's day – the best bit of the cheese gone. A calamity sure enough. Who gets that bit? The Headmaster I suppose, Old Beaky?'

'No Tony! Good Lord no! A hundred times no! That's the whole point of the tradition: NOBODY gets the best bit. It's thrown away! As there is not enough for all, then no-one gets any. It's a parable about fairness and equality – 'all in the same boat rowing together' as our boating song goes.' As Peter started on his fifth bottle of Guinness, Paul Radburn asked,

'But what's it got to do with the judo lads. Why blame them?'

'Oh yes. Well, when the judo chappies had finished their chat they were left alone in the Great Hall for a while. None of the 'oiks' or Masters would ever defile the 'Great Cheese' – perish the thought. The judo fellows were the only ones with the opportunity.' A waiter came and once again whispered to Alfie. 'Sorry lads – bit of a flap. Seems we've run out of canapes. Can't understand it – there's only fifty people here and I ordered four hundred of the bloody things.' Three judoka guiltily glanced at the nearby heavy curtains, behind which were hidden ten empty silver platters.

⌒

In April, a few months after his return from Japan, Peter Donnelly won the British Open for the second time and subsequently received the letter which formally guaranteed his place in the British Judo Team for the Moscow Olympics. He was surprised that he did not feel particularly elated. He had achieved the goal that had driven him for at least five years but felt only a sense of anti-climatical relief. David Starbrook had retired and Peter had established himself as Britain's dominant light heavyweight judoka. He was a major force on the European and World stage having won a bronze medal in the recent European Championships in Vienna and was ranked fifth in the world.

He was acutely aware of how many people had contributed to his success: Kevin Murphy, his first coach who insisted that he did the basics well; Kenny Webber and Pete Barnett who added their own techniques and a touch of fire; all the players he'd scrapped with in his formative years; Bob Trevis, Roy Muller, Danny Murphy and then the 'Solihull mob' – hard men all! Latterly the elite international level fighters, Brian Jacks above all, who took his performance to the highest level; the team managers and coaches, Ray Ross, Dave Starbrook and most importantly 'Mac' who had taught him how to fight. He would always be grateful to the generous Arnold Humphreys the millionaire businessman who had sponsored him and allowed him to train full time. The more he thought the more he realised that every medal he had won was in fact a team effort. He also knew also that his commitment to training had put tremendous demands on his family life.

In the past, at times of hardship, failure or injury, he had agonised why he had chosen judo to be his obsession – but over the years realised that it was the other way round.

Judo had chosen him.

Some Dojo Knights: Tony Underwood; Peter Donnelly; Bob Trevis; Christo Murphy; Fred Stansbie.

Chapter Eighteen
The Dojo Knights

ROYSTON MULLER IS a first-rate fellow and excellent friend. He is quite exceptional in his way. His greatest attribute and lowest failing are the same quality. Roy is not a meanderer; he is not a beat-around-the-bush merchant. No, if there is a destination to be reached the only route, he will take will be a straight line from A to B. Neither will he look at a vermillion sunset and weep at its decaying majesty; he is more likely to sniff the country air and wonder, 'who's farted?' If there is a topic which divides opinion Roy knows the correct side of the debate – his. He sees the world through functional eyes. A while back we were in the splendour that is Girona cathedral in Catalonia. This thirteenth century edifice combines power with beauty. I stood transfixed appreciating the intricate carvings of a magnificent altar screen. Peter Donnelly was enrapt, lost in transcendental thought viewing treasures stripped from the Incas and galleon brought to old Spain. Roy beckoned us...

'Look at that!'

'What?'

'The bracket that's holding up the heating pipe. Hand forged, that is – you can still see the hammer marks.'

∽

For the second time in less than a day Roy's arrival elicited surprise. Peter Donnelly was eating lunch in the Crystal Palace restaurant. The morning's training session had been hard and he was looking forward to the compulsory few hours bed-rest in the afternoon. Life as a full-time athlete was tough. He felt a tap on his shoulder and turned around, surprised to see his friend. 'Hello Roy, what are you doing here?' The two friends shook hands.

'I'm on holiday for a couple of weeks so I decided to fly over to see you and the Midland lads. Some of the Swedish boys I've been training are fighting in the London Open next week so I thought I'd come along with them and watch the lads scrap. You know how it is. We flew in yesterday and as it was a late flight we stayed in a hotel. Guess who I bumped into?'

'No!' said Peter. Roy Muller ignored this rebuff and carried on.

'Well, it was Danny Murphy and I tell you Peter he has gone completely down the pan. He's really let himself go and I'm pretty sure he is into some deep shit – bad stuff, drugs and the like, if you know what I mean.'

'Danny? I don't believe it! Roy, not for the first time you're talking through your pipe. Anyway, what's up – what's going on?' Roy warmed to his story.

'We checked into the hotel and I could hear a band playing somewhere, good stuff – *Hey Joe! Born to be Wild*, that sort of thing. I went to investigate. It was coming from a pub next door so I went in. At first, I thought I was wrong, but I wasn't! It was Danny Murphy on stage with a load of obvious druggies. The band was pretty good though, I'll give them that. At the break I went over to speak to him. Caught him off guard I did and he told me the lot.' He waited silently, pausing for effect, until finally Peter Donnelly gave in.

'Okay, what did he say?'

'He said he'd packed in the psychology bullshit, don't know why - money for old rope in my opinion. But then he said he was a sort of male prostitute for both sorts, men or women he didn't care.' Peter Donnelly stared blankly and then shook his head slightly in resigned bemusement.

'Bullshit, Roy. Complete nonsense! He's a bit of a hippy I'll give you that, but you're talking rubbish!'

'I'm not!' Roy protested forcefully. 'He told me himself. He charges money to be sexually humiliated. I've read about it. They probably piss on him or worse, and that 'pays the rent.' He's a 'rent boy' – that's what it means. He sells sex to pay the rent! And he 'cuts grass' – that's drug talk. They buy genuine marijuana and mix it, or 'cut' it with kitchen herbs, oregano, basil or something, then sell it again to make a profit. The same thing with 'bush.' It's all drug talk Peter – I'm surprised you don't know. He said he'd do anything for a bit of LSD! Sends you barmy that does – you think you can fly and see God! Anyway, the name of the band is a giveaway. *Rough Trade* – that's when a posh gay bloke picks up a 'bit of rough' off the street. No, Peter it all adds up. Danny has gone bad ways and I'm going to do something!'

'How come you know so much about it Roy? And what do you mean you're going to do something?' Muller waved his forefinger from left to right – a habitual gesture,

'I keep my eyes open and my wits about me – you've got to these days. And I'm going to rescue him – rescue him from his bad ways and get him back on the mat. That'll sort him out. He might be a pratt – but he's our pratt. I'm going to kidnap him and stay with him for a week to get the drugs out of his system. 'Cold chicken' they call it.'

'Muller, you're mad as a fish. They put instructions on shampoo bottles for people like you. Stark raving mad you are – and I think you'll find its 'turkey.' And what do you think Danny will do when you try this kidnapping stunt? He's no powder-puff, and he'll cut up rough.'

'Don't worry, I've thought it all through!'

'Roy, I've known Danny since we were kids and none of what you're saying makes sense. It just can't be true.'

'Well, I don't care too much if it's true or not – if I'm right, I'm right - and if I'm not it's good for a laugh!'

⌐

Roy Muller made his goodbyes with the promise that he would see Peter the following week at the championships. He drove to Birmingham in a rental car convinced of the importance of his mission. As he drove, he considered his plan: He would phone around a bunch of the good judo boys and explain that they were going to kidnap Danny Murphy for his own good. Someone would stay with him while he dried out and went 'wild turkey' or whatever it was called. He was pretty sure from films and what he'd heard that in the first stages of drug withdrawal the person went mad and thrashed about a lot. He needed some handcuffs.

The next day he arose quite early and felt pleased with himself. It was good to have a project, something to do as it were. In this case he was on a noble quest – like a mediaeval knight in shining armour. He got dressed, had toast and coffee and drove to Harry Wyatt's hardware store in the centre of Great Barr. The sign outside proclaimed 'Why go to town? We stock everything you need!'

'Morning Roy – what can I do you for?' Harry was a balding man with glasses, running to fat and dressed in a habitual brown cow gown; two biros and a steel ruler stuck out of his chest pocket. He and Roy had been at school together. Harry was of that irritating sort who called male customers 'young man,' regardless of age.

'Hello Harry. I need a pair of handcuffs. Have you got any?'

'Handcuffs you say?' He slowly shook his head, rubbed his chin and grimaced. 'I don't think so Roy – I sold the last pair a few days ago. They're due in next week' It didn't matter what Harry didn't have; he always gave the same trite response.

'You could try the joke shop...'

'No Harry, I don't want a toy, some plastic junk from Hong Kong. I want real handcuffs that work.' Harry thought for a while and then his face brightened.

'I know the very place – not that I go there mind. Ann Summers, the sex shop on The Parade. I hear they do a very good range of bondage gear and intimate apparatus. I've never been obviously – but I hear the quality is very good.'

⤺

The assistant was a young woman wearing a very low-cut black PVC dress, red high-heels, black fishnet stockings with similar matching scarlet lipstick and nail varnish. Her hair was long, straight and predictably jet black. A name, 'Anthea,' was tattooed in copperplate script on the plentiful uncovered pale skin of her left breast. Roy leaned forward and peered closely. He removed his glasses, and squinted to better read.

'I'm not here for myself, Anthea,' said Royston, 'but have you got any handcuffs - for a friend?' The assistant was unabashed.

'Of course, Sir. By the way, my name's Heather – Anthea is my girlfriend. Is your 'friend' male or female?' Roy could see the implications of her enquiry.

'He's male... but he's just a mate. No hanky-panky, shirt-lifting or anything like that – just a mate. Not that there's anything wrong with...' Royston's words evaporated and Heather unblinkingly helped.

'With being Gay, Sir?'

'That's it exactly. Nothing wrong with it at all. Perfectly reasonable thing to do – being Gay that is... But the handcuffs are nothing to do with sex. I just need to handcuff him.'

'Of course, you do, Sir. Now what type would your 'friend' prefer?' This puzzled Royston, he was not expecting a choice. Heather recognised his difficulty.

'We have fur-lined or perhaps padded satin? They are quite safe if your friend wishes to thrash about without hurting his wrists. But if he prefers a rougher experience our 'Brutal SS' range is popular. I hear the spikes add to the erotic fun.' Royston felt it necessary to clarify the position.

'No, you've got it wrong love. We're not 'bondos!' She looked at him quizzically.

'Bondos?'

'Yes - I mean no! I'm not a bondo and neither is he.' She looked mildly perplexed.

'Of course you're not Sir. Who is? Anyway, for this week only the cuffs come with a free gift. She showed him a tray of what looked like large glass dummies, you know the things babies suck. He had no idea what they were, but Royston could never resist a bargain.

⌐

Roy Muller is by no means an idiot – but he does march to a different drum.

He knew that kidnap was technically against the law, but kidnapping a friend for his own good was, without doubt, eminently reasonable. He fingered the handcuffs and noted they were of good quality, but ridiculously expensive he thought. As for the free gifts, he examined them and wondered where they might fit. There are only two openings in the human body. He thought about sucking on one, but could see no point to it. As for the other orifice - the sizes seemed unrealistic. He hid them away – 'they might come in handy,' he thought. 'Who knows?'

He also knew that his rescue mission was not a solo job. He needed reinforcements – a driver and at least two others ought to be enough – but who? Danny was a big bloke who, though a university wallah, came from the pits like the rest of the crowd and, as Peter had said, could cut up rough. He must be well over powered so that nobody would get hurt. He needed two or three heavy or at least light heavy-weights. He made a list and began a series of phone calls. Tony Weaver was his first call.

'Hello Weave, it's Roy Muller. You okay?'

'Worse now I'm speaking to you. Smashed yourself up on that motorbike yet?'

'Not yet. Weave, I've got a problem, not my problem but I thought you could help, give me a hand so to speak. You know Danny Murphy?'

'Course I bloody well know him.'

'What do you think of him?' Tony Weaver answered with a series of questions.

'What you on about Muller? What sort of a question is that? What you on about? What's going on?'

'Just answer. What do you think of him?'

'I think he's a smart arsed pratt. Good on the mat. Clever bastard – that sort of thing.'

'Would you help him out if he got into trouble?'

'Of course, I would! He's a prick - obviously, but aren't we all? Why what's up?'

'He's gone bad ways. Male prostitution, drug addiction, dealing – that sort of thing.'

'Bugger off, Muller! If anyone's on drugs it's you!'

'It's true Tony. I met him last week – playing in a band with a load of druggies, and smoking a spliff. But I've got a plan to save him from himself...'

Later Roy made similar calls to Tony Underwood, Bryan Drew, Dave Walker and Dave Law.

⌒

I was sitting alone in my flat pondering – attempting to take stock of the changes that had occurred in my life. It had been a good idea to relinquish the therapy practice and re-assign clients. I had enough problems of my own and it would have been hypocritical to pretend that I could guide people in their own struggle for personal stability or development. I was happy, all things considered, and at last felt that I had made some good decisions. My life seemed to be re-assembling in better order.

It was a huge relief to disentangle myself from Rosalind. I still ached for her and hurt as though bereaved but at least I had the strength to stay away. Playing in the band helped greatly. I was learning new skills; I had a powerful focus and very importantly I was having some fun! Seeing Roy Muller again was also unreservedly good. I've always felt here is something irrepressible about the guy. He is an eccentric to be sure – but a truly great idiot and the world is a better place with lunatics like him in it. The house in Cheshire was sold to Barry and Anna and at a considerable profit. I had spoken with Helen and her hatred seemed less – she also had a new partner about which I was pleased and simultaneously resentful.

The idea of travel, perhaps to the Greek islands, appealed... My thoughts were interrupted when the doorbell rang. I put down the copy of *My family and Other Animals* the excellent book by Gerald Durrell set in Corfu – undoubtedly why I was currently drawn to an adventure in Greece. The doorbell rang again and I reluctantly

I opened the door. I was very surprised to see Roy Muller and even more so to see Tony Underwood and Bryan Drew at his side.

'Hello Roy. This is a surprise – twice in a week, people will talk.' I looked at the other two impressively muscled hulks. 'Hello Bryan, Tony. Good to see you both. What brings you here?' Royston answered.

'Nothing much. We're just going for a drink. Weave and Lawman are in the car. We were passing and thought you might like to join us.' I considered this a bit odd. Although we all knew each other well, none of us were 'drinking buddies' as the Americans say. It seemed rude to refuse but I was not that keen mainly because the band had a gig on the forthcoming Friday which only gave me two evenings to sort out the bass line to *Dear Prudence* and I was finding it tricky. I was no Paul McCartney and had set the evening aside to practice.

'I'm sorry lads but I'm really quite busy. Some other time.'

'Fair enough. But just come and say 'hello' to the others.' My doorstep was only ten yards from Roy's monstrous Mercedes. Sure enough, they were in the back but both got out as I waved and started to walk to greet them.

'Code Red! Code Red!' Muller shouted and my arms were immediately pinned as Bryan held me in an almighty bear hug from behind. I couldn't move – the guy had been a 'Britain's Strongest Man' finalist. I was not alarmed in the slightest. The judo mob were odd. I remember at Bob Trevis' wedding when Tony Underwood had been stripped naked and chained into a telephone box. No harm was done and a passing 'beat bobby' saw fit to take a group photograph with a Polaroid camera that had been brought along for the purpose. I was not even much concerned when Weaver and Lawman held an arm each while Muller secured my wrists with strange looking spikey handcuffs. I was bundled into the back of the Mercedes. The ever-practical Roy Muller said he'd better go into my flat and check that I hadn't left the gas on. 'Okay fellas, very funny. What's going on?' Roy returned and sat in the driving seat. He turned around to speak.

'We've kidnapped you Danny. For your own good mind. It's more of a rescue really. You'll thank us in the end.' His voice was curious; patient as when telling a child not to run with scissors.

'Kidnapped me! What for? Is this a charity stunt or something? Who do you think is going to pay a ransom? The always sensible Dave Law spoke sharply as Roy started the car.

'Listen up! Roy says you've got yourself in a mess, sex and drugs and rock and roll...Is that right Murph?'

'What! The only sex I get these days is twenty minutes every morning with a copy of *Razzle*. As for drugs I've never taken anything stronger than Disprin unless you count the odd whiskey.' A white Ford Cortina with the passenger window open pulled alongside Muller's Mercedes. It was Dave Walker. I shouted to him. 'Dave, DAVE! Talk to these idiots – they're trying to kidnap me!' He looked puzzled but waved affably and shouted back.

'Hello Danny, Muller said you needed some help. Are you moving house?'

'Don't listen to him Dave – or any of you!' said Royston. 'Close your ears to anything he says! I told you this would happen. The first thing they do is to lie! Listen to me! In the next stage he'll start to cry and shake. He'll probably be sick as well. Have you got that plastic bag ready Weave? I don't want his puke on the upholstery.' His voice harshened as he attempted to become forceful. 'Listen to me Danny. This is what will happen. I'm taking you to my place and one of us will sit with you while you go through 'wild turkey' and then, if you're up to it, we're going down to Crystal Palace for the London Open on Saturday. Donnelly's not fighting nor Neil Adams – too close to the Olympics, but Walker, Bryan and Weave are having a bash. It should be a good day out.' I looked at the handcuffs and noticed that the chain links were alternately stamped with the lightning symbol of Hitler's 'SS' and the Nazi swastika. It dawned on me that my judo brothers might be serious.

'O for God's sake! You idiot Roy! And the rest of you are bloody stupid for believing the crazy bastard! Everyone knows if there was a job for madmen, he'd be too demented to get it.'

'Stay calm everyone – this is the still the first stage,,,' Royston seemed happy.

'Stay calm! Stay bloody calm! You're mad – all of you!' Roy revved up the engine and looked resolutely forward. A Ford Cortina pulled in front of us and braked; momentarily Royston's eyes fiercely glinted red, demon like, in the rear-view mirror, perhaps due to the reflection of brake lights.

I watched him arrive, the large, lean, muscular torso of a man dressed in jeans, tee-shirt and black shoes. To begin with that was all my view allowed as his head and shoulders were above the level of the Mercedes' windows. I had a flash-memory of our first meeting as children at the Victory Hall Budokan. The rear door was pulled open and the smiling, powerful frame of Peter Donnelly leaned into the car. 'Hello Danny – I thought you might need some help dealing with these dopes.' He spoke commandingly to our band of brothers. 'Who do you lot think you are – the Knights of the Round Table?'

'No!' said Royston 'The Mad Muller,' his eyes on fire. '*WE*, are 'The Dojo Knights!'

~

And so, the tale is done: –

'I never had friends later on in life like the one's I made in judo – Jesus, does anyone?'

~

Dojo Knights

Part Two

Chapter Nineteen
The Histories of The Dojo Knights

INTRODUCTION A BRIEF History of Violence, Jousting and Judo.

In the beginning, just after God had created light, messed around with the firmament, separated the waters of the air made, made fish and birds, that sort of thing, He made mankind. To begin with Adam and Eve got along well in paradise, but soon Eve got bored, and started talking to snakes and ate the fruit of the tree of knowledge. She gave a chunk to Adam who liked it and for some reason this made them both interested in sex. Seemingly, this annoyed God who threw them out of the Garden of Eden and told them to find somewhere else to live.

Anyway, shortly afterwards, I suppose about nine months later, Cain was born – their first son. A while later Abel came along. I don't believe the Bible mentions the age difference between the two boys but I think it is safe to assume that it would not have been much – about a year. I mean, there was no birth control and Adam and Eve didn't have a lot to do in their spare time. The boys must have gotten on each other's nerves. There was no-one else to play with for a start and brothers fight. Career choice was limited and when they grew older Cain decided to be an arable farmer and Abel kept sheep. The family was acutely aware that they had annoyed God and tried desperately to get into His good books by sending Him presents; the mechanism for delivering such gifts left much to be desired. I don't think they had thought this through. Yes, they made a big fire and burnt the offerings. Cain incinerated his farm produce, wheat, broccoli, cauliflower - that sort of stuff and Abel burnt a lamb. (I assume the lamb was dead because the thought of him dousing it with oil and setting fire to the fleece is very offensive. A blazing lamb charging around a middle eastern field is no way to please anyone - let alone God who is very picky about such things.)

It puzzles me that God preferred Abel's gift of over-cooked meat to the carbonised vegetables that Cain sent skywards. (For my part I most certainly do prefer the smell of a barbecue to that of a garden bonfire, but I am certain that a just God would not be so biased.)

On a fateful night, when they were coming home from their respective fields, having worked a long hard day, the brothers met.

'How did the burnt offering thing go today?' Abel asked of Cain.

'Pretty shit to be honest with you,' said Cain. 'God didn't like the burnt veg at all. How about you?'

'Oh, not so bad, you know. God thought the lamb smelled very tasty – He was mightily pleased!'

'You prick!' Said Cain and in the ensuing disagreement, Cain Killed Abel stone dead. Later God asked him where his brother was.

'No, idea,' said Cain. 'The last time I saw him he was doing something or other with a row of beans.'

'He wasn't dead then?' asked God.

'No,' said Cain. 'Perfectly alive and healthy – not a bit dead no, not at all.'

⌒

The truth of the matter is that from the very beginning humans are violent and like fighting – hence the beginning of combat sports.

⌒

Born in 1519, the future Henry II of France married Catherine de Medici in 1533 when they were both fourteen years old. His father, King Francis I, who reportedly supervised the consummation, announced that they had both shown valour in the 'joust.' Now I don't know about you but my father hanging around the bedroom when I was a teenager checking upon how well I was performing the sexual act, would have been most off putting. I mean, how did he score the event? Did he award marks for style?

Catherine was rich but not pretty and Henry was soon in the arms of Diane de Poitiers, a beautiful, ambitious widow in her mid-thirties. Henry had other mistresses but his two great loves were really hunting and jousting. He succeeded his father to the French throne on his 28th birthday.

In June 1559 a tournament was held in Paris to celebrate a peace treaty between France and Spain. King Henry was to enter the joust before a glittering audience of lords and ladies, including Queen Catherine and Diane de Poitiers. He fought well, as usual sporting the 'favours' or colours of his lover Diane. This can't have gone down well with his wife. In the first contest the Count of Montgomery, almost unseated Henry which royally annoyed the young king and put him into a sulk. Queen Catherine tried to persuade the king to withdraw from the competition:

'Stop nagging me woman,' he said. 'Leave me alone, I'm fine. I want another crack at that Montgomery bastard. Knock me off my horse? Will he buggery!' Henry insisted on another bash at the Count, who did his best to refuse but King Henry was having none of it. 'Fight you little tosser or you're in deep shit.'

Montgomery's lance struck the king's helmet and a long splinter pierced Henry's eye and penetrated his brain. The medics extracted the shard of broken lance - along with the King's eyeball and a touch of grey-matter. Surprisingly he did not die immediately. He hung around for a bit, forgiving people, Montgomery and the like. I suppose he knew he was about to die and thought it best to do a good deed or two to get on the right side of God. Catherine took command, kept watch by her husband's bedside and refused to allow Diane de Poitiers into the room. After a few days Henry's soul ascended into the 'great jousting tilt in the sky.' Kate then banished little Diane from court and ordered her to return all the jewels and gifts Henry had given her. The Count Montgomery prudently retired to his estate in Normandy. To no avail; Catherine, who hated him, soon found an opportunity to have him beheaded.

After the death of Henry there was an almighty clamour with the Health and Safety killjoys of the day calling for jousting to be banned. In the end they settled on making it safer and brought in new rules and standards. Lances became lighter, blunter and designed to snap. The 'old timers' complained and said that the sport had gone soft and was 'not like it used to be in our day.'

⌒

This ramble has precious little to do with judo. Except that there were knights of England, France, Spain, Germany and so forth, travelling around Europe from competition to competition in search of fame and success more than fortune. Jousts were the exhilarating combat sport of the day – a little like judo in the sixties and seventies. Judoka travelled from competition to competition seeking a win and visited different clubs in the hope of learning something new which might give them a competitive edge. Rivalries and friendships soon formed as these 'Dojo Knights' fought each other again and again while travelling the competition circuit.

In the sixties and seventies judo was a growing sport in Europe and particularly in Great Britain. It was a young sport; the British Judo Association being formed in 1948 and the Amateur Judo Association and British Judo Council only a few years later.

Great players were emerging and becoming known both to domestic audiences and on the world stage. This new era was the realm of David Starbrook, Brian Jacks and Angelo Parisi to name but three; other names would soon join this famous list. But there were also exceptional players for whom there is no history. 'Hard knocks' from around the country that in a larger sport would be well-known premier players. I have tried to give a few of these a mention also.

⌒

1. David Starbrook 9th Dan; MBE - "The Great Knight"
Olympic Team Coach

Significant Competition Performances
Olympic Silver Medallist Munich 1972
Olympic Bronze Medallist Montreal 1976
World Bronze Medallist x 2 1971;1973
European Silver Medallist 1973
European Bronze Medallist x 2 1974;1975
European Team Championships Gold Medallist 1971
European team Championships Bronze Medallist x 2 1972;1973
European Club Championships Gold Medallist 1971
European Club Championships Bronze Medallist x 2 1972;1973
British Open Champion x 9
Dutch Open Champion x 2
German Open Champion

(Author's Note: - This magnificent record is much foreshortened!)

Personal Statement
It is true to say that I had a very disrupted childhood. My early experiences certainly have affected my life, but you cannot choose your own beginnings and you must have the strength of character to make the best of things.

I was born in 1945 but my father was not around. I found out much later in life that I was a 'war baby' – one of thousands of children whose fathers were soldiers based in England during the Second World War. My mother had married a Canadian soldier sometime in 1942. I was told that he never came back from the war – which was true. I assumed that he had been killed but this turned out not to be the case, he had returned to Canada. Understandably my mother spoke little on this matter. I do not resent her for the way my life went; times were very hard, and she did what she could. But it is to my lasting regret that I never met my dad who was still alive when I won the Olympic bronze medal in Montreal in 1976. Had I known this I would have liked to have acknowledged him and my Canadian roots when I was being interviewed by the press. I think that the Canadian Sergeant would have been proud of the achievements of his son, David Colin Hawkins.

I was taken to a Catholic children's home when I was very young which was far from easy; the regime was very tough to say the least. I was about two years old and the home was St Anne's in Brighton. Discipline was harsh and included being tied to the legs of a kitchen table or locked in a cupboard for being too boisterous. At the age of five I was moved to another home for older boys. This was called St Mary's and the treatment we received there forms the subject of two books called 'The Boys from St Mary's.' I am mentioned in a chapter entitled 'Yes, We Did eat Ants' (and very tasty there were too!). Something happened to me at St Mary's and I spent many weeks in hospital. Unfortunately, my memory of this time is very vague My final move was to a home originally called 'St Joseph's Home for Destitute Catholic Boys' – a rather unpleasant name don't you think? By the time I arrived, it had changed its designation to be a Reform School, a corrective institution for troublesome boys aged eleven years or older. So, at the tender age of nine years, I was living in an institution for delinquent lads. I was unaware of this until last year (2019) when I requested and received my care papers. This came as a bit of a shock as, to my knowledge, I had never been in trouble - I was just a little boy, sometimes naughty in the ways that children are! I must mention that the stories you hear of how the Fathers, Brothers, and older lads abused vulnerable children in Catholic care homes, are completely supported by my own experiences.

I left at the age of fifteen with no academic qualifications and pretty poor at reading and writing. Truth be told, as I was a big powerful lad, I spent as much time working as a farm labourer (I was sent there by the school) as I did in lessons – so it is hardly surprising! On leaving school I went to live with my mother, but this was all very strange. I had been brought up in care with every aspect of my life organised and when this stopped, I found it difficult to cope. I was not aware of it, but as inmate referred to as much by number (I was number 35) as by name, I suppose I had become institutionalised. One odd thing about being raised by nuns, is that I am quietly spoken and do not have the strong accent that is often associated with Londoners. It is amusing to look back on the fact that, when living with my mother, other lads in the area though I was 'posh', and this caused a great deal of friction. What, me 'Posh' of all things!

I am not naturally aggressive in the 'thuggish' sense of the word, but I have always enjoyed physical tasks and sports. I was a good schoolboy boxer and won a few competitions, but as people have noticed over the years, I have a prominent 'chiselled' jawline. this would have been an ideal target for opponents had I continued in the sport; I am glad I took up judo! The chapter in this book where I 'meet' Peter Donnelly and Danny Murphy is quite accurate regarding how I started in the sport. By chance. I saw a poster in Shoreditch Evening Institute and thought I would give it a go. The rest as they say is history. One thing that is missed out is the fact that the law regarding National Service was changed in the early sixties; – my birthday was three weeks before the cut-off date otherwise I would have spent two years in the British Army and my life would have been completely different! Nevertheless, at nineteen I was a late starter to judo – most of the top players then and now start at a much younger age.

When I began training at the Renshuden my judo techniques and abilities quickly improved due to a combination of good coaching, more and better players to practice with, and getting myself into excellent physical shape. I owe a lot to my first coaches; Steve Wisdom and Patsy Walker (who were also at the Evening Institute class), Harry Wyn, Ray Ross, Jim McWade and Dave Barnard at the Renshuden. I should also like to say that one of my mentors and most respected men in Judo at the time, T. P. Leggett was also a great influence on me. It was he who gave me his first 6th Dan belt which was embroidered in Japanese. I am extremely honoured and proud of this and it is entrusted to my young friend Deryn to ensure its safe keeping. I believe that he saw 'something special' in me and could maybe glimpse into the future as this gift was before my exploits at the Olympics. There have been many more influences over the years, including my great friend and motivator Tony 'Mac' MacConnell.

I am quite a sociable person and would like to thank and acknowledge all those clubs, players and squad members who trained with me, and helped mould me into the player that I became. I also enjoyed training on my own: one of my favourite routines was to run around Regent's Park in heavy hobnailed boots. This became quite the thing to do amongst the judo crowd, but I think I still hold the record for the fastest circuit! Also, you would be surprised of how many things you can use a broomstick for when exercising alone. 'Harry Potter' has nothing on me!

I trained very hard at the Renshuden and developed arrange of techniques which gave me success both in the club and in my first competitions. These were the *ashi-wazas, taio-toshi and harai-goshi*. These are still favourite techniques although I like *uchi-mata* and it was with this throw that I beat Ischii, the Japanese/Brazilian, in the Munich Olympics which guaranteed me the Silver Medal which I won. To me, every medal is a success; I only thought of one competition at a time, and when that was done focussed completely on my next fight.

I look back with pride at the first time I won the British championship – I had no idea then that this was only the first in a long line of wins. Winning the Olympic Silver medal was a great achievement of which I am proud, but it was also a moment of tremendous disappointment as I was hoping for the Gold Medal. The author of this book, Christo Murphy has made it clear that he feels that I was, to say the least, very unlucky. The repechage system meant that I had to beat Chochoshvili twice to win gold, but he only needed to draw with me (one win each) to become Olympic Champion – unfair to say the least. I really have nothing further to add to this – but it was a moment of utter disappointment for me. I feel a bit the same about the Bronze Medal I won at the Montreal Olympics and my two World Championship bronze medals; each a success tinged with disappointment – but as they say, 'that's life' and you just have to keep moving forward.

All-in-all judo has been pretty good to me. I have made great friends, met the royal family and have travelled the world. I remember being delighted to be awarded the Winston Churchill Scholarship in 1973, to train in Japan. It was a fantastic experience (it was also the only sponsorship that I ever got!) I must mention that while training at the Kodokan I was sharing a top floor room with the great Keith Remfry. Quite slowly to begin with, the room started to shake and then the furniture began to bounce violently around. It was very scary, and we were both terrified! It was the only time I've been in an earthquake, and I don't want to be in another!

Looking back at my troubled beginnings it is true to say that judo changed my life completely. That 'retarded,' mistreated little boy, brought up in an institution always knew that he was more than the negative labels that were pinned to his back. I hope that my family and friends are proud of my achievements both on and off the judo mat. Never give in - especially when life is tough.

I hope my story gives some encouragement to young players; my advice is to take one step at a time – you can't jump to the top, you get there through hard work, dedication and a positive attitude. Never regard a loss in competition as 'defeat' – it is just a step in the learning process.

Finally, I have very few regrets about judo or my life in general – as I have said before you just have to make the best of things. I would have appreciated being invited to the 2012 Olympic Games in London my hometown – but was not, and this was a sadness. As a double Olympic Medallist, multiple British Champion, double World Championship medallist I thought I had earned that right. I was pleased to receive my ninth Dan, there is only one British player graded higher – but again this seemed to be given as an afterthought, without any importance being attached to the honour. I saw a film once about a great American boxer; 'It was called 'Somebody Up There Likes me.' A film about my life might have a different title...

~

2. Peter Donnelly 7th Dan - "The Knight Errant"
National Coach for Wales

Significant Competition Performances
Junior British Champion Aged 12
Espoir Champion Aged 16

British Open Champion x 2 1980; 1981
European Bronze Medallist
World Championships Vienna – 5th Place 1975
World Championships Paris - 5th Place 1979
Moscow Olympics 1980 – Team Captain 7th Place
(*Author's Note – At Peter's request this is a much-truncated list and I refer readers to JudoInside for further elaboration*)

Personal Statement
Possibly the most fortuitous meeting of my judo career was with a 10-year-old lad in my class at primary school named Roy Bernard. He fanned my flames of interest in the sport which coincidentally my father had also suggested I should try. He took me along to the Budokan Judo Club, Castle Bromwich. (The story told earlier in this book about meeting Kevin and Danny Murphy has elements of truth in it – it certainly captures the flavour of my first club.) Starting at ten years of age I became British champion for my age group at Crystal Palace two years later

I have said many times in my career that I did not choose judo, rather judo chose me. I had an aptitude for it and stuck at it because I liked it – it's easy to like something that you're good at.

My final year in Judo was 1980 and I was approaching the age of 30 I was British open champion, European bronze medallist, fifth in the world Championships, Paris, a Moscow Olympian and British Team captain.

I was fortunate in having coaches that were perfect for my development through time starting with Kevin Murphy, Ken Webber, and Peter Barnett. Kevin was an excellent coach to begin with. He believed that the secret to judo was to learn the basics well. Kenny Webber made me appreciate the vital importance of breaking my opponent's balance and correct body positioning – *Kuzushi and tsukuri*. When I trained with my dear friend Bob Trevis, he instilled into me the importance of good ne-waza. We must have spent thousands of hour training together and I owe him a great deal. I have said many times as a coach that the best way to improve your standing judo is to become good on the ground because you are then confident that if a throw fails and you end up in *newaza* you are not only NOT at a disadvantage but are in your comfort zone. Good *newaza* adds confidence to your standing attacks – any proficiency I gained was in large part thanks to Bob.

Finally, Tony McConnell and Dave Starbrook put the jigsaw altogether and taught me how to compete internationally – they taught me how to win on the world stage!

I was lucky enough to have been given the opportunity to 'go full time' and trained at Crystal Palace with many months spent in Japan. Huge influences in my Judo career came in the form of the judo world greats which are Neil Adams, Brian Jacks, Angelo Parisi and the great Dave Starbrook.

All-in-all judo and I are even. There are some fights I lost and should have won; there are other fights I won and should have lost.

I think I got more out of it than it did out of me. At the end of the day, it's only a game!

∿

3. Richard Barraclough 8th Dan - "The Gentleman Knight"
Vice President - British Judo Association
Vice-President – British Student's Sport Association

Significant Competition Performances

Judo
European Student Championship Gold Medallist 1965
Team GB Representative World Championships 1965
Midland Area Champion 1968
Northwest Area Champion 1968
Northeast Area Champion 1968
British Team Trials Gold Medallist 1970
Team GB Representative European Championships 1970

Olympic Freestyle Wrestling
Team GB Representative European Championships 1967

British Freestyle Champion – 1970;1971;1972
Team GB World Championship Representative – 1971
Team GB Representative Munich Olympics 1972

Sambo Wrestling
World Sambo Bronze Medallist - 1975

Greco-Roman Wrestling
Common Market Games 1973
British Champion x 2 – 1970; 1975

Personal Statement
I was born and raised in a quite isolated Yorkshire village called Upper Cumberworth, which was about eight miles from Huddersfield, the nearest town. My parents had a farm and a haulage business and so from a very early age I became used to heavy, hard work. This is probably why I had great natural strength. When I was sixteen my dad bought me a motorbike so that I could attend college in Huddersfield. On enrolment day we were told of the leisure activities the college had to offer and I opted for judo and weightlifting. The coach was a blue belt named Tommy Downs; black belts were in short supply in those days. I was strong and fit and did well quickly in the small college club. Tommy suggested that I needed to train with better players and so I joined Huddersfield JC. It was a great club housed in an old cricket pavilion, long and narrow smelling of sweat, liniment and ageing woodwork. The mat was canvas covered sawdust – not a bit like the modern tatami. The coaches were both blue belts – Len Penistone and Len Booth. Len was a fine player and won the Goldberg-Vass tournament in London.

I improved quite rapidly and gained my black belt in just a couple of years and had wins in local and area championships – my victory against David Peake, an international player, comes to mind. In 1965 I won the European Student Judo Championships and was selected to fight in the World Student Games to be held later that year. My lifelong friend and great judo player tony Sweeney suggested that we went to Japan to train in preparation for this event – and we did!

I trained at Tenri University, perhaps the top fighting university in Japan at the time. It was a fantastic experience, but the training regime was unbelievably hard with a 'brutality' that was completely different to what was acceptable in western judo. (The young *Sempai* were quite happy to give you a whack with a bokken – a wooden training sword, if you were not working hard enough! I was impressed and influenced by Matshusita Saburo and hence refined my *harai-goshi* which was my favourite throw equally with *ippon-seoi-nage*. I suppose that I am most remembered for *kata-garuma* which I could utilise in both wrestling and judo. Although I scored many an *ippon* with this throw I mainly used it as a take-down as I liked *ne-waza* and did well 'on the ground.'

Rather than picking a specific contest win of which I am proud I would rather highlight a year – 1970. Within three months I won the British Greco-Roman Wrestling championship, the British Freestyle Wrestling championship and in judo the British Team Trials. The latter event I won with twelve consecutive ippons (including against the great Roy Inman). In the Greco-Roman championship I defeated Ron Grinstead, a multiple British Championship and a world class player. In freestyle wrestling I beat Chris Martin, who wrestled professionally as 'Caswell Martin.' He was a great wrestler who had beaten me previously. He had a tremendous physique and was explosive in action. He was leading me by one point; in the final round I threw him with *hiza-garuma* and then managed to get behind him to score a couple of points which gave me the win. It was a good year!

Judo and wrestling have provided me with a lifetime of experience – almost all very positive but I do have one regret – I never won a British Open judo championship. I was at my peak in 1970 but was also doing very well at wrestling. I remember wanting very much to compete at the forthcoming, 1972 Munich Olympics and must have made the implicit choice to be selected as a wrestler. When I started doing well as a competitive judo player the British Open was in its infancy and did not seem to be that important to me. Also, the dates of the judo and wrestling open events were close. I had broken a toe and was recovering well enough but decided to skip the judo competition to give myself a few more weeks to heal. Anyway, the British Open (judo) was won by Roy Inman. I won the British Open (wrestling) but I had an *ippon* win against Roy a few weeks later in the trials for the British Team to compete in the European Championships. Looking back on this time I think I made a poor decision – a British Open win would have been a welcome addition to my record, and I denied myself that chance. Hindsight is a wonderful thing!

I must mention my great friend and icon of British Judo – the sadly late Tony MacConnell. I met him in 1962. My parents had retired to Cleveleys near Blackpool. I used to visit on vacation from university. At first, I hated it, as to me, 'home', was the beautiful Yorkshire village where I had grown up. And then I met Tony Mac! He was coaching judo at the Keidokwai. I was a brown belt at the time but under Tony's exceptional skills and hard training regime soon gained my black belt; international selection in 1963 and Team GB selection for the 1965 Rio de Janeiro World Championships. I owe 'Mac' a lot – so does British Judo.

I don't know whether to blame or thank Tony for perhaps my maddest adventure as a young man. He was a natural sportsman; cyclist, fell-runner, judoka and 'dabbled' at wrestling. He dabbled so successfully that in 1968 he was selected to represent GB at the European Championships to be held in Skopje and was flown out along with Andy Bailey, another Mancunian champion wrestler. The international governing body for wrestling was promoting Sambo at the time, and on the back of the Skopje Games a 'clinic' was arranged to which four additional top players were invited – but had to make independent travel plans. So, one bright summer morning myself, Steve Pullen and two others hefty guys piled into my VW Beetle and set out to drive to Yugoslavia! I don't know how we put up with nearly two thousand miles non-stop driving, and each other. Four days in a small tin box with poor ventilation in high temperatures was a memorable experience! We arrived without mishap and watched Tony fight. Before we left, he was full of confidence, playfully boasting of the medal he would win. The reality of wrestling top eastern European players, very hard men, was brought home when he quickly lost to a Hungarian and a Pole.

With the competition and training camp finished we found ourselves with nothing to do and 'hooked' up with a similar group of pretty girls. There followed a brief few days of fun and flirtation. They took us to a beautiful secluded riverside spot where Tony in a fit of high spirits ran and dived into the water, I suppose to make a bit of an impression. He did in a way; the shallows were only a foot deep and he removed bits of his manly chest and abdomen on the gravelled bottom. We found this hilarious and thanked him for the entertainment.

Andy Bailey's parents were at that time on holiday in a villa in Venice. This seemed quite close and more or less on the way back to England so we decided that it would be nice to pay them a visit. Obviously, we couldn't leave Tony to fly home so the six of us set off to drive the 750 miles to Venice. My Beetle groaned under the weight and was somewhat snug! What could go wrong? Following our map, we drove for about four hours in the blistering heat – and then literally ran out of road. It had been destroyed in a recent earthquake. We had no alternative but to turn round and drive back to Skopje. That Volkswagen was a great car; we cancelled the Venice trip and eventually made it back to England.

I've had many influences in my life – Tony Sweeney for example, but without doubt the greatest was Tony MacConnell. He was an inspirational coach; he was so full of fun and energy that it was impossible not to be inspired by him. I spent thousands of hours on the judo mat with him. I don't think he knew how to take training easy and he never gave up. He is much missed.

To finish I'd like to say a bit about the Munich Olympics and the terrorist attack. The opening ceremony was fantastic – so much tradition and history. I have never thought of myself as particularly patriotic but at that occasion I was overcome with pride that I was there representing my country. It was a very moving and emotional experience. There were a few 'standout' moments for me at the games: Olga Korbut in the gymnastics; Wolferman of Germany winning the javelin with every voice in the stadium cheering the javelin on its way; Dan Grable the brilliant American won his wrestling gold without conceding a point; Wim Ruska winning both Open weight and Heavyweight Gold – but the high spot was, of course, Dave Starbrook winning his Silver medal.

The terrorist attack was a terrible tragedy. Many of the Israeli victims were wrestlers – a few of whom I had met. Some of the sadness of the massacre has stayed with me. At the time I never met any athlete who thought that the games should have been cancelled – we had all put in so much effort that everyone wanted to compete.

Finally, my life was greatly enhanced through my participation in judo and wrestling as an internationalist an Olympian and as a coach. But people take to our sport for different reasons; some just for fun and to exercise, others to gain confidence or to learn self-defence and a small number transition to top level competition. To all I would say, value your training partners – you need them and they are your greatest asset. So, choose a good club with a good coach; learn the basics well and practice them a lot! Respect and listen to your coach – he or she knows a great deal; use their experience to improve your performance.

It is important to always keep in mind that you learn your fighting skills on the mat. You might need to use weights to build your core strength or do cardio-vascular exercise to improve stamina but nothing can replace the hard hours spent on the tatami!

Many ambitious young players never consider their life after competition days have ended. This is a big mistake! Education is important and building a career path that will take you through life is vital. (This is less of an issue in the USA where most sport is tied into the university system and so players train alongside receiving a good education. We are improving in this in GB – but there is a long way to go!) – Good Luck!

∼

4. Colin Charles Draycott 8th Dan - "Sir Colin Le Beau"

Senior Vice-President – British Judo Association
Director – International Judo Federation

Significant Competition Performances

AJA   National Open Champion x 3.
AJA   National Team Member. On five occasions, five gold medals.
Open Home International Tournaments
Five-man teams – three gold medals.
Open Olympic Trials 1964 Selected as a Light Heavyweight, Final Pool
WMA World Championships, Tokyo, Heavyweight Silver Medallist
(Authors' Note – This is a selection from a much longer list}

Personal Statement

I started Judo when a visiting judo coach started a club in a village near to mine in a public house called The Ram. My father said it was a magical art and I should go and listen to the introduction. I was 14 years of age at the time and it was a Seniors class. It was thanks to one or two of the seniors saying, "Let him join", that they let me in!

I liked it very much. I had done competitive swimming as a youngster and competitive boxing and immediately took to the discipline and respect that this sport had.

Within 18 months, the coach decided he couldn't travel that distance any longer and I was the only one that was graded to any significance and I re-formed the club in another public house and started teaching from that day on. I had no trouble sticking to my judo - I loved it.

I don't have any judo heroes – in fact, I had no heroes in my life. I had grown up during the Second World War and I suppose my only hero was the man who came home when I was six – my father, and that's possibly how it stayed all my life.

My first coach was a first dan who started the club, but I then started to go to the Leicester club, which was run by Harry Ewen. Harry was the Chairman of the AJA. He was a super guy – very much like a second father. Of course, I didn't understand, and no-one else did in my area, about the politics of the Associations. I was number

28 when they started the BJC and I was somewhere in the first 100 in the AJA. I joined the BJA in 1959 and I had to take all my grades again by line up.

I was fortunate in being right and left-handed and I had a variety of throws that I favoured, although I suppose *hidari tsurikomi* goshi was my ultimate favourite.

I think all my wins were enjoyable at the time, and I would not want to select one or other out from the rest.

I have had numerous great times through judo – more than I can put down on paper and as far as bad times are concerned, these have only been when I have lost friends (this last year my lifetime friend Tony MacConnell).

Talking about ambitions in Judo, fortunately I hope I have still plenty of goals left to fulfil. I am still working hard in judo, hopefully to improve judo for young people who join it.

I don't think I have had any rivals as such, and if I cast my mind back along the way all I can say to youngsters is 'Join a Judo Club.' This is the biggest friendship group in the world. Wherever you go in judo you can make friends. I have made more friends in my life than most people would in twenty lifetimes. Judo is full of them, and I am fortunate to still be one of those who meets once a month with old friends.

There have been many judo players who I have admired – far too many for me to mention, however there is one person who everyone in judo has admired. I was fortunate enough to be his friend before he died and that was Anton Geesink, and he taught everybody the way that you can win if you try. He was the first to beat all the past masters of the sport. And possibly one other great friend of mine and a great friend to most people in Great Britain is Kisaburo Watanabe. There is one person currently who I admire greatly as he has done so much for judo in his twenty years as President of the IJF – Marius Vizer.

Judo for me was great, however I chose to get out of the competition years as I very quickly realized that I had to make more of my life for my family, and unfortunately, this is where judo lets down many of its greatest players, by not preparing them for when they finish competition. A pathway to learning so that players make a success of life after judo should be an integral part of the sport's organization. It is a very difficult decision to make – whether or not to pursue a competitive career full time.

My message to young players is very simple. You must do your best, stick to the rules, stick to the principles of discipline and respect; if you get good enough, think of your future beyond your judo years.

I love my judo and I must say everyone in judo – we are one great big family.

~

5. Roy Muller 6th Dan - "The Jester"
National Coach Sweden

Significant Competition Performances
British Commonwealth U73 Kg Veteran Silver Medallist 2019
National Champion of Sweden U73 Kg.
World Veteran Silver Medallist x 2; World Veteran Bronze Medallist x 2
British Championship (Closed) Bronze Medallist; North Eastern Championship Gold Medallist U73 Kg;
BJA Northwest U73 Champion
AJA National Champion U73; Midland Area U73 Kg Gold Medallist x 4
British Kurash Gold Medallist
(Author's Note – This is an author chosen selection from a much larger supplied list.)

Personal Statement
I grew up in a rough area, a council estate about five miles from the city centre of Birmingham. It was not the worst of places but neither was it the best. For all my adult life and competitive career, I weighed in at about 70 kilos and I'm still the same weight now.

I was quite skinny as a child and not strong which led me to be bullied at school. I decided to do something about this as a young teenager and chose to learn judo. I loved the sport straight away. Training gave me a great deal of confidence and competitions were perfect for me; I loved the excitement! As I progressed at judo my confidence improved and the bullying stopped. It was all instigated by one lad who was a violent thug and I am not ashamed to say that he came my way again when I was about seventeen and I flattened him. I am not proud of this but he was a bully who had tormented me at school and I think it was no more than natural justice.

As I become more involved in judo, I began to know who were the top players at competitions. Brian Jacks and David Starbrook were the standout players of that generation. My greatest admiration went to Danny DaCosta because he was a tremendous lightweight champion but, on his day, could defeat all comers.

I owe a lot to my first coaches, 'Lofty' Nicholls at Great Barr JC (my first club) and Peter Barnett at Solihull JC. Peter was a great coach and he attracted top players from the midlands to his club to take advantage of his expertise and knowledge.

In judo everyone begins their competition career with the throws they have been first taught and as you progress choose those that suit you best for whatever reason. My first contest technique was a fast, low *taio-toshi*. I used other throws of course but that was my main technique. A strange thing happened in one event, the Midland Area Open-weight – I reached the final against Gerry White, a great player who had been reserve for the Olympic team. It was in the days when there were at least six rounds to reach the final and I had won every fight with a clean *ashi-waza!* From that day these throws never left me! I had not trained for them but I won a lot of contests with them, against players, on paper, much better than I was.

Despite what I have just said I never really had a favourite technique – I would try to win with whatever came my way but cannot deny that often this was an *ashi-waza*. However, there is one win which I still recall with pride, amusement and some surprise. Back 'in the day' it was always the case that we entered two events, your own weight and the open-weight category. I was in the final of this event against a guy who was about 120 kilos and he had been laying out his opponents all day. I attacked him with *hane-goshi* and he went over for a clean *ippon!* I think we were both surprised.

Judo has been very good to me – I have had a great life through the sport and met wonderful people. There have been plenty of good times and none bad. Two things stand out. I was lucky enough to get a job as a national coach in Sweden and had a fantastic time. I was also pleased to get my sixth dan as I know I have the competition pedigree to deserve it.

Some daft things have happened through judo. For example, I was presented with a Samurai sword at a competition in Germany. When returning I took a gamble and shoved it in with my judo gear. All went well until I was surrounded by six SWAT style armed guards at the checkout pointing machine guns at my head. One of the officers asked me if I did martial arts and I replied that I did. Anyway, I left the sword and was relieved to get out of Germany realising I could have been shot!

Finally, the player I most admire is probably my mate Peter Donnelly. He came from the mean streets of Shard End to become British Champion and an Olympian, and then managed to carve out a very successful career in banking and finance **without** any formal qualifications – just the will to succeed.

Judo changed my life completely, (as I believe it changed Peter's) it gave me the confidence to face the world head on. It gave me lifelong friends and success both on and off the mat.

My last word to any young aspiring players would be this: do not let judo control your life. Ensure you have the skills to make a living outside of judo. I have met too many great judoka who have not done well in life because they committed themselves totally to judo but had no plan for the rest of their life after the glory days were over.

~

6. Anthony Underwood 6th Dan - "The Phantom Knight"
Competition Coach BJC

Significant Competition Performances
BJA Goldberg Vass Champion; Southern Area L/Heavy Champion; Midland and Southern Area Team Member

AJA National Open Champion; National L/H Champion x 2; National Silver Medallist x 4; National Team Member x Often BJC/MOSJ National Open Champion; National L/H Champion x 2; National L/H Silver Medallist x 4
Mercian Judo Society Open Weight Champion
(Author's Note – This is a much-shortened list at Tony's request)

Personal Statement
I started Judo by mistake by going into the wrong room when looking for weight training when I was nearly 17. I took to it, read up on it and liked the way a big heavy guy could be made weightless for a split second as if by magic. That and the mantra 'maximum efficiency with minimum effort' fitted my personality.

I set myself progressive goals, first to be the best at *ukemi* in the club, so I could fight and not get injured. I succeeded quite quickly. Then while learning different throws I set the objective of being very hard to throw, so I could then concentrate on my throwing techniques without worrying too much about being dumped. That took a bit longer. I listened to my instructor who did *uchi-mata* and was roughly my size. I found it hard to get between the legs and so the *uchi-mata* developed into a variation of hane-*goshi*. That in turn became *uki-goshi*. When attacking fast, a strong *tsukuri and kuzushi* brought my opponents onto my hip and I just flicked them over. If the contest was slower and there was more resistance it developed into a *tsuri-komi* version. The fact is that 'my technique' was two throws and depending upon what I felt when I turned in, I used *uki* or *tsuri-komi*, - hence people have different opinions as to the nature of 'my' throw.

I decided my judo needed more balance and so developed a foot throw to the 'other' side - *tsuri-komi-ashi* and sometimes *hiza-guruma* on very tall people. A backward throw was essential and *o-soto-gari* fitted the bill. I developed *nidan ko-soto-gari* follow up 'round the back' if needed. To keep my opponent unsettled I did foot sweeps as direct attacks and as 'set up' techniques. All this led me to disregard groundwork and as I was hard to throw, I don't believe my competition performance suffered too much.

I didn't want Judo to take up all my time. I never had a specific coach. I could not tolerate being pushed into what I didn't want to do, train with groups according to someone else's decision or be expected to fight whenever or wherever a coach decided. (If there was a war on being told what to do is fair enough but not for an amateur sport.) I valued personal freedom and personal responsibility far above any wish to be a 'professional' judo player and I had a career to pursue. It was apparent to me that a 'system' Judoka would be unwanted after his competitive career had finished and would likely be scratching about for a living or getting depressed at glories lost with prospects diminished.

I never lost my temper fighting even when my opponents did. I think it made them even more irrational when they were faced with my calm response. I was on the mat to do a job and the opponent was in the way. I tried to develop a cold emotionless approach. I never listened to mat-side coaching. Only I was on the mat and no-one else could have any idea why I could or could not do a particular move. When fighting I solely relied upon myself. Having said that if I heard something funny from a coach or spectator I would sometimes reply, which confused my opponent. I would never have said this at the time, but I always expected to win. I would silently speak to myself, 'How do I defeat this one? He won't be able to do much with me' When I came off, I never showed emotion, so nobody would know by my looks how I got on. Even today I cringe when a player jumps up to celebrate a win or shows anger at a loss.

I was thrown three times with Ippon, (not counting the time by Chris Murphy which was off the mat). Harry Hobbs *ippon-seoi* got me up and over and dislocated my shoulder in the process. Tony Bucknell countered me with *ura-nage* when trying my *tsurikomi-goshi*. That taught me to 'hook in' with my foot as soon as I felt resistance. I was never caught like it again. Mike Smith caught me with *de-ashi-harai* of all things, as I came out of a turn. I lost quite a few times on decisions; I would not compete in *ne-waza* mainly which I believe went against me and I ran out of steam in extra-time. I lost twice in finals to Roy Inman in this manner, and I believe there is a tendency when the match is even to award it to the well-known international player.

Quite a few years after I turned thirty the veteran's events started. I felt, like quite a few people, that my performance would just be a shadow of my previous self, so limited my fighting to club practice. I believe that the difference between good and average players is down to speed, timing and flexibility. With age you lose these and your performance declines.

I have never pushed for or wanted a higher grade, unlike many who still practice. If I didn't win with *ippon* or at least *waza-ari* failure, I considered the contest a failure. I was never pleased to win by decision. Losing by *ippon* or *waza-ari*, invariably on the ground was just my silly fault for entering *ne-waza* in the first place. The older I get the more I realise how much I value fellow judoka. I have a special sentiment and respect for those old friends who have died.

Judo never dominated my life; it was just done for my pleasure and as a compensation to my sedentary work. My professional career was full of targets and problem solving and so judo was a good safety valve. As a result, my body has not faired too badly and apart from the odd rheumatic pains due to driving forty thousand miles a year when working and being slightly bow legged. I am in better than average condition for my age. My knees and hips are as good as anyone's and I have not had to have replacements as have many of my judo friends.

They used to say Malcolm Collins 'collected nutters' and I am basically the same. Hence the forming the *Yudansha-kwai* – 'Old Codgers' group became a must for me. Each member is a distinct and very independent character who would not tolerate being regimented. My personality suits in that I act more like a facilitator to the group. I do the organising of meetings and outings as no-one else wishes to do this chore and so I press ahead without fear of dictating.

Watching modern Judo doesn't interest me - not even the Olympics. To me the refereeing rules have interfered with the flow of what is really a stylised fight – judo has become too sanitised. I suppose that I differed from fighters like Bob Trevis, an all-round 'street fighter' if ever there was one, and many of others for whom a driving motivation was winning competitions. I felt more like an artist doing his job of trying to make it look effortless and immune to emotion. I am not the ideal to use as an example for a future internationalist or Olympian - but then I don't think judo fits well as an Olympic sport. Devoting oneself completely to training in the hope of achieving the highest goals probably isn't worth the effort and can severely limit one's future life prospects I believe that judo serves people best as an amateur recreation tied as it is with an important personal philosophy. It should add to your personality – not dominate it.

I have forgotten most of my fights but looking back a few stand out. I enjoyed my two ten-minute finals with Roy Inman. We were well matched we ended up passing the time talking. Roy said, 'I will murder you on the ground' and my reply was 'I hope you can break-fall after you fly through the air.' We then chatted about where we were going for our holidays. The second fight, a year later started just after we bowed with him saying 'how was your holiday?' Many people still talk about my throw on Colin McIver; I remember the competition for a different reason. In my next fight I threw another guy off the mat twice and on the mat for *waza-ari* but stumbled and he held me for *ippon*. When I sat down Bob Trevis was very annoyed that I'd lost after the McIver win, but I saw the funny side of it

To aspiring players, I would say this. Times have changed since my contest years, when judo was a truly amateur art for all pockets. Firstly, work out why you are doing Judo, how dedicated you want to be, how good you are and how it will affect your work and family life. Where do you want to be in ten or fifteen years when past your prime? What are your life plans after that? Do a detailed decision analysis as used in business, and update it regularly and talk to others who have gone through it all and achieved success as well as those who failed. For instance, I am a disappointment to many friends as I know I could have achieved a lot more; others think I did very well without having total commitment.

I know what my objectives were and am not disappointed at all.

(Author's note – I have dubbed Tony 'The Phantom' as an homage to the late great Roy Inman who fought Tony in two BJC finals. Roy referred

to him as the 'Floater' in reference to Tony's lightness of touch in both attack and defence.)

~

7. David Law 3rd Dan - "The Mechanic"

Significant Competition Performances
AJA Team GB v France Winning Team Captain 1988
London Area Open L/Heavyweight Gold Medallist 1970
Midland Area Open Heavyweight Silver Medallist 1968
AJA sponsored England v France v Germany Winning Team Captain 1967
AJA sponsored England v Scotland Winning team Captain x2
North-west Open – Winning Team Captain 1966
(Author's Note – Author selected from a longer list)

Personal Statement
I grew up in a very tough part of inner-city Birmingham called Aston; the police always patrolled in pairs in case there was trouble. I went to Upper Thomas Street school which had a terrible reputation at the time and I can remember there was a lot of fighting amongst the pupils. The school had a boxing club which was quite successful and turned out many good boxers. I gave it a go but it wasn't for me.

One of the 'tough guys' in the area was Pat Roach who was a bit of a tear-a-way but a good friend and when I was about fourteen, he suggested that I give judo a go. He was training at the 'Tin Hut' Budokan and he more or less dragged me along. From the first time I stepped onto the judo mat I knew it was going to be my sport. The coach was Kevin Murphy and I got on well with him. He was of the 'old school.' He expected everyone to work hard and be disciplined. I liked the fact that the sport was very fair; you would push each other to the limit and at the end be pleased – win or lose.

There were not many black-belts in Birmingham in the early days. I was really impressed by Jimmy White who seemed amazing – fast with a great *taio-toshi*. The stand out player was, of course, Pat Roach. He could beat everyone on (or off) the mat. His favourite throw was *hane-goshi)* – an odd choice for such a big man. I did a lot of training with Pat – he had a set of keys and we would turn up in the daytime two or three times each week and have a workout. That was hard work I tell you!

At championships it was hard not to be impressed by Colin Draycott who was a great fighter, much better than most of his opposition. In the sixties and seventies, I was almost exclusively an AJA player and other fighters that I liked to watch were Bob Trevis, who was as hard as nails and Tony Underwood (when he left the BJA.) I attended a few coaching week-ends run by Kenshiro Abbe and he was amazing in the early years. I think the man was a genius of judo.

I remember him taking a line-up of all the players on the course and throwing them one-by-one with the throw which he named beforehand. It was quite amazing, and he was not a young man!

As far as techniques go, I tried to copy the *uchi-mata* that was bringing my friend Chris Murphy so much success but then developed my own style of *harai-goshi*. I had very strong hands and arms, I think because of my job as a mechanic – I did very little weight training. I held low with both hands and pulled my opponent onto my hips. It was unorthodox but seemed to work. I recall one competition when I was captain of the AJA Team in a three-cornered match against France and Holland. I was fighting heavyweight and my Dutch opponent was about six-foot three and twenty stone. My training with Pat Roach paid off as I threw him and when he landed the whole stage shook!

I sometimes regret that I did not take my training to a higher level; I do not think that I reached my potential. On the other hand, I did run a successful business, made money and raised my family. I think that to be a top player you must be single minded, and that comes with its own problems. I know many great players, including Olympic players, that have ended their fighting days with a full trophy cabinet but nothing else – and then find the rest of their lives a struggle.

I suppose the type of player I admire most is the one that can produce good skilful judo with stylish throws; Brian Jacks is an obvious example and from the Midlands – Tony Underwood and the great Neil Adams.

Judo has had a massive effect on me. It has given me the confidence to face the world head on and the courage to get up after you've taken one of the 'knocks' that life throws at you. Above all it's given me lifelong friends. There is something about the mates you make on the judo mat – you go 'head-to-head' with someone and the friendship gets stronger and stays for ever.

Finally, my advice to young players: keep healthy, don't smoke and don't drink too much and stay away from drugs! As far as judo is concerned practice, practice, practice – but make sure that it's good practice and get you techniques right. No point in practicing a mistake. Above all listen to your coach and older players. When you're young you're full of energy and enthusiasm but know nothing about life. Listen to them – they know more than you!

∼

8. David Walker 6th Dan - "The Hammer"

Significant Competition Performances
World Championships (Masters) Gold Medallist x 2
Dutch Open Championship Bronze Medallist 1972
British Championships Gold Medallist Open-weight 1984
British Championships Bronze Medallist O95Kg x 3 : 1980; 1993; 1996
British Trials Bronze Medallist O95kg 1994
British Olympic Training Squad member
(Author's Note: - This is a selection from a much longer list)

Personal Statement
I grew up to the south of Birmingham on the edge of the 'Black Country.' Nobody chooses where they are born or their parents – it's just the luck of the draw. In my case it was bad luck, as my mother and father were both hopeless cases and he was also a violent drunk. As I say bad luck – but in life you must make the best of the hand you are dealt; there is no point whingeing you just have to be strong and make the best of things. I left home at the age of fourteen and had to make my own way in the world. Obviously, my education suffered

but trust me, at that time it was the least of my worries! In some ways my early experiences made me stronger – they toughened me up. And I learned to keep my temper and stay calm which has been a good quality throughout my life: I make sure that I always stay in control.

I started judo as the result of a street fight but I was already interested in it because of one programme on the television. It was called 'The Avengers' and the star was Honor Blackman who used judo in her fights with the 'bad guys.' I was very impressed. As for the street-fight I had two friends, both of whom went to a special school for children with learning difficulties and they were being picked on by local 'yobs. I hate unfairness and joined in on the side of my friends but then the rest of the gang came along and we had no alternative but to 'run for it!' I ran into the local school where a judo evening class was going on. This was a stroke of luck because I loved what I saw and the coach, Stan Turbin, let me join in and I never looked back.

I found that the people that I met in judo were almost always decent, good honest people. Most of the friends that I made have stayed friends all my life. In some ways judo has provided the family that I never had. Right from the start I loved the sport: I liked the discipline and the good manners and I was very lucky to meet Peter Barnett who became my coach. He was one of the best around and I don't think anyone knew more about judo than he did. It is no surprise to me that Solihull became such a great fighting club. He was a good person too. He taught me my favourite two throws, *uchi-mata* and *tomoe-nage* and made me practice them until it hurt!

I have always believed in keeping fit and think in judo your body has to be in top class condition to do the sport well. By the late sixties I was in very good shape and my techniques were improving. I began to win local and national competitions. I trained with the Olympic squad which was both an honour and very hard work! I am still proud of my performance in the Dutch Open in 1972 – I was still very young. I am obviously pleased with my achievements in the World Masters Championships; to become World Champion is a great privilege.

A few people have mentioned to me that it is incredible that I stayed in competition judo for so long. And it is true that I medalled in major championships over a period of thirty years. To be honest I just loved judo so much that I just kept fit and kept going.

It sounds dramatic but judo has given me everything; it has given me a life. Considering how bad things were as a child I dread to think what would have happened to me without the sport. It gave me the confidence and a reason to get through life and I have met wonderful people along the way – not to mention having as friends and acquaintances some of the best players in the world such as Neil Adams and Brian Jacks. I respect and admire them as gentlemen and for the fantastic judo skills they possess.

My only regret is that I never made the Olympic team but I have no complaints – some things just don't quite go your way, which is fair enough as the other guy is trying hard too!

The only advice I would give to young players is to concentrate upon improving their techniques. There is no easy fix – it's just training and dedication. There is no magic – just work on improving techniques, and make sure your body is in top class condition

~

9. Anthony Weaver 5th Dan - "Iron Hands"
Chairman Solihull Judo Club
Senior Coach

Significant Competition Performances

Judo
British Team Championship Gold Medallist x 2; Bronze Medallist
British Open Silver Medallist L/Heavyweight
British Closed Silver Medallist L/Heavyweight
Midland Area L/Heavyweight Champion
Western Area L/Heavyweight Champion
Amsterdam Open L/Heavyweight Gold Medallist
Olympic Freestyle Wrestling
Midland Area Mid-Heavyweight Champion x 2

Personal Statement

Unlike many judo players I came to the sport quite late in life. I must admit that as a nineteen-year-old I was 'going nowhere.' I had not done particularly well at school; I was clever enough but lacked discipline. I had a few labouring jobs where the fact that I was naturally strong helped and I enjoyed physical work. In the evening I worked as a barman in a Solihull hotel to bring in some extra money. One of the guests, turned out to be a high-grade judo player and in conversation with him one night he said that I looked strong and fit and suggested that I visit a judo club. The first time I went on a judo mat was at the police club in Deritend, Birmingham. I loved it! (In spite of the fact that I met Roy Muller who is mentioned in this book!) The following week I joined Solihull Judo Club. That was more than fifty years ago and I have been a member ever since.

Judo provided something that was missing from my life – discipline. As a younger teen-ager I was forever getting into fights. Judo allowed me to channel this energy properly and I could burn off my natural aggression on the mat. I don't know if the two things are connected but within a month of me starting judo one of the managers (Ms Dauncey) elevated me from my labouring job and I was placed on a trainee management scheme. In the course of time, I moved to Pearl Assurance as a salesman. I worked very hard and eventually rose to a very senior position. As every judo coach knows hard work brings success and I found this true in my professional life and of course in judo.

I was very lucky to have Peter Barnett as my club coach and Geoff Gleeson when I was training with the national squad. From Peter I learned the importance of pace and tempo when fighting, that and the importance of putting together a series of combinations in attack. I had a variety of favoured techniques over the years; I liked to use *te-garuma* as a counter and most of the 'leg-grab' technique which fitted in very well when I was training as both a judoka and a freestyle wrestler. I think it was a great mistake banning these techniques from judo! It is said that the removal of such techniques was to distinguish judo from wrestling; I think it was to counter the dominance of the Russians and East-Europeans in the sport. I suppose I am influenced as a wrestler because I used to like to take my opponents into ground-work. I have never had a judo 'hero' although there are many players I admire – Neil Adams and Peter Donnelly come to mind – and Geoff Fountain who had beautiful, skilful judo. But I would like to mention that in wrestling, Greco-Roman style, Aleksandr Karelin (3x Olympic Champion) was my ideal as a sport's 'hero.'

I had so many good times through judo that it is impossible to make a list. The crowd of friends made at Solihull Judo Club and at National Squad training remain with me to this day; Peter Donnelly, Chris Adams, Les Hudspith, Geoff Hobbs were the 'best of the best' and our crazy nights at the 'Rum Runner' are best not mentioned!

I had so many good times that it is hard to think of a disappointment. I would like to have achieved a full 'International Flag' – but it just eluded me. As with so many other players I don't think it was lack of ability that stopped me. They say that you need 10,000 hours training to even be able to compete at the highest levels and perhaps that I started late, might have held me back a little. But really, I think it was the inability to commit myself to full-time training. On the other hand, I did remarkably well in my professional life and I don't think this success would have been possible without the stability and discipline that I found in judo.

I am not sure of the advice I would give to a young up and coming player. I suppose the first thing is to make sure that you have an excellent coach. You can't do it on your own – good coaching is vital. Secondly, I think you must do a lot of auxiliary training; top class judo requires your body to be in first-class condition. Finally, you must real want to get to the top because it is a hard struggle to which you commit the best years of your life – with no guarantee that you will succeed.

~

10. Robert Murray Trevis 3rd Dan - "The Rock"

Significant Competition Performances

AJA
Open Champion
Dan Grade Middleweight Champion x 2
Midland Area Champion x 3
BJA
Midland Area Champion 1968
Midland Area Representative National Teams
BJC
Midland Area Champion 1968
International Team Representative

Personal Statement

When I was a kid in the 1960s, I have to admit to being a bit of a tearaway. I don't know exactly why this was; I resented authority and did not like being told what to do. I started getting into trouble – nothing serious but I had a few scrapes with the law. The result of this was that I was sent to what is now known as a 'Young Offenders Institution' but then was referred to as a 'Borstal.' Everything was very ordered and organised and the discipline was very strict. When it was time for me to leave it was suggested that I should take up sport as a safe release for my energies, and I took up judo. I went back to school at Bierton Road and did a bit of school judo, and loved it. If I remember correctly the coach was Harry Underwood – a blue belt which seemed a high grade in those days.

The first club I trained at seriously was at the Morris Commercial Cars Social Club – but it was always known as simply 'The Morris.' It was an AJA club and the instructor was Pat Collins. I absolutely loved the sport and progressed very quickly to brown belt. I was naturally very strong and never found it necessary to do much weight training. I started to train at Kenny Webber's club the *Ren-do-kan* in addition to the Morris. Kenny was a great coach and he helped me improve in many ways but mainly getting my *tsukuri* and *kuzushi* in order. My main throws at that time were *harai-goshi* (which I would convert into *maki-komi* if there was a lot of resistance); *uchi-mata* and *hane-goshi*. These remained my favourite techniques throughout my career.

The Morris became well known at a club and we had many great players join or visit the club. Peter Donnelly, Tony Underwood and Christo Murphy became members and the 'Solihull Mob' often visited; Les Hudspith, Dave Southall, Dave Walker and Ronnie Knight all practiced at one time or another.

I started to win a lot of local *kyu* grade competitions including the AJA midland area event. I stuck at judo for two reasons; firstly, I was quite good at it and enjoyed winning; secondly the atmosphere and friendship in judo at that time was really good. I was graded to black belt by the National coach of the AJA – Norman Grundy. The system at the time was to take a 'line-up' which was supposed to be one each of the lower colours and then three brown belts. Grundy didn't think the opposition was good enough so I had to fight and beat every player on the course – which I did. I think I scored twenty-seven wins in succession.

I had a really good year in 1968 when I won the Midland Area events of the three major judo associations. There were lots of other wins which I can recall with pride: In 1972 there was a club team event promoted by the BJA to raise money for the team travelling to the Munich Olympics. The Morris team had done very well; it had won the AJA nationals; the BJA Midland Area and 'The Tatami' Open Championship. The team was normally Tony Underwood, Peter Donnelly, Christo Murphy, Fred Stansbie and myself. For this event Christo was injured and replaced by Geoff Fountain, a really talented middleweight who was a multiple area champion. Peter couldn't fight, I forget why, and was replaced by Dave Porter We had an easy run to the semi-finals where we met the *Renshuden* – the famous club from London. We won the first three fights which gave us the victory. I beat Alexander, Tony beat Krobells and Geoff beat Cullen (all international players). We beat our rivals Solihull JC in the final. A very happy day!

Another contest I will never forget was when I fought the great Dave Starbrook in the British Trials. He was a phenomenal player

– it was like fighting someone made of iron bars. I managed to roll him over and score a good *waza-ari*. I kept this lead until the last seven seconds of the match when he tied me up in *ne-waza* and nearly ripped my arm off with *juji-gatame*. In the same event the following year I beat Roy Inman and my next fight would have been against Brian Jacks – but I had to withdraw. I had badly twisted my knee fighting Roy and could hardly stand. There would have been no point stepping onto the mat with Brian with my leg as damaged as it was.

There were too many good times to list! But judo was different then – the players seemed closer and the club atmosphere was terrific. When we travelled to a championship from the Morris, we would book two coaches to take players and supporters to the event. Win or lose we would return happy – made even happier with the help of the half-dozen crates of beer we would take onto the coach! Another occasion that comes to mind was when Kevin Murphy (coach at the Budokan and AJA General Secretary) treated a crowd of us to a night out at a city club called the 'Pink Elephant.' I can't remember what the occasion was, but we had a mad time and it must have cost him a fortune! Kevin and myself often 'crossed swords' as they say – but he was a good guy and we respected each other.

The only 'bad' time I can recall was when I was disqualified in the AJA National final fighting Keith 'Tiger' Brown. He was a great player, normally BJA, and was as tough as they come. I had narrowly beaten him once before. It was a rough scrap and we both lost our tempers. (This is mentioned earlier in the book; something was said between us as we locked heads and I blew up – but in truth I can't remember what it was. I lost my temper before Keith, and now I wish I'd kept calm.)

My only regret concerning judo is that I did not take it more seriously. I was my own worst enemy. I had some good wins against international players but never committed myself fully to the sport. It would have been nice to have represented Team GB but I realise now that international level performance requires total commitment. The only one of 'our crowd' who managed to get to the Olympics was Peter Donnelly and being his close friend, I know of the pressure it put on his life.

Looking back, it is difficult to imagine my life without judo – in fact I don't think I would have had a satisfactory life. The friends I made sixty years ago are still friends. I fought some great and famous players but admire everyone who stuck at the sport – it's a hard game. The great players are one thing but the sport is made of all the others that can put in a hard shift on the mat – players like Geoff Fountain, Tony Underwood, Christo Murphy and of course Peter.

I've been to a few judo clubs recently – with my grandchildren! Perhaps it's just me getting old but the atmosphere doesn't seem the same. So, my advice to any young player is to enjoy it! It's a sport after all and if you are not having fun then what's the point?

~

11. Bryan Drew 4th Dan - "Warhorse"

Significant Competition Performances
British Open Heavyweight Gold medallist 1977
British Closed Heavyweight Gold Medallist 1978
British Open Gold Medallist (AJA) Heavyweight 1973
British Team Gold Medallist (AJA) 1973
National Team Champion Heavyweight x 2 1979;1980
Midland Area Heavyweight Champion BJA; AJA *(multiple occasions)*
AJA Internationalist
National Club Team Championship Gold Medallist 1974
Member of the 1976 Olympic Squad

Personal Statement
As a teenager I have to admit that I was 'going off the rails' as they say. My life lacked any form of structure or discipline and I suppose I considered myself to be a 'hard knock' on the streets. The only thing I was doing usefully with my life was boxing. I was a member of a local club and had won a few bouts. I had one victory against a lad from area – I knew him and he was another 'street-fighter.' This had a bad ending, for me at least. Coming back from the cinema with another couple of mates we took a short cut along the canal bank and found

ourselves surrounded by his gang. To make an unpleasant long story brief, a fight started and he came at me with a knife and I got stabbed. Worse was to come; it was apparent that I needed hospital treatment. His gang and my mates tried to calm the situation but when I was nearly unconscious, he stabbed again and had severe abdominal injuries. It took me a long time to recover - and I'd lost interest in boxing!

I don't think I was a nice person back then, in fact I was an arrogant, aggressive young idiot. I got in trouble with the police on a few occasions ... then two things happened at about the same which turned my life around. Firstly, I met a beautiful girl who said that if I didn't straighten myself out, she would have nothing to do with me. Secondly, I went along to a judo club. Of course, I opened my mouth out of bravado and said all the wrong things; I insulted a few people and asked if I could borrow the 'pyjamas' – the usual stupid stuff. Anyway, I did a few breakfalls and made a nuisance of myself until a small blue belt got hold of me and threw me all over the place. Then he held me down and I couldn't get out even though I was much bigger and stronger. And then he threw me about some more. I couldn't believe it. It was a magic moment - as if I'd seen the light! I also knew that the girl meant her threat so I stopped being a thug, became addicted to judo and married the beautiful girl who is still my wife!

I have been asked 'why did you stick at judo?' I liked it of course but more than that I hated to lose. So, every time I was dumped it was a motivator to do better. Winning is a great encourager, but for me losing made me learn more and try harder.

I went to a couple of clubs to begin with but then settled on the 3Ks where the coach was Malcolm Collins. I loved the club and loved Malcolm who died a few years back and I was privileged to say a few words at his funeral. He was a great man and is sadly missed. Trevor Smith was also a coach at the club and gradually they helped me refine my techniques. I developed a very powerful *uchi-mata* and I had a lot of success with that throw. I quite liked counter techniques and scored a *waza-ari* against Angelo Parisi with this in the British trials. Unfortunately, he came back and won the contest – but dumping a world great (with *ura-nage*) is a good memory! The 3Ks was a great club with many fine players at one time or another. It was an honour to be head coach there for 14 years. It was where Dennis Stewart, British Champion and Olympic medallist began his career – I remember him as a teenager and it was clear that he had great potential.

There were lots of great players at that time and it is difficult to pick out any specific influences. I was impressed by Dave Starbrook – who could not be? It was a privilege to be on the mat with him! I also admired the skills of Keith Cannaby from Solihull – he was a lightweight but with really good judo. And then there is Bob Trevis! We are good friends now but when we were young men we did not get on. He was a rough customer – but so was I, and suppose given our personalities it's not surprising tempers flared.

My life in judo was full of good times both on and off the mat. Winning the British Open was a high-spot of course – Ian Thompson and Arthur Mapp (soon to be Olympic bronze medallist) took the other podium places. I suppose that was the time (1977) I should have committed myself to full-time dedicated training in the hope of a slot at the Moscow Olympics – but life always has its complications and it was not to be. Instead, I built up a very successful business, ably partnered by my wife and later on my son Keith became a director. You can't do everything can you?

As for fun – there are really not enough pages to list the japes and scrapes which I shared with the judo crowd. Myself, and a few lads from the 3Ks decided to start a rock band. My 'audition' was simple. 'Get yourself a drum kit and you're in!' I couldn't drum at the time but quickly learned. I did have quite a good singing voice and very soon we were playing around the pubs and clubs of the Black Country – and being paid! The band was called 'The 2nd Dans' – and there is no reason to explain why! Even the spell when I was on the 'Britain's Strongest Man' circuit had its roots in the hard training I was doing on the judo mat.

Looking back, the one judo personality I truly admired was my old coach and friend, Malcolm Collins. He dedicated his life to judo particularly regarding the British School Judo Association, which he managed and nurtured along with Kenny Webber. I would also like to pay tribute to Kevin Murphy who was an immense contributor to judo, particularly in the midland area. (He took me Mike Smith, Mike Davis and others on our first (AJA) International competition to Hildesheim in Germany – we won but that is the least of my memories of a mad trip!) I am a 'Black Country' man to my core and being as successful as I was in the midlands means a great deal.

Judo did so much for me; I really don't know where I would have ended up without the discipline and perspective that judo put into my life and created order from chaos. This process was helped by my wife who has also kept me in line! In judo I could work off any frustrations on the *tatami* and at the end of a hard fight realise that my opponent was not an enemy. It seems strange sometimes that the people I fought hardest with became friends!

Finally, I have no secret to give to younger players who might wish to become good at the sport. I have no secret because there isn't one. Practice! Practice! Practice! – that's all there is to it. Practice *uchikomi* until it hurts. I was one of Britain's strongest men so trust me – strength alone doesn't work. It is vital to have good technique.

~

12. Danny Murphy - "The Unknown Knight"

Significant Competition Performance
I could walk across a judo mat without making a fool of myself – a fact of which I am proud and make no other claim!

Personal Statement
I would like to thank the 'Dojo Knights' who have given richly of their time in the writing of this book. It does not surprise me that they have been as fearless in sharing their lives as they were in competition.

I would like to thank the many additional people who made this book possible:

For reading the book and making constructive suggestions I thank:

Bryony Hill
Neil Harrison
Wendy Allen
Joey Murphy
Richard Tracey

And for putting up with me, my loving wife
Eilish

Christo Murphy 2021

Printed in Great Britain
by Amazon